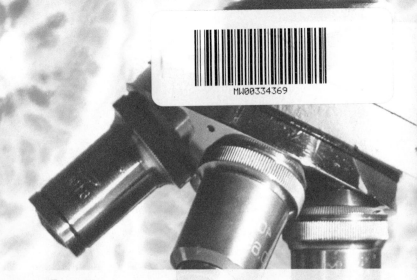

second edition

Introduction to the
BIOMEDICAL
SCIENCES
Laboratory Manual

Ivy Fitzgerald

Kendall Hunt
publishing company

The original images in the histology lab were photographed by Akayla Singleton (unless noted) and all of the other images were drawn or photographed by Elizabeth Troutwine. Both are students at Missouri State University.
Screen shots throughout: Used with permission from Microsoft.

Cover image © Shutterstock, Inc.

www.kendallhunt.com
Send all inquiries to:
4050 Westmark Drive
Dubuque, IA 52004-1840

Copyright © 2019, 2020 by Kendall Hunt Publishing Company

ISBN 978-1-7924-2507-3

Published in the United States of America

BRIEF CONTENTS

CONTENTS

Introduction to the Biomedical Sciences Safety Sheet
Compiled From Student and Instructor Suggestions

1. Know the location of safety devices such as the eye wash station, the shower station, the fire extinguisher, the fire alarm activator, and the first aid kit.

2. Know the location of stairways, building exits, and designated storm shelter areas. The fire alarm is loud. The tornado siren is quiet. In the event of a tornado warning, go to a designated shelter area. In the event of a building evacuation, use the stairs, not the elevator.

3. Place backpacks, cell phones, etc., in the area indicated by your laboratory instructor and keep aisles free of clutter. Keep only those items needed to do your work at your laboratory bench.

4. Always wear closed-toed shoes to lab. Bring your goggles or laboratory glasses to every lab.

5. Confine long hair, loose clothing, and jewelry.

6. Come to lab prepared, having studied the pertinent information from the lab manual.

7. Label items requiring identification. Check labels before using solutions. Organize your workspace for safety and efficiency.

8. Clean up your work area after use, wash glassware, and dispose of waste. Use water and paper towels to clean and dry any spillage.

9. Wash your hands at the end of the laboratory period after working with chemicals or biological materials.

10. Listen carefully to instructions and suggestions given by the laboratory instructor. Keep quiet and respectful of others so everyone can hear when additional instructions need to be given during a laboratory period. Share necessary information.

11. Be considerate of other people's needs and limitations. Ask for help from the instructor when necessary. Be both a participator and leader in your group as appropriate. Help your laboratory partners when appropriate, but encourage them to do their own work when individual work is required.

12. Always be alert. Use common sense. Don't overreact in an emergency. Be responsible for your personal safety.

13. The phone number for Campus Safety and Transportation is 417-836-5509, the number for the City of Springfield Fire and Police is 911.

14. Adhere to commonsense rules. The laboratory is no place for "horseplay." Such behavior is **NOT tolerated** and will result in <u>**automatic dismissal from the course**</u>.

LABORATORY A

Microscopy

VOCABULARY

compound	oculars	objective	stage
stage clip	stage aperture	coarse focus knob	fine focus knob
illuminator	iris diaphragm	condenser	rheostat
base	arm	slide	cover slip
magnification	resolving power	field of view	depth of field
parfocal	parcentral	contrast	bright-field
dark-field	Rheinberg	protist	

SKILLS

Use a compound and a dissecting microscope.
Make a wet mount slide.
Get a specimen on a slide in focus at each magnification power.
Be able to move the stage to view different parts of the specimen.

INTRODUCTION

Microscopy is the study of things too small to be seen with the naked eye. The human eye can see things down to about 100 μm. A red blood cell has a diameter of about 7 μm. Bacteria are around 1 μm across. To be able to see these and other objects, we need convex lenses to produce magnified images. In this lab we will learn about light microscopes.

The first **compound** light microscope—a microscope with more than one lens— was created at the end of the sixteenth century by Hans and Zacharias Janssen, a father and son who made eyeglasses. Their microscopes magnified objects 3–9x. Galileo Galilei made his first microscope in 1609. Antonie van Leeuwenhoek, who lived from 1632–1723, created the highest power early microscopes. He produced tiny, almost circular, single lens microscopes, the best of which had magnifying power of more than 200x. He was the first person to visualize living, moving cells. Microscopy became a field of interest thanks to Robert Hooke's book "Micrographia" published in 1665, which contained drawings of objects viewed under a microscope, with as much as 50x magnification.

Today, using oil immersion, light microscopes can reach a total magnification of about 1,500x. The magnification that can be achieved with light microscopy is limited by the wavelength of visible light: the smallest resolution possible is about half the wavelength of the light used. Violet light has the shortest wavelength of visible light, about 400 nm, so the smallest resolution possible is about 200 nm. Even smaller objects can be visualized not with light but with electrons. A beam of electrons is accelerated to get very short wavelengths, giving very high resolution images. In **transmission electron microscopy** (TEM), an electron beam is transmitted through a very thin sample and the electrons that pass through the sample are detected to provide a grayscale image of the fraction of electrons that pass through the sample at each location. TEM gives a resolution of details as small as 0.2 nm. An alternate technique scans the electron beam across the surface of a sample (**scanning electron microscopy**, SEM) and the secondary electrons generated by the surface of the object are detected to give a grayscale image of the number of electrons detected. SEM uses lower-energy electrons than TEM, to prevent transmission of the electrons through the sample, therefore the resolution of SEM is lower, about 2 nm.

Microscope Parts

In this lab we will learn about compound light microscopes and dissecting microscopes. **Compound microscopes** are used to view thin specimens, such as a section of tissue or small organisms, for example yeast or bacteria. The specimen must be thin enough to allow light to pass through it. The image produced is upside down and backward. A **dissecting microscope** is used to aid the human eye's vision of small objects, such as fruit flies. Dissecting microscopes magnify objects up to 40x, but the image is true, so these microscopes are useful for manipulating small objects or dissecting small organisms. Specimens are illuminated from above, allowing visualization of the surface of the object, and thus thickness of the sample is not a concern. Both types of microscopes are composed of many parts.

The **oculars**, or ocular lenses, or eyepieces, are the part of the microscope to which you put your eye(s). Some microscopes have one eyepiece and some have two (binocular). The oculars magnify the sample 10x. The distance between the two ocular lenses can be adjusted to fit the distance between your eyes. Adjust the distance between the oculars by pushing or pulling on the eyepiece housing (not the glass!). If possible, use both oculars to view the sample, however, if you have trouble using both eyes at once, you can close one eye to view.

If one of your eyes is weaker than the other, this difference can be compensated for by adjusting the focus of the eyepieces independently (diopter adjustment). Start by twisting both eyepieces so that the line on the housing of the eyepiece lines up with the zero focus position on the eyepiece. Focus the microscope so the sample is in crisp focus using the 10x objective. Now move to the lower magnification 4x objective. Close one eye and adjust the eyepiece until the specimen is in crisp focus (do not use the focus knobs). Switch eyes and focus that eyepiece. Record the position of each eyepiece using the graded scale printed on the eyepiece housing for future use. If the image you see through the microscope is blurry and you can't get it in focus, check the eyepiece positions and set both lenses to zero.

In one of the eyepieces, there may be a pointer or ruler. This is useful for describing the location or size of a specimen. If you can't see the pointer, try looking through the oculars one at a time (close one eye, then close the other).

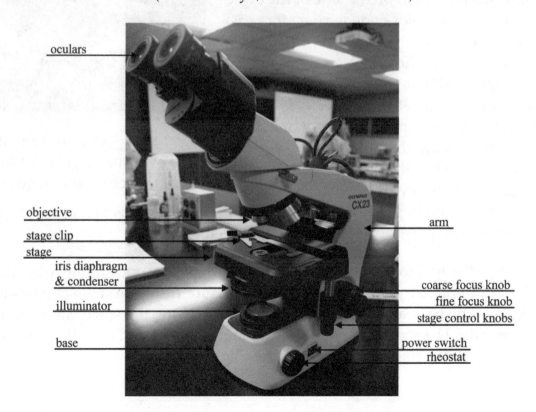

Figure A1   Labeled parts of a compound light microscope.

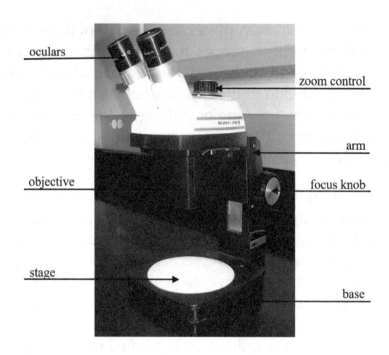

Figure A2   Labeled parts of dissecting microscope.

Objectives, or objective lenses, magnify the sample. Each objective has a different magnification, which is marked on the side of the objective, and has a color-coded ring for easy reference. The larger the objective, the high its magnifying power. The microscopes in this lab are equipped with three objectives—4x, 10x, 40x. You can switch between objectives by simply rotating the nosepiece—do *not* move the stage before rotating the nosepiece or you will have to start over with focusing your sample. The larger objectives will be very close to the

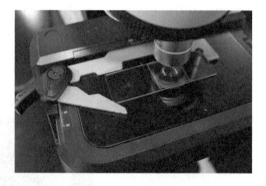

Figure A3   The position of a slide over the stage aperture, held in place by the stage clip.

slide when they are in position, but if the sample was in focus at a lower magnification, the higher-power objectives will not touch the slide.

The **stage** is the horizontal surface on which the microscope slide is placed. The slide is held in place by the **stage clip**. The pressure from the stage clip holds the slide against the back and side of the slide holder. Note, the stage clip is NOT on top of the slide. The specimen on the slide should be centered over the **stage aperture**, the hole in the stage through which the light shines.

The **stage adjustment knobs** hang down from the side of the stage. One knob moves the slide in the x-direction (left-right); the other knob moves the slide in the y-direction (front-back). You will have to practice to get used to which direction to move the knobs to move the slide the direction you want.

The z-direction—the distance between the sample and the objective—is changed by the focus knobs, which move the stage. The **coarse focus knob** (or **coarse adjustment knob**) moves the stage quickly and the **fine focus knob** (or **fine adjustment knob**) moves the stage slowly (little movement for a lot of twisting). The fine focus knob is the smaller knob in the center of the large coarse focus knob on our microscopes.

The **illuminator** is the microscope's light source.

The **iris diaphragm** is used to adjust the size of the circle of light entering the stage aperture. We will keep it all the way open and it shouldn't be adjusted.

The **condenser** collects and focuses the light from the illuminator, so the sample field of view and the objective are uniformly illuminated. The condenser is also where filters can be added. Usually the condenser should not be touched.

The **power switch** turns the microscope light off and on.

The **rheostat** adjusts the brightness of the light. The rheostat should be turned all the way down before the microscope is put away. For some microscopes, when the rheostat is at the lowest position, the light is off. If you plug in and turn on the microscope and there is no light, check the setting of the rheostat.

The bottom of the microscope is the **base** and the vertical bar is the **arm**.

To view a specimen, it is placed on a microscope slide, usually in liquid, and covered by a cover slip. A **slide** is a long, thick piece of glass or possibly plastic and a **cover slip** is a small, thin square of glass or plastic.

A magnified image of the sample is visible through the oculars of a light microscope. To create this image, light from the illuminator is focused by the condenser through the stage aperture onto the sample on the slide. The light transmitted through the sample is collected by the objective lens, which magnifies and focuses the light on the oculars. The oculars also magnify and focus the light, this time on the viewer's eyes.

Figure A4   Placement of a cover slip on a slide.

Slide Preparation

To prepare a slide, place one drop of a liquid sample on a slide and carefully cover it with a cover slip by placing one edge of the cover slip against the slide and slowly lowering, and then dropping, the cover slip over the sample. The cover slip should move evenly across the sample as it lowers, creating an even film of the sample without bubbles.

A sample with low contrast, such as translucent human cells, can be stained to make the cells easier to see. Methylene blue is one type of dye used. When preparing a slide, add one drop of dye to the slide, then add the sample to the dye.

Slide Care

Prepared slides need to be taken care of to prevent them from getting broken. Slides should be stored in a slide box all facing the same direction, aligned straight across the box, with the label upright.

Microscope Care

Do not touch the glass of the oculars or objectives because this will leave fingerprints and possibly scratch the glass. The glass of the microscope's parts should be cleaned only with lens paper. Please ask your instructor for help in you believe your microscope's lenses need cleaning.

Starting with a Microscope

1. Hold on to the microscope's arm and base when moving it.
2. Set up the microscope on a level, dry, stable surface.
3. Remove the dust cover and plug in the microscope.

4. Turn on the microscope and turn up the rheostat.

5. Move the lowest-power objective over the aperture in the stage.

6. Secure your slide with the stage clip and center the slide specimen over the aperture.

7. Watching from the side, raise the stage up, toward the objective, as far as it go with the coarse objective knob (but do not hit the objective).

8. Bring the sample into focus by moving the stage *away* from the objective with the coarse focus knob.

9. Once you can see the specimen, use the fine focus knob to bring the sample into crisp focus.

10. To view the sample at higher magnification, carefully turn the objective nose-piece without bumping the stage or focus knobs.

11. Refocus your view using the fine focus knob.

Putting away a Microscope

1. Remove the slide from stage.
2. Put the lowest objective lens in place over the stage aperture.
3. Move the stage as low as possible.
4. Reposition the stage clip so it is all the way back and centered.
5. Turn the rheostat to its lowest setting.
6. Turn the power switch off.
7. Unplug the cord and put it in its holding pocket.
8. Put on the dust cover.

Microscopy Terms

Magnification is how much bigger the image is than the object is.

Total magnification is the amount the image is enlarged; both the objective and the oculars are magnifying. To calculate the total magnification, multiply together the objective magnifying power and the ocular magnifying power. Objectives commonly have magnifying power of 4x, 10x, or 40x. Oculars have a magnifying power of 10x. If a specimen is viewed through the oculars when a 4x objective is in place, the total magnification is 4x × 10x = 40x.

☑   If an object is viewed with a 35x objective, what is the total magnification? _____

Resolving power is the ability to distinguish features that are close together as separate. Details tend to blur with magnification. Higher resolution gives crisper images.

Figure A5   Two dots close together may blur into one shape at high magnification. Whether these dots appear as one shape or two depends on the resolving power of the microscope.

The **field of view** is how much of the sample can be viewed in the x- and y-directions, so how far across the sample is visible. The field of view decreases as magnification increases: the greater the magnification, the smaller the field of view.

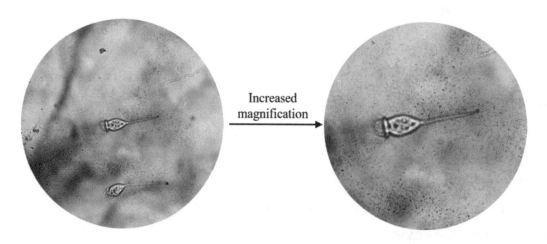

Figure A6   Increased magnification decreases the field of view. At increased magnification, only the Stentor at the center of the field of view is visible.

☑   If you are looking for a specimen on a slide, which objective would you want to use? Why? _____

The **depth of field** is how much of the sample, in the z-direction, is in focus. The depth of field decreases as magnification increases: the greater the magnification, the smaller the depth of field.

☑   If you are looking at a relatively thick sample on a slide, and you wanted the full depth to be in focus, which objective would you want to use? Why? _____
_____

☑ If we picture the area that is in focus at different magnifications as a cylinder, which would represent what is in focus at low magnification and which for high magnification? Explain why.

_____

_____

Compound microscopes are engineered to be parfocal and parcentral. **Parfocal** means that the field of view remains in focus when the objectives are changed—you shouldn't have to adjust the focus when you change objectives. This is an ideal, so in most cases, you will need to move the fine focus knob a little bit to get your specimen back in focus when you change magnification. **Parcentral** means that the center of the field of view stays in place when the objective is changed. Remember, the field of view will be smaller when you move to a higher magnification, but the center of the field of view at a lower magnification will still be at the center at a higher magnification.

☑ Before you change objectives, where should you place the specimen you want to view at higher magnification?

_____

☑ After you change objectives, how hard should it be to see your specimen of interest in crisp focus? _____. What is it about your microscope that makes this true?

_____

Contrast refers to the range of light in an image, from the brightest white to the darkest black. Contrast is what allows you to make out details.

ACTIVITY 1: USING A LIGHT MICROSCOPE

In this activity, we will look at several prepared slides to become familiar with using the microscope and we will practice making wet-mount slides.

PROTOCOLS FOR ACTIVITY 1

To create a wet-mount slide of your cheek cells:

1. Place a drop of methylene blue in the center of a slide.
2. Use a tooth pick to scrape the inside of your cheek (don't hurt yourself, but do use firm pressure).
3. Rub the tooth pick in the methylene blue on the slide.
4. Carefully cover the dye with a cover slip.
5. View your cheek cells under the microscope.

To create a wet-mount slide of your skin cells:

1. Wash your hands and thoroughly dry them if your hands are dirty or have lotion on them.
2. Tear a square of double-sided tape from the roll, touching it as little as possible.
3. Affix the tape to the center of a slide.
4. Press the tape (and slide) firmly against the skin on the top of your hand, such as the flesh between your thumb and pointer finger. Do not twist or drag the slide.
5. Place one drop of methylene blue onto the tape.
6. Carefully cover the tape and methylene blue with a cover slide.
7. View your skin cells under the microscope.

To create a wet-mount slide of your hair:

1. Place a drop of water in the center of a slide.
2. Collect a hair from your head.
3. Lay the hair in the water.
4. Cover with a cover slip.
5. View your hair under the microscope.

Cleanup:

- Wash off slides and put on tray.
- Throw plastic cover slips in the trash.
- Throw toothpicks in the trash.

Name _____ Section _____ Date _____

ACTIVITY 1: MICROSCOPY COMPLETION

1. Look at the letter e. Draw how it looks on the slide and how it looks under the microscope:

On slide (by eye)	Through microscope
	total magnification: _____x

When you move the stage to the right, what direction does the e move?

When you move the stage away from you (back), what direction does the e move?

2. Look at the slide with three threads. Which color thread is on top? Which color thread is on the bottom?

3. Draw a picture of your stained cheek cells and stained skin cells.

cheek cells

total magnification: _____x

skin cells

total magnification: _____x

4. Draw a picture of your hair.

total magnification: _____x

ACTIVITY 2: FILTERS

INTRODUCTION

Usually when we use the microscopes in lab we will be doing **bright-field microscopy**: we will use the bright light on the microscope to illuminate the sample on the slide for us to view. The contrast in bright-field microscopy comes from light being absorbed by the sample, changing the brightness of the sample relative to the surrounding light. But there are other types of microscopy. Filters can be added to the microscope to change the amount, color, or polarization of the light illuminating the sample.

In **dark-field microscopy**, the majority of the light is blocked by a filter on the condenser that has an opaque center. This gives the background area, around the specimen, a dark appearance. The light from the outer, transparent ring of the filter illuminates and is scattered by the specimen. Only the light scattered by the specimen reaches the objective, making it appear to glow. Dark-field microscopy produces high contrast: a bright specimen on a dark background. Dark-field microscopy is useful for viewing samples that have different densities, such as the cytosol or vacuoles of an organism, because different density substances refract light differently, giving contrast to these structures. Likewise, small edges diffract light well and show up clearly in dark-field microscopy, for example, viewing silica-shelled diatoms. Other small structures that diffract light, such as cilia, also appear clearly in dark-field microscopy.

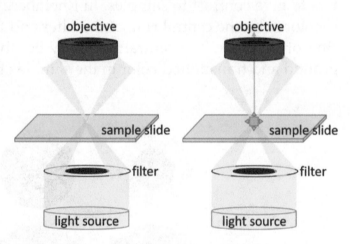

Figure A7 Simplified diagram of dark-field microscopy.

The disadvantage of dark-field microscopy is that most of the light from the illuminator is blocked, so samples appear dim. To compensate, the rheostat needs to be turned up and the iris diaphragm needs to be opened. Even so, images are only seen clearly using low-power objectives (because more light is collected at lower magnification).

☑   What are the advantages and disadvantages of bright-field versus dark-field microscopy?

Bright-Field Advantages/ Dark-Field Disadvantages	Dark-Field Advantages/ Bright-Field Disadvantages

Rheinberg microscopy is a variant of dark-field microscopy that uses colored filters to give contrast to samples. In Rheinberg microscopy, the image background is colored by the central ring of the filter and the specimen is colored by the outer ring of the filter. The central ring may be divided to provide both a dark background and transmitted color in the sample object.

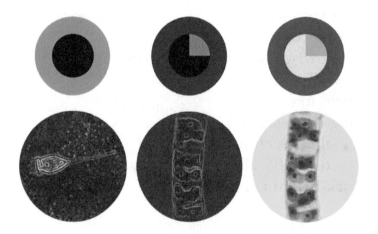

Figure A8   Examples of Rheinberg filters and resulting images (simulated).

☑   In Activity 1, we stained colorless check and skin cells with methylene blue. How else could we increase the contrast of these cells to aid visualization? _____

_____

Polarized light has all of the light waves traveling with the same orientation. To do polarized-light microscopy, cover the light source with a polarizing filter. This will polarize the light entering the microscope. Then cover the ocular lenses with polarizing filters. If the ocular filters are aligned with the filter on the light source, the light will pass through the oculars and the image will be bright. As the filter on the oculars is rotated, more and more of the light rays will be blocked by the filter, making the image dimmer. However, if the light has already been rotated by the sample, at a certain rotation that light will be able to pass through the ocular filter, and the structure that rotated the light will glow.

ACTIVITY 3: PROTISTS

INTRODUCTION

Protists are from the kingdom Protista from the domain Eukarya. Protists are microscopic eukaryotic organisms, which are usually unicellular and usually live in water. Protists can be divided into three categories: animal-like protists, which are called protozoa; plant-like protists, which are called algae; and fungus-like protists.

Pond water is teeming with protozoa. Some are motile and move by means of cilia (like paramecia), or flagella, or cytoplasmic extensions (like amoeba), and others don't have a means of locomotion.

Organisms from the genus *Colpidium* are unicellular, freshwater, ciliated protozoa. The most striking feature of this organism is their vacuoles for digestion.

Organisms from the genus *Stentor* are freshwater, filter-feeding, ciliated protozoa. Stentor are one of the largest unicellular organisms, growing to as large as 2 mm. Stentor can be seen in two forms: ovoid (egg-shaped) when swimming or horn-shaped when attached by its stalk to a surface. Stentor can often be found in nature attached to algae or detritus. Features to look for in *Stentor* include the contractile vacuoles that collect and remove water from the cell and the ring of cilia *Stentor* use to move water to collect food.

Organisms in the genus *Tetrahymena* are unicellular, freshwater, ciliated protozoa. *Tetrahymena* contain vacuoles inside and cilia outside that can be viewed with a microscope. To help visualize the vacuoles of *Tetrahymena*, equal volumes of **India ink** and *Tetrahymena* culture can be mixed. *Tetrahymena* bring in fluid and material from outside the cell by the process of endocytosis. This process creates vacuoles, which hold the fluid. Thus, vacuoles that are formed after the addition of the India ink will be colored by it. Likewise, the pink dye **carmine,** can be used to stain the vacuoles of *Tetrahymena*. A toothpick can be used to transfer a little of the solid carmine into a small amount of the *Tetrahymena* culture.

Because protozoa are motile, they can be hard to see (they swim away too quickly!). Therefore, **Protoslo** can be added to the culture to slow them down. Protoslo is a viscous fluid containing cellulose. A drop of Protoslo can be added to a drop of cell culture on a slide.

☑ How could you determine if other species of protists do endocytosis? _____
_____

Name _____ Section _____ Date _____

ACTIVITY 2 & 3 COMPLETION: PROTISTS WITH FILTERS

Draw and label pictures of samples you view. Color in the filters you use.

Name _____ Section _____ Date _____

MICROSCOPY COMPREHENSION

1. Explain the steps, in your own words, for looking at a new slide. Do not refer to the directions in the lab while writing your response.

2. How do you prepare the microscope for storage after you're done using it? Explain in your own words.

3. If the ocular magnifies 10x and the objective magnifies 23x, what is the total magnification of the sample?

4. What kind of samples do you view with a compound light microscope?
   What kind of samples do you view with a dissecting microscope? Give your own examples.

5. Explain the difference between the coarse focus and the fine focus. Which do you use first? Which do you use with a high-power objective?

6. Describe the orientation of the magnified image, as seen through a compound micro-scope, relative to the sample's orientation.

7. With which objective do you start? Which one do you use next? Which one do you use last?

8. Name each part of the microscope shown below:

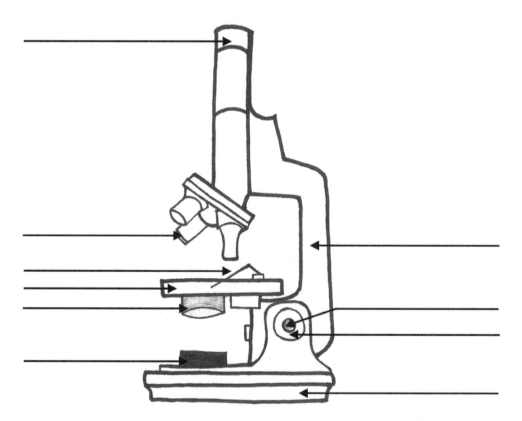

Name _____ Section _____ Date _____

MICROSCOPY REVIEW QUESTIONS

1. Name the parts of a compound light microscope and what they do.

2. List the microscopy terms from this lab and explain what they mean.

3. Explain how to carry, set up, put away, and care for a light microscope.

4. Explain, in your own words, how a light microscope creates magnified images.

5. Two students are sharing a microscope. One is very near-sighted and is not using her glasses. When her partner, with normal vision, looks through the microscope, how does the image appear to him? What does he need to do to make the image clear for him?

6. Think about the definitions of parfocal and parcentral; what is the same for both of the definitions?

7. What is the relationship between magnification and depth of field?

8. What is the relationship between magnification and field of view?

9. List the benefits and limitations of dark-field microscopy.

10. List the benefits and limitations of bright-field microscopy.

11. For each if the filters shown, color in the visual field appropriately.

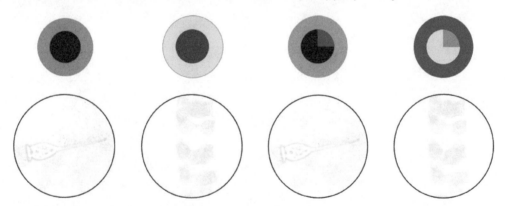

12. What kind of microscopy would you use to view the vacuoles in *Colpidium*?

13. What kind of microscopy would you use to view the cilia in *Stentor*?

14. What kind of microscopy would you use to view the vacuoles containing India ink in *Tetrahymena*?

15. Dr. Fitzgerald posits that TEM is to compound microscope as SEM is to a dissecting microscope. Explain why.

LABORATORY B

Data Analysis with Excel

OBJECTIVE
- Learn about the functionality of Excel to do calculations and make graphs.

VOCABULARY

mean	median	mode	range
x-axis, y-axis	independent variable	dependent variable	scatter plot
trendline	R^2	line graph	histogram
bin	Gaussian distribution	standard deviation	

SKILLS

Implement Excel to do calculations and make graphs.

INTRODUCTION

Statistics

Mean, median, and mode are different measures of centrality (the middle of the data). The **mean**, or average, is calculated by adding up all of the values and dividing by the number of values.

Values 5, 5, 6, 8, 9, 10, 11.
Mean: (5+5+6+8+9+10+11) / 7 = 7.714
Median: 5, 5, 6, **8**, 9, 10, 11.
Mode: **5, 5**, 6, 8, 9, 10, 11.
Range: 5 − 11 or 11 − 5 = 6

The **median** is found by listing the values in order from smallest to largest and finding the middle term. If there is an even number of terms, then the average of the two middle terms is the median.

The **mode** is the most common value from the set.

The **range** is the spread of the values. It can be given as a range, listing the lowest and highest values, or it can be calculated as the difference between the highest and lowest values (high–low).

Graphs

The *x*-**axis** is the horizontal axis. The value of the **independent variable**—the one you control—is plotted on the *x*-axis. The *y*-**axis** is the vertical axis. The value of the **dependent variable**—the variable affected by the independent variable—is plotted on the *y*-axis.

A **scatter plot** is a graph that depicts data pairs as points. Each point represents one value of the independent variable and its resulting dependent variable value. Thus, the *x*- and *y*-values are *correlated*—they have a cause-and-effect relationship. A **trendline** can be drawn through the data. This is the best-fit line that shows the ideal relationship between the independent variable and the dependent variable.

If the *x*- and *y*- values are uncorrelated, there is no cause-and-effect relationship and there will be no trendline that clearly fits the data.

The coefficient of determination, or **R^2** value, measures the goodness-of-fit of the data to the linear regression trendline. An R^2 value of 1 is a perfect fit. The closer the R^2 value is to 1, the better the fit of the trendline to the data.

A **line graph** shows connected points to give a smooth curve. This converts a discrete number of measurements into a continuous representation of the data. From this, you can extrapolate the value of points that were not measured.

A **histogram** shows the frequency of a value occurring in the data. Unlike other types of graphs, only one set of data is used. On the *x*-axis of a histogram are **bin** values. This is how the data is grouped for the frequency count. The values in the data set can be analyzed individually or in intervals. The *y*-axis shows the frequency of the values in the bins appearing in the data set. The bin size is picked by the analyst, so in this sense it is the independent variable. And the frequency is dependent on the bin size. Thus, the same data, sorted into bins of different intervals, will give different histograms (see Figure B2).

Bin Values Typed in Excel	Value Ranges in Bin
5	1–5
10	6–10
15	11–15
20	16–20

☑ If the following values were typed into Excel and used as bin values, write the range of values that would fall into each bin.

10 _____   2 _____

20 _____   4 _____

30 _____   6 _____

Data often clusters around the data mean, and tapers off as you move away from the mean. This data fit is called a **Gaussian distribution**, normal distribution, or bell curve.

If a data set does have a normal distribution, then there is an expected rate at which the data frequency will decrease as the values move away from the mean. The **standard deviation** is the measure of how "spread out" the data are. The smaller the standard deviation of the data, the smaller the spread of the data; the larger the standard deviation, the farther spread the data is.

If you are using an average to calculate the "true" value from several experimental observations, the standard deviation gives you a sense of the range in which the true value most likely falls. The smaller the standard deviation, the more confidence you have that the average of the experimental results accurately reflects the true value of the thing being measured.

☑ If you could take a medicine with a concentration of 650 ± 500 µg/mg or a medicine with a concentration of 650 ± 5 µg/mg, which one should you take to minimize your chance for an overdose? Why? _____

_____

The two histograms in Figure B1 are graphed with the same *x*-axis range. The histogram on the left has a smaller standard deviation, and has a narrower distribution. The graph of the right has a larger standard deviation and the bars of the histogram extend further to the right and the left of the mean.

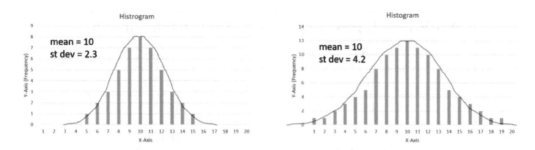

Figure B1   Gaussian curves centered at the same mean with different standard deviations.

If a data set shows a Gaussian distribution, then you would expect 68% of the data to fall within one standard deviation of the mean (mean ± st dev). You would find this range by subtracting the standard deviation from the mean to get the low end of the range and adding the standard deviation to the mean to get the high end of the range. We expect 95% of the data to fall within two standard deviations of the mean (mean ± 2 × st dev).

☑   For the two histograms shown in Figure B1, calculate the range in which you would expect 68% of the data to fall and the range for 95% of the data.

	Left-Hand Graph	Right-Hand Graph
68%		
95%		

Data

2	3	8	12	12	14	16	16	17	18
21	21	22	31	33	41	41	44	47	49
52	52	54	55	56	62	64	65	66	67
68	71	78	79	85	86	92	94	96	99

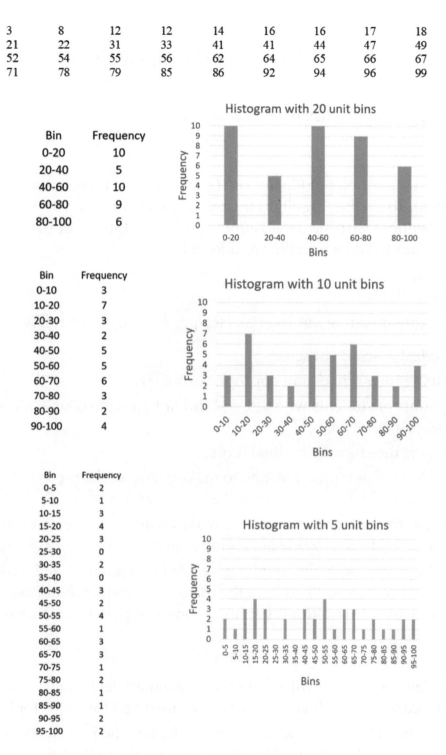

Bin	Frequency
0-20	10
20-40	5
40-60	10
60-80	9
80-100	6

Bin	Frequency
0-10	3
10-20	7
20-30	3
30-40	2
40-50	5
50-60	5
60-70	6
70-80	3
80-90	2
90-100	4

Bin	Frequency
0-5	2
5-10	1
10-15	3
15-20	4
20-25	3
25-30	0
30-35	2
35-40	0
40-45	3
45-50	2
50-55	4
55-60	1
60-65	3
65-70	3
70-75	1
75-80	2
80-85	1
85-90	1
90-95	2
95-100	2

Figure B2   Histograms created using the same data set and different bin sizes.

ACTIVITY

Refer to the "Excel Commands" section (pages 31–36) to supplement these instructions.

Open the Excel Data.xlsx file found on Blackboard.

Scatter Plot

1. Make a scatter plot of Final Score (*y*-axis) versus Pretest Assessment Score (*x*-axis). To do this, highlight the two columns of data you want to graph. The independent variable data column must be to the left of the dependent variable column. Add a trendline and R^2 value.

Histograms

2. After downloading the ToolPak (see pg. 33), create the following histograms:

   a. Pretest assessment scores

   b. Final scores (choose an appropriate bin size)

   c. Counts of students who did and did not pass the course for each pretest assessment score.

   - Sort the students by final score.
   - Use the histogram function to make counts of the pretest scores for students who had a final grade below 725 (Not Pass).
   - Use the histogram function to make counts of the pretest scores for students who had a final grade of 725 and above (Pass).
   - Copy and paste the column generated for Pass next to the column generated for Not Pass and highlight the three columns (bin, Not Pass, Pass) and create a "Clustered Column" bar histogram using Insert Recommended Chart.

Mean, Median, Range, and Standard Deviation

3. Calculate the mean, median, range, and standard deviation for the **pretest assessment scores** and the **final scores**. You can use Excel functions for these calculations.

4. Using the values you calculated in 3, calculate the pretest score value that is one standard deviation below the mean and the pretest score that is one standard deviation above the mean.

5. If the pretest scores fit a perfect Gaussian distribution, 68% of students would get scores within one standard deviation above or below the mean. What percentage of the students scored within one standard deviation of the mean? Express your answer as a percentage.

6. Upload your graphs to Blackboard.

Name _____ Section _____ Date _____

EXCEL COMPLETION

Record your answers to the Activity here.

1. Interpret the scatter plot you created: Is there a direct correlation between pretest score and the final score? Explain your answer. _____

   _____

   _____

2. Interpret the histograms you created: What is the most common pretest assessment score?

   _____

   What is the most common final score range (bin range)? _____

   Does a student's pretest assessment score predict whether or not they will pass the course? Explain your answer. _____

   _____

3.

	Mean	**Median**	**Range**	**St. Dev.**
Pretest				
Final				

4. Pretest mean −1 st dev _____ pretest mean +1 st dev _____

5. % students ±1 st dev _____

6. Upload your graphs to Blackboard.

EXCEL COMMANDS

To **select data:**

With the mouse, click and do not let the right button up on the first cell

Keeping the mouse button depressed, move the mouse over the other cells you want selected

To quickly **select all the data in a column:**

Click the column letter

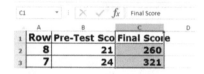

To quickly **select multiple columns:**

Click the column letter, holding the right-click button down

Drag over the next column letters

To quickly **select two nonadjacent columns:**

Click the column letter of the first column

Press and hold the Ctrl key

Click the column letter of the next column

To quickly **select only nonblank cells** in a column:

Click the first value

Press and hold Ctrl, Shift, and down arrow

If starting from the bottom of the column, press and hold Ctrl, Shift, up arrow

To **graph** data:

Highlight the data you want to graph

Click "Insert"

Click "Recommended Charts"

To add **axis titles and trendlines** to graphs:

Click the green plus sign

Select the features you want

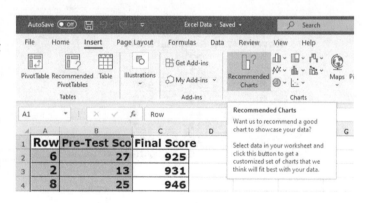

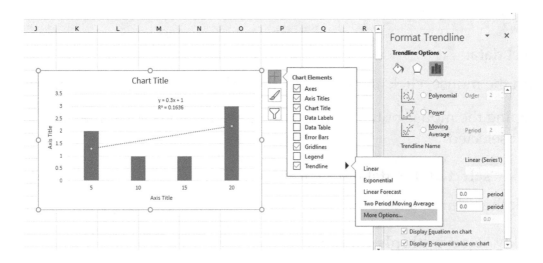

To **change a chart or axis title:**

Click inside the text box

Delete and type your title

To **sort data** from the smallest to largest:

Select all data (so that each row stays together)

Click "Data"

Click "Sort"

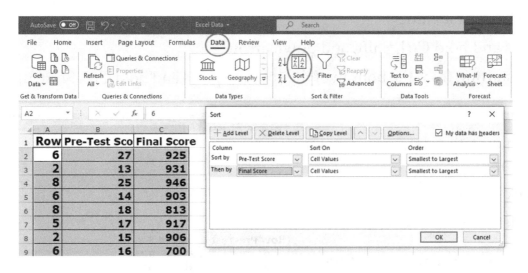

For Macs, it looks like:

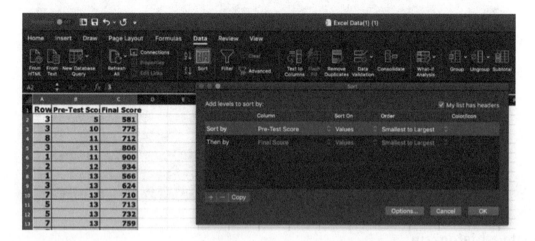

PC: To **load the ToolPak** that contains the *histogram function:*

Click "File"

Click "Options"

Click "Add-Ins"

Click "Go" toward the bottom of the pop-up window (NOT OK)

Click the box next to Analysis ToolPack

Click OK

Mac: To **load the ToolPak** that contains the *histogram function:*

Click "Tools"

Select "Excel Add-ins…"

Select "Analysis ToolPak"

Click "Add-Ins"

Click OK

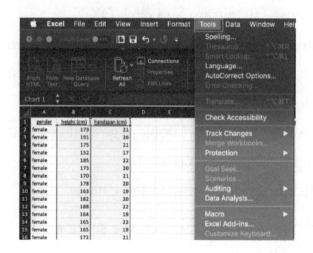

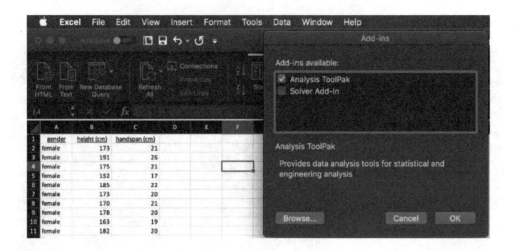

To create a **histogram:**

A histogram displays the frequency each value appears in the data.

Type the bins you want into a column in Excel.

Bins are the values for which the frequency will be counted. Bin size can grow by 1, so you get every number, or by some other interval. For example, the bins 5, 10, 15, 20 would find the frequency of numbers between one and five, between six and ten, between eleven and fifteen, and between sixteen and twenty. Auto filling can be useful to create a column of bin values.

Click "Data"

Click "Data Analysis" (far right)

Choose Histogram and click OK

For Input Range, select the data values (cannot select column letter for this)

For Bin Range, select the bin values (cannot select column letter for this)

Click OK

A new Excel workbook page will be created with your bins and frequencies

Highlight values (no text)

Click Insert, Recommended Charts

To graph **two histograms on the same axes:**

Using the steps above, produce frequency calculations for both data sets using the same bin size and range.

Paste the bin values and both frequency columns into neighboring columns

Select all three columns and click Insert, Recommended Charts

To create a **calculation**

> Type =
>
> Type name of function,
>
> > For example =AVERAGE, =MEDIAN, =STDEVA
> >
> > Note, "RANGE" and "MEAN" are not functions in Excel
>
> Type (
>
> Highlight the cells you want to use in the calculation
>
> Type) and press Return

To quickly **autofill** data to **extend a list:**

> Type the first three values you want into the cells of a column
>
> Highlight the cells with these values
>
> Click and hold on the green square at the bottom right-hand corner of the bottom cell (cursor will become a bold, black plus sign when over the green square.)
>
> Drag down to fill values in the column until you reach your desired final cell
>
> This works for constant or changing values (see images below)

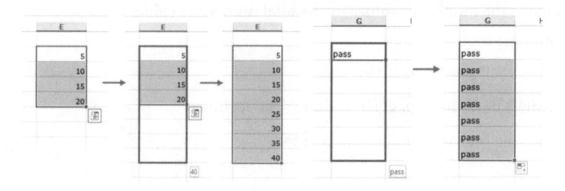

To quickly **autofill** a formula to **extend a calculation:**

> Type the equation you want into the first cell of the column
>
> Highlight the cell with this equation
>
> Click and hold on the green square at the bottom right-hand corner of cell (cursor will become a bold, black plus sign when over the green square)
>
> Drag down to fill the column until you reach your desired final cell

For example, if you wanted to calculate the percentage for each value in a column, you can create your formula in the next column, referencing the cell with the value you want to use in the calculation. Then press enter.

	A	B
	Pre-Test Score (out of 50)	%
1		
2	12	=A2/50*100
3	17	
4	19	
5	22	
6	36	

Highlight the cell with this equation

Click and hold on the green square at the bottom right-hand corner of cell (cursor will become a bold, black plus sign when over the green square)

Drag down to fill the column until you reach your desired final cell. The reference cell will automatically change.

If you don't want the formula to change, add a $ to the cell reference:

A2 will always reference cell A2, regardless of the direction of fill.

	A	B		B
	Pre-Test Score (out of 50)	%		%
1				
2	12	=A2/50*100	→	24
3	17	=A3/50*100		34
4	19	=A4/50*100		38
5	22	=A5/50*100		44
6	36	=A6/50*100		72

$A2 will always reference cells in column A, but which row can change.

A$2 will always reference cells in row 2, but the column can change.

To **calculate percentage:**

Divide the number of values by the total number of values

Multiple by 100

For example, $6/10 \times 100\% = 60\%$

To create a **new sheet** (page) inside an Excel document

Click the plus sign at the bottom of the page

Paste function:

You can chose to paste a formula, the number generated by a formula (losing the formula), or a format.

Copy the cell you want to paste, click the cell where you want to paste, then right click. Select the icon you want under Paste Options or choose Paste Special to get a menu. This menu also gives the option to **transpose** the data's rows and columns.

Name _____ Section _____ Date _____

DATA ANALYSIS COMPREHENSION

1. A data point is written (x, y), where x is the x-value and y is the y-value.

   a. Graph the following data points: (2, 1), (4, 2), (8, 4).

   b. Label the axes "independent variable" and "dependent variable."

   c. Draw a trendline through the data points.

   d. Would you expect the R^2 value for this graph to be close to 1 or close to 0? Explain.

   _____

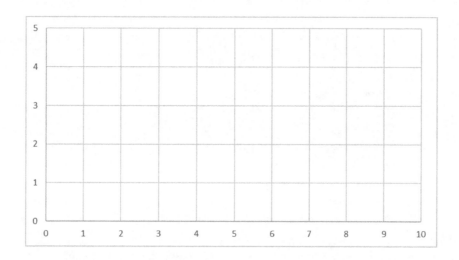

2. Create two histograms for the following data set, one with a bin size of 1 and the other with a bin size of 2. Data: 1, 2, 2, 4, 5, 7, 7, 7, 9.

3. Calculate the mean, median, mode, and range for this data set: 20, 20, 30, 50, 80.

Mean:

Median:

Mode:

Range:

4a. For each graph, draw in the appropriate trendline, to the best of your ability (hint: Use a ruler to get a straight line).

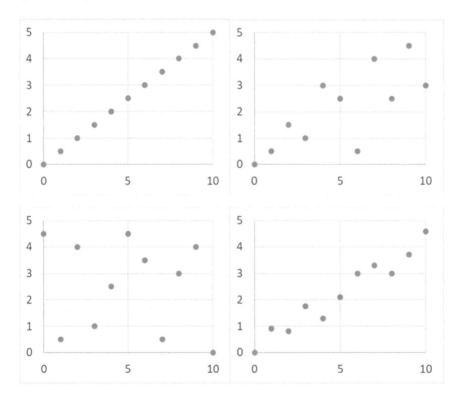

b. The graphs shown have R^2 values of 0, 0.6, 0.95, and 1.0. Match each R^2 value to the correct graph and write the R^2 value onto the graph.

Name _____ Section _____ Date _____

DATA ANALYSIS REVIEW QUESTIONS

1. If a graph of the average daytime temperature of each month was made . . .

   a. What would be the independent variable?

   b. What would be the dependent variable?

   c. Which axis would be labeled with the names of the months of the year?

   d. Which axis would be labeled with degrees?

2. If the height (in centimeters) of a child by age (in years) was plotted . . .

   a. What would you label the x-axis?

   b. What would you label the y-axis?

3. Using the data points (1, 3), (2, 5), (3, 2), (4, 1), (5, 2), (6, 3), (7, 5), (8, 1), (9, 4), (10, 2), for which the first value in each pair is the x-value and the second value in each pair is the y-value, (x, y),

   a. Create a scatter plot

   b. Create a line graph

   c. Create a histogram showing the frequency of the y-values. What are your x-axis values going to be for this graph? What bin size would best represent this data?

4. Calculate the mean, median, mode, and range for the following data sets:

   a. 1, 1, 2, 5, 6

   b. 5, 5, 10, 30, 50

   c. 1, 4, 15, 40, 40

   d. 5, 15, 30, 100, 100

5. What function would you use in Excel to calculate the standard deviation of a data set (i.e., what would you type)?

6. Match each of the words in the word box to the season with which they are associated. Then create your own histogram by filling in the appropriate number of boxes in the graph below for the number of items in the word box that correlate with each season.

Word Box

snorkel	wreath	orange leaves
ice skating	nesting birds	beach ball
daffodils	snowman	ice cream

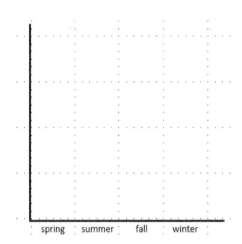

spring   summer   fall   winter

7. The graphs below were made with Excel, using the Histogram function.

   a. For each, state the bin size and what range of numbers fall into each bin for the first three *x*-values.

   b. All four graphs present the same data set. Which graph do you think best communicates the data? Explain your choice.

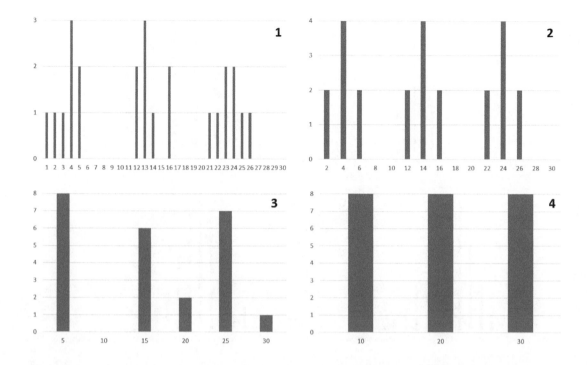

8. a. Match each mean and standard deviation to its corresponding histogram below:

    i. Mean = 100, standard deviation = 15

    ii. Mean = 100, standard deviation = 30

    iii. Mean = 160, standard deviation = 1.5

    iv. Mean = 70, standard deviation = 15

  b. For each mean and standard deviation given above, calculate the value range in which 68% and 95% of the data falls.

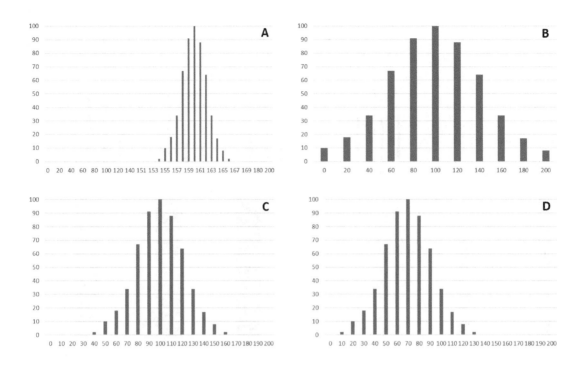

9. a. When is a line graph useful?

   b. When would a line graph be incongruous?

10. Reproduce this data set in a column in Excel, one value per cell: 1, 2, 2.5, 2.6, 2.7, 3, 3.2, 3.8, 4, 5.

    a. Use Excel functions to calculate the mean, median, and standard deviation of this data.

    b. Graph this data as a scatter plot (highlight the column and click Insert → Recommended Charts; Excel will automatically assign x-values). Add a trendline and display the trendline equation and R^2 value on the graph.

    c. Does the trendline show a good fit to the data? Explain your answer.

11. Reproduce this data set in a column in Excel, one value per cell: 9, 7, 6, 5, 3, 2.5, 2, 1.5, 1, 0.8.

    a. Use Excel functions to calculate the mean, median, and standard deviation of this data.

    b. Graph this data as a scatter plot. Add a trendline and display the trendline equation and R^2 value on the graph.

    c. Does the trendline show a good fit to the data? Explain your answer.

12. Reproduce this data set in a column in Excel, one value per cell: 7, 9, 10, 9, 6, 4, 1.7, 0.5, 1.5, 5.

    a. Use Excel functions to calculate the mean, median, and standard deviation of this data.

    b. Graph this data as a scatter plot. Add a trendline and display the trendline equation and R^2 value on the graph.

    c. Does the trendline show a good fit to the data? Explain your answer.

Databases

VOCABULARY

primary literature   peer-review   review

SKILLS

Use PubMed to find research articles.
Use OMIM to find information about human genetic disorders.

ACTIVITY 1: LITERATURE DATABASE SEARCH

INTRODUCTION

Scientific research is communicated through the publication of articles (papers) in scientific journals. **Primary literature** is original research and is **peer-reviewed**—assessed for quality by another scientist in the field—before it's published. **Review** papers, which compile what is currently known in a field, combine the findings of many primary research articles into one paper. Both primary literature and reviews are easily accessed on the web from scientific databases (subscriptions are needed in some cases). In order to make searching these databases more convenient, search engines have been created. The most widely used for medical and biological research is the U.S. National Library of Medicine's "PubMed."

In this activity we are going to search for primary literature using the National Center for Biotechnology Information (NCBI) database:

1. Go to NCBI homepage: http://www.ncbi.nlm.nih.gov/
2. Click on link to PubMed (on right sidebar). This will take you to the PubMed homepage.

Skill 1: Search for Journal Articles by Author

You will type your search query in the search box. When searching for an author enter the last name; the author's first and middle initial can also be used.

3. Let's look up how many papers Dr. **Daniel P. Romero** has. Let's see how what we search changes the results. Search for the following names and write down how many results you get:

   Romero _____

   Romero DP _____

   Romero Daniel P _____

4. Search "Romero DP" again and hit the "**Review**" option on the left under Article types. How many of his papers are reviews? _____

5. Go to **Advanced** under the search bar. In the dropdown menu that says "All Fields" select **Author–last**. Then type in Romero DP. Click Search.
   - How many results did you get? (Did you unselect "Review"?) _____
   - How many of these are available as free full text (option on left-hand side of screen)? _____
   - Download one of these articles and email the PDF as an attachment to the instructor.

Skill 2: Search for Publications that Cited a Paper

6. Click on one of Dr. Romero's papers. In the third section of the right-hand side, there is a "Related information" header. At the bottom of that list is "**Cited in PMC**." Click that. How many other papers in the database cited that paper? _____

Skill 3: Search for Journal Articles by Keyword

7. Return to PubMed. In the search box type the keyword or subject of interest: **heart**.

   How many article are there on the Heart? (Did you unselect "Free full text"?) _____

   How many are reviews? _____

8. Refine your search to Human Heart.

   (Note: You can just type the two words without an "and" between them)

   How many articles are on Human Heart? _____

   How many are reviews? _____

9. If you put the two words together in a phrase, use a "+" to link them together. (Note: Do not put spaces between them and put it in the order you want it to appear.)

   How many articles are on Human+Heart? _____

Skill 4: Limiting the Search by Date

10. Searches can be limited by date of publication. Search **seizures** and date limit using the Publication dates option on the left-hand side.

    How many articles on seizures were published in the last month? _____

    How many articles on seizures were published in March 2008? _____

    How many of these articles are available as free full text? _____

Your results can be recorded on the completion form on page 51.

ACTIVITY 2: ONLINE MENDELIAN INHERITANCE IN MAN (OMIM)

OMIM is a catalog of human genes and genetic disorders authored and edited at the Johns Hopkins University School of Medicine and provided on the internet by the NCBI.

We are going to search for a genetic disease and genes associated with it.

1. Go to https://www.ncbi.nlm.nih.gov/omim?db=OMIM
2. Pick a genetic disease and enter it in the search bar.
3. Click on one of the search results. If you cannot answer the following questions from the result you chose, go back and choose another one.

   What disease are you searching? _____

   How many genes have been linked to that disease? _____

   What is the first gene/locus name that comes up? _____

Here is an example. Do NOT use this example for the above questions; pick your own disease.

1. Go to http://www.ncbi.nlm.nih.gov/sites/entrez?db=OMIM
2. Type the genetic disease you are interested in into the search engine (such as depression).

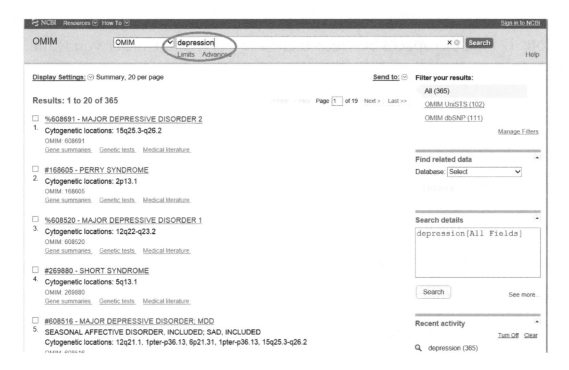

3. Click the blue link to open. (#608516. MAJOR DEPRESSIVE DISORDER; MDD)

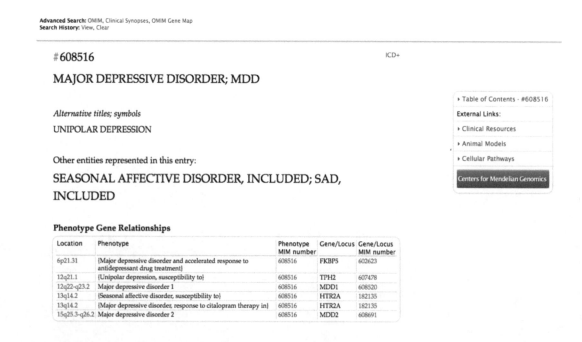

Advanced Search: OMIM, Clinical Synopses, OMIM Gene Map
Search History: View, Clear

#608516   ICD+

MAJOR DEPRESSIVE DISORDER; MDD

Alternative titles; symbols

UNIPOLAR DEPRESSION

Other entities represented in this entry:

SEASONAL AFFECTIVE DISORDER, INCLUDED; SAD,
INCLUDED

▸ Table of Contents - #608516

External Links:

▸ Clinical Resources

▸ Animal Models

▸ Cellular Pathways

Centers for Mendelian Genomics

Phenotype Gene Relationships

Location	Phenotype	Phenotype MIM number	Gene/Locus	Gene/Locus MIM number
6p21.31	{Major depressive disorder and accelerated response to antidepressant drug treatment}	608516	FKBP5	602623
12q21.1	{Unipolar depression, susceptibility to}	608516	TPH2	607478
12q22-q23.2	Major depressive disorder 1	608516	MDD1	608520
13q14.2	{Seasonal affective disorder, susceptibility to}	608516	HTR2A	182135
13q14.2	{Major depressive disorder, response to citalopram therapy in}	608516	HTR2A	182135
15q25.3-q26.2	Major depressive disorder 2	608516	MDD2	608691

4. Locate the chart displaying the genetic disease, phenotype, phenotype MIM number, Gene/Locus, and Gene/Locus MIM number. Determine how many genes are associated with this disease and write down the first one on the list. For this example it would be: 5 (HTR2A appears twice), and FKBP5

Name _____ Section _____ Date _____

ACTIVITY 1 & 2 COMPLETION

Record your results for each search

PubMed

3. Romero _____

   Romero DP _____

   Romero Daniel P _____

4. Romero DP reviews _____

5. Author–last: Romero DP _____

   Free full text _____

   Download one of these articles and email to the instructor.

6. Cited in PMC _____

7. Heart _____

   Heart reviews _____

8. Human Heart _____

   Human Heart reviews _____

9. Human + Heart _____

10. Seizures last month _____

    Seizures March 2008 _____

    Free full text _____

OMIM

What disease did you search? _____

How many genes have been linked to that disease? _____

What is the first gene/locus name that came up? _____

LABORATORY

D

Metric System and the Scientific Method

OBJECTIVES

- Learn the steps of the Scientific Method.
- Learn about the standard units of measurement and prefixes of the metric system.
- Learn about instruments used in science.

VOCABULARY

hypothesis	experiment	variables	independent variable
dependent variable	controlled variable	quantitative	qualitative
accuracy	precision	data	observation
result	interpretation	discussion	conclusion
meter	liter	gram	degrees Celsius
scientific notation	instrument	error	kilo-
centi-	milli-	micro-	nano-
graduated cylinder	pipette	micropipette	beaker
meniscus	graduation	aspirate	

SKILLS

Form a hypothesis.
Apply the steps of the Scientific Method.
Identify types of error.
Convert between U.S. standard units and metric units.
Convert between prefixes in the metric system.
Correctly write numbers and units.
Correctly use graduated cylinders, pipettes, and micropipettes.
Use an electronic balance.
Calculate percent error.
Use a ruler and calculate area and volume.

INTRODUCTION
SCIENTIFIC METHOD

The scientific method is a way to methodically work through a problem to get an answer. It involves asking a question, posing a hypothesis, testing the hypothesis (experimenting), collecting data, interpreting the data, and making a conclusion. The findings of the experiment then need to be communicated to others.

A **hypothesis** is an "educated guess" or statement of what the experimenter thinks is going on, given their background knowledge. A hypothesis is written the the form of a statement, such as "I hypothesize that . . ." or "My hypothesis is that . . ." Note that a hypothesis is only possible after sufficient background research or observation has been conducted to have a reasoned guess about the phenomenon under investigation.

An **experiment** is a test designed to provide data that will show if the hypothesis is false. An experiment includes an **independent variable**, which is varied, a **dependent variable**, which is measured, and **controlled variables** that are held constant. Only one variable should be changed at a time, so the effect of that variable can be measured. It is important to take into account all of the things that could affect the outcome of the experiment and make sure these variables stay the same for each experimental iteration.

An experiment is set up so that the dependent variable can be observed at the end. The observed result, or **observation,** may be measured (with a ruler, thermometer, scale, etc.) or described with the senses (smell, color, sound, etc.). Measurable observations are **quantitative**. Unmeasurable observations are **qualitative**.

An experiment should be repeated several times to see if the same results are achieved each time. When quantitative observations are made, you want to be as accurate and as precise as possible. "**Accuracy**" refers to how close you are to the "true" value. For example, I am about 1.6 m tall. If I measure myself and find that I am 2.00 m tall, I have poor accuracy. "**Precision**" is used two ways: How close together repeated measurements are to each other and how many decimal places a measurement has. We will focus on the first definition in this course. Accuracy and precision are independent. If you take multiple measurements, the measurements can all be very close to the true value (high accuracy) and all be very close in value to one another (high precision); the measurements can average to be very close to the true value (high accuracy) although the individual measurements differ greatly from one another (low precision); the measurements can be far from the true value (low accuracy) but all be very close to each other in value (high precision); or the measurements can be far from the true value (low accuracy) and far apart from one another (low precision).

The information gained from each iteration of the experiment is the **data**. A **result** is the statement of data in words. The data is analyzed for meaning—it's interpreted. An **interpretation** is the analyst's explanation for the relationship between the independent and dependent variables as shown by the data. In a scientific article, this may be called the **discussion**.

From the interpretation, conclusions are drawn. A **conclusion** is usually bigger picture and more widely applicable than an interpretation. Finally, findings from the experiment need to be **communicated**.

Here's an example: Mendel studied inheritance in pea plants in the mid-1800s. He would plant peas, carefully cross-pollinate the resulting plants, plant their offspring peas, and count the number of plants with different traits that resulted. Here are four sets of Mendel's data:

Round peas 5,474	Yellow peas 705	Tall plants 787	Axial pods 651
Wrinkled peas 1,850	Green peas 224	Short plants 277	Terminal pods 207
Ratio 2.96:1	Ratio 3.15:1	Ratio 2.84:1	Ratio 3.14:1

One result Mendel got was he counted 5,474 round peas and 1,850 wrinkled peas from a cross of two parent plants with round peas, each of which had one parent with round peas and one parent with wrinkled peas.

From his data, Mendel drew the following interpretations: the round pea trait (phenotype) is dominant and the wrinkled pea trait is recessive; yellow color is dominant and green pea color is recessive; the tall trait is dominant over the short trait; axial pods are dominant and terminal pods are recessive.

By looking at the ratios of the dominant traits to the recessive traits for each of the traits he studied, Mendel noticed that they all had ratios close to 3:1 dominant : recessive. He concluded the following things: Physical traits are determined by inheritable units (genes); there are dominant and recessive versions of traits (alleles of a gene); an individual has two copies of each inheritable unit, one from their mother and one from their father; having one or two copies of the dominant allele of the gene causes the dominant physical trait; having two copies of the recessive allele of the gene results in the recessive version of the trait to appear. During the formation of sex cells, an individual's two copies of a trait separate, so that each sex cell has only one copy of each gene. Mendel tried to communicate his findings—he sent letter to prominent scientists, including Darwin—but the significance of his discoveries was not recognized. (See the Genetics Lab I for more information.)

Notice that each interpretation is an explanation of the reason he got the results he collected and that the conclusions are visionary for how inheritance works.

METRIC SYSTEM

The International System of Units (*Système International d'Unités*, abbreviated **SI**), is the modern metric system established in 1960 by the General Conference on Weights and Measures, an international organization that works to maintain standardized definitions and practices of measurements.

The metric system has been adopted for all measurements by most of the world, with the major exception being the United States. In the US, the metric system is used by the military, industry, and science, though most day-to-day units are from the U. S. Customary System (USCS), which is derived from the British Imperial system of measurements. Since both systems are standardized, conversion factors exist for transforming a value from one unit to another unit. See table D1 for a list of useful conversion factors for interconverting between USCS and SI units.

Table D1   Conversions between U.S. Customary System and Metric System Units.

Measurement	USCS	Metric	Conversion
length	feet (ft), inch (in)	meter (m)	$1\ ft \approx 0.305\ m$ $1\ in = 2.54\ cm$
Area	square feet (ft²), square inches (in²)	square meter (m²)	$1\ ft^2 \approx 0.093\ m^2$ $1\ in^2 \approx 6.45\ cm^2$
Volume	cubic feet (ft³)	cubic meter (m³)	$1\ ft^3 \approx 0.028\ m^3$
Volume	gallon (gal)	liter (L), cubic centimeter (cm³)	$1\ gal \approx 3.8\ L$ $1\ mL = 1\ cm^3$
Mass	pound (lb), ounce (oz)	gram (g)	$1\ lb \approx 454\ g$ $1\ oz \approx 28.35\ g$
Density		grams/milliliter (g/mL)	water $= 1\ g/ml$
Temperature	Fahrenheit (°F)	Celsius (°C) Kelvin (K)	$(°F{-}32)/1.8 = °C$ $K = °C + 273.15$

☑   If water has a density of 1 g/mL, how much volume does 1 g of water take up?

_____

☑   If (°F – 32)/1.8 = °C, what is the formula for converting °C to °F?

_____

Metric System Base Units

Length: *meter* (m)
Volume: *liter* (L)
Mass: *gram* (g)
Temperature: *degrees Celsius* (°C)
        Also used: *Kelvin* (K)
Time: *seconds* (s)

When we write numbers, we like "nice" numbers, such as between 1 and 100. We tend to avoid fractions, decimals, and numbers with a lot of digits. To achieve "nice" numbers, we can scale numbers up and down using prefixes that are added to the base unit's name. Here are some examples:

One meter is pretty big (about 3 ft). If you want to measure something smaller, then you can use *centimeters* (cm), which are 1/100 of a meter, or *millimeters* (mm), which are 1/1,000 of a meter.
        1 m = 100 cm = 1,000 mm
        The width of my index finger is 10 mm or 1 cm or 0.01 m.

One gram is pretty small. A teaspoon of salt weighs 6 grams. If you want to measure something bigger, then you can use *kilograms* (kg), which are 1,000 grams.
        My cat weighs 4,000 g or 4 kg.

One liter is a bit big (think of a 1 L soda). If you want to measure something smaller, then you can use *milliliters* (mL), which are 1/1,000 of a liter.
        Eye drops are sold in 30 mL or 0.030 L bottles.

Alternately, numbers can be expressed in **scientific notation**. In scientific notation, one number before the decimal is written and then a power of ten in given. For example 100 would be 1.00×10^2 and 0.01 would be 1×10^{-2}. Displaying numbers in scientific notation is convenient for discussing their "order of magnitude." 8,341 and 9,045 would be written 8.341×10^3 and 9.045×10^3, respectively. Both are to the 10^3 power, so they have the same order of magnitude—the same "bigness," if you will. However, the number 723, or 7.23×10^2, is one order of magnitude smaller than the previous two numbers.

Conversions

Conversions are set up like fractions, with the numerator on top and the denominator on bottom, and numbers are multiplied and divided to get to the final answer. The way to know where a number goes in the setup is by using the units. Your starting value, the value you want to convert, is placed first in the equation and it is in the numerator (you can draw a line and put a one under it if this helps you).

Next you will write your conversion factor as a fraction, with the unit you want to solve for (end with) on top and the value with the units you started with in the denominator. If you are interconverting between multiple units, you will add the next conversion factor, so that the next unit you want is on top and the next unit you want to eliminate is on bottom. Then you multiply together the numbers on top and divide by the numbers on bottom.

Table D2   Metric system prefixes for powers greater than base.

Prefix	Abbreviation	Ordinary Notation	Scientific Notation
exo-	E	1,000,000,000,000,000,000	1.0×10^{18}
peta-	P	1,000,000,000,000,000	1.0×10^{15}
tera-	T	1,000,000,000,000	1.0×10^{12}
giga-	G	1,000,000,000	1.0×10^{9}
mega-	M	1,000,000	1.0×10^{6}
kilo-	k	1,000	1.0×10^{3}
hecto-	h	100	1.0×10^{2}
deka-	da	10	1.0×10^{1}

There are two ways to think of the conversion between prefixes smaller than the base unit in the metric system. Pick which way makes more sense to you and then always do your conversions that way.

Table D3   Metric system prefixes for powers smaller than base.

Prefix	Abbreviation	Base Unit Equivalence in Ordinary Notation	Base Unit Equivalence in Scientific Notation	Conversion Factor
deci-	d	0.1	1.0×10^{-1}	10 d in base
centi-	c	0.01	1.0×10^{-2}	100 c in base
milli-	m	0.001	1.0×10^{-3}	1,000 m in base
micro-	μ	0.000001	1.0×10^{-6}	1×10^{6} μ in base
nano-	n	0.000000001	1.0×10^{-9}	1×10^{9} n in base
pico-	p	0.000000000001	1.0×10^{-12}	1×10^{12} p in base
femto-	f	0.000000000000001	1.0×10^{-15}	1×10^{15} f in base
atto-	a	0.000000000000000001	1.0×10^{-18}	1×10^{18} a in base

Examples of converting between USCS and SI units:

Convert 5 inch to centimeters. There are 2.54 cm in 1 inch.

$$5 \text{ in} \times \frac{2.54 \text{ cm}}{1 \text{ in}} = 12.7 \text{ cm}$$

Convert 50 oz to liters. There are 29.5735 mL in 1 oz.

$$50 \text{ oz} \times \frac{29.5735 \text{ mL}}{1 \text{ oz}} \times \frac{1 \text{ L}}{1000 \text{ mL}} = 1.479 \text{ L}$$

Examples of converting between SI unit prefixes:

You can either remember what fraction of the base the prefix is or how many of the prefixes are in the base. For instance, if you want to convert 1 m to cm, you can set up the conversion two ways:

$$1\text{m} \times \frac{1 \text{ cm}}{0.01 \text{ m}} = 100 \text{ cm} \quad \text{OR} \quad 1\text{m} \times \frac{100 \text{ cm}}{1 \text{ m}} = 100 \text{ cm}$$

Convert from 4 m to nm:

$$4\text{m} \times \frac{1 \text{ nm}}{1 \times 10^{-9} \text{ m}} = 4 \times 10^9 \text{ nm} \quad \text{OR} \quad 4\text{m} \times \frac{1 \times 10^9 \text{ nm}}{1 \text{ m}} = 4 \times 10^9 \text{ nm}$$

☑ Set up the conversion of 1 m to mm using both methods.

_____

_____

Whichever way makes more sense to you, memorize the values for centi-, milli-, micro-, nano-, and pico-. You also need to memorize kilo-.

When converting between different prefixes, say from kilometers to centimeters, it is often easiest to convert to the base unit, in this case, meters, in an intermediate step:

Convert 8 km to cm:

$$8 \text{ km} \times \frac{1000 \text{ m}}{1 \text{ km}} \times \frac{100 \text{ cm}}{1 \text{ m}} = 800{,}000 \text{ cm}$$

When doing conversions, check your work to make sure your answer makes sense. For example, if you are converting from meters to nanometers, you should get a very big number, because nanometers are tiny. You can think of this as "cutting up" the bigger meter unit into lots of smaller nanometer units. If you are converting from nanometer to meters, you should get a very small number (less than one) because you are "putting together" very tiny units into a larger unit.

Remember, a positive sign on the superscript in scientific notation is a big number (lots of digits) and a negative superscript is a small number (less than one).

☑   If 1 inch equals 2.54 cm, how many millimeters does 1 inch equal? _____

☑   Lab A stated that the human eye can resolve things down to about 100 μm and that TEM has a resolution of about 0.2 nm. How many times smaller an object can be resolved with TEM than with the eye? _____

Rules for Writing Values

Include a lead zero before the decimal for numbers less than one: 0.15
Do not add a period (.) or "s" to an abbreviation: 10 cm (not 10 cm. or 10 cms)
Put a space between a number and its units: 10 cm
When writing a ratio, do not put spaces between units: g/ml

☑   Convert 12 pg to nanograms. Make sure to format your answer correctly.

_____

INSTRUMENTS

An **instrument** is a device that allows us to measure something. An instrument must be calibrated—compared to a standard—so it can measure with accuracy and precision. Even so, instruments are not perfect; there is error associated with them.

Table D4   Instruments used to make different types of measurements.

Type of Measurement	Instruments Used
Length	Ruler, measuring tape
Volume (liquid)	Graduated cylinder, pipette, micropipette
Mass	Scale, balance
Time	Clock, timer, stopwatch
Temperature	Thermometer, probe

☑ Which instrument would you use to measure the amount of milk you pour on your cereal for breakfast? _____

SOURCES OF ERROR

When we make measurements, our measured values often differ from the "true" value. These differences are due to error. There are three categories of errors that cause inaccuracies: systematic errors, random errors, and human errors.

A **systematic error** is a repeated error, it occurs with every measurement. Once a systematic error is identified, a correction or compensation should be achievable to eliminate or ameliorate the error. There are four types of systematic errors: instrumental, observational, environmental, and theoretical. If an **instrument** is miscalibrated, it will always be wrong by the same amount. If a person is making their **observations** consistently, but in the wrong way, this is a systematic observational error. An **environmental** error is a consistent error caused by the conditions of the experimental site, such as a damaged electrical power supply that has low voltage, thus causing measured currents to be consistently too low. **Theoretical** errors are due to simplifications of the math or model used in the experiment.

Random errors are due to fluctuations in observation method or environment. Random errors will cause some measurements to be too high and some measurements to be too low. Statistical methods can be applied to calculate the effect of random errors.

A **human error** is a mistake. Measurements affected by human error should not be included in data analysis.

☑ Students measure their height and record it in cm. The class data has the following values: 1.57, 162.6, 172.7, 177.8, 182.9. Do you see an example of human error? Explain. _____

_____

☑ After everyone had taken their measurements, a student noticed that the ruler posted on the wall doesn't touch the floor, that it starts an inch off the ground. What kind of error was incorporated into the class data?

_____

ACTIVITY 1: MEASUREMENTS OF LIQUID VOLUMES

INTRODUCTION

In Activity 1, we will practice using tools for liquid measurements, namely a graduated cylinder, a pipette, and a micropipette.

Graduated cylinders are made of either glass or plastic. They have **graduations**, or markings, on the side, that indicate the exact volume at that mark. Typically markings are in milliliters and vary in the size of the marked increments (every 1 mL, 10 mL, etc.). A graduated cylinder is named according to the largest volume it holds; e.g.,: a 100-mL graduated cylinder measures a maximum of 100 mL.

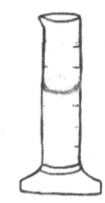

To read a graduated cylinder, the cylinder must be placed on a flat, level surface and your eyes need to be level with the liquid's surface. The liquid may form a **meniscus**, or U-shaped curve, due to adhesion of the liquid with the walls of the graduated cylinder. The correct reading of the volume of the liquid is from the bottom of the meniscus.

Graduated cylinders are usually filled by pouring. When pouring from a larger storage container to a smaller graduated cylinder, it is useful to pour the liquid into an intermediate-sized beaker, to prevent spilling. A funnel may also be used to prevent spilling.

Figure D1 Drawing of a graduated cylinder with meniscus

Pipettes are made of either glass or plastic. They have graduations that indicate the exact volume at that mark. Typically markings are in milliliters and vary in the size of the marked increments (every 0.1 mL, 1 mL, etc.). A pipette is named according to the largest volume it holds; e.g., a 10-mL pipette measures a maximum of 10 mL. Pipettes with a maximum volume between 1 mL and 25 mL are commonly available.

Pipettes are filled by **aspirating** (sucking) fluid up into them using a bulb or pump. There are a number of different styles of pipette bulbs. The simplest type is a bulb that you use by squeezing the air out of the bulb, inserting the tip of the pipette into the fluid you want to measure, and re-inflating the bulb. More complicated ones have multiple valves. We will use a Pipet Helper in lab. To use, squeeze the aspiration bulb. Then press up on the lever to draw up liquid. Dispense liquid by pressing down on the lever. The small, round button is the blow-out function. Your lab instructor will demonstrate use.

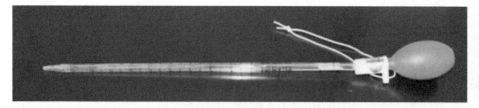

Figure D2   A pipette with attached bulb (left) and another type of bulb (right).

Figure D3   Pipette with Pipet Helper.

Micropipettes are for measuring very small volumes, usually less than a milliliter. The smallest micropipettes can measure as little as 0.1 µL accurately! The largest micropipettes will dispense as much as 5 mL. Common micropipettes include the P20, P200, and P1000. The numbers give the largest volume, in microliters, that the pipettes can measure. Micropipettes can accurately measure volumes within a certain range, and this range is marked on the side of the micropipettes. Pipettes should NOT be used outside their marked range. Pipettes are most accurate in the middle of their marked range and less accurate at the extremes. In this lab we will use a P200, which has a range of use between 20 µL and 200 µL, and a P1000, which can be used for volumes between 100 and 1000 µL (note: 1000 µL = 1 mL). Micropipettes are calibrated to ensure accuracy. Mistreatment of the micropipette, such as setting it to a volume outside its range, will mess up the calibration, leading to inaccurate measurements.

Micropipettes MUST be used with a plastic tip. The fluid is drawn up into the plastic tip and the tip is discarded after the fluid is dispensed. You must be very careful to make sure fluid never enters the barrel of the micropipette itself.

Beakers also have volume markings. However, beakers have very low precision at these markings, because they are so wide compared to their height. Because of this, beakers say "approximate value" or ±5%.

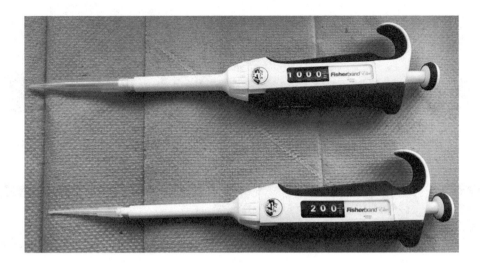

Figure D4 A P1000 micropipette with attached blue tip (top) set to aspirate 1000 μL and a P200 micropipette with attached yellow tip (bottom) set to aspirate 200 μL.

PROTOCOLS

To use a pipette:

1. Hold onto the pipette near the top.
2. Firmly attach the bulb to the top end by pressing and twisting to get a snug fit. Take care not to shatter a glass pipette while doing this.
3. Remove the air from the bulb.
4. Insert the tip of the pipette under the surface of the fluid (do not push the pipette deep into the fluid).
5. Aspirate (suck) the fluid into the pipette by inflating the bulb.
6. Hold the pipette vertically at eye level and check the fluid volume. Adjust as necessary.
7. Squeeze the bulb to release the fluid into the desired receptacle.

Special care needs to be taken when pipetting viscous (thick) fluids. These are slow to aspirate and slow to dispense and may form air bubbles.

To use a micropipette:

1. Turn the dial by twisting the plunger to set the micropipette to aspirate the desired volume. Make sure the correct volume appears in the window on the side of the micropipette.

2. Firmly attach a tip to the micropipette by pressing the end of the micropipette into a tip (of the right size) in the tip box. The P200 uses a yellow tip and the P1000 uses a blue tip.

3. Depress the plunger to the first stop with your thumb and hold the plunger down.

4. Place the very end of the tip into the fluid you want to measure. The end of the tip should stay under the fluid surface the whole time you are drawing it up into the tip, but not very much of the tip should be in the fluid.

5. While the end of the tip remains submerged, slowly lift your thumb up to let the plunger up.

6. Once the plunger is fully released, remove the tip from the solution. If the outside of the tip has a drop of fluid on it, gently wipe the tip against the mouth of the container to remove it.

7. Move the micropipette over the vessel into which you want to dispense the fluid.

8. Slowly depress the plunger to expel the liquid from the pipette tip. Stop at the first stop. If fluid remains in the tip, press the plunger down to the second stop to completely empty the tip.

9. After the fluid is dispensed, remove the tip by pressing the tip ejector button to pop the tip off the end.

While there is fluid in the micropipette or a wet tip on the micropipette, NEVER turn the pipette upside down or past horizontal. Doing so will result in fluid entering the barrel of the micropipette.

The micropipette tips are all sterilized by being autoclaved (see Microbiology Lab F) before being placed in the lab. Please close the lid of the tip container when not using it to minimize contamination from the air. When working with biological samples or sterile solutions, it is critical to maintain sterility. Make sure you do not touch the micropipette tip to anything that is not sterile. If you do, discard the tip and replace it. This will be critical in Microbiology Lab F, but is not important for this lab.

Name _____ Section _____ Date _____

ACTIVITY 1: LIQUID VOLUMES COMPLETION

Skill 1: Using a Graduated Cylinder

1. Set the digital scale to grams (g). (Make sure to include units when recording mass!)

2. Place an empty beaker on a digital scale and record the weight of the beaker: _____

3. Measure 7.5 mL of water using a graduated cylinder.

4. Pour the 7.5 mL of water from the graduate cylinder into the beaker and weigh the beaker with water: _____

5. Compute the mass of the water: _____

6. Convert the mass of water into volume. (Hint: The density of water is 1.0 g/mL.) Show your work.

7. Calculate the percent error of the graduated cylinder. The volume of water calculated from the mass is the "experimental value" and the volume read from the graduated cylinder is the "expected value."

   Percent error = <u>(experimental value − expected value)</u> × 100
   expected value

☑ What does a positive percent error mean? _____
_____

☑ What does a negative percent error mean? _____
_____

Skill 2: Using a Pipette

1. Set the digital scale to grams (g). (Make sure to include units when recording mass!)

2. Place an empty beaker on a digital scale and record the weight of the beaker: _____

3. Measure 7.5 mL of water using a pipette.

4. Dispense the 7.5 mL of water from the pipette into the beaker and weigh the beaker with water: _____

5. Compute the mass of the water: _____

6. Convert the mass of water into volume. (Hint: The density of water is 1.0 g/mL.) Show your work.

7. Calculate the percent error of the pipette (see 7. from the graduated cylinder).

Skill 3: Using Micropipettes

1. Set the digital scale to grams (g). (Make sure to include units when recording mass!)

2. Place an empty weigh boat on a digital scale and record the weight of the weigh boat: _____

3. Measure 150 µL of water using a P1000 micropipette.

☑   Convert 150 µL to mL.

_____

4. Dispense the 150 µL of water from the micropipette into the weigh boat and weigh the weigh boat with water: _____

5. Compute the mass of the water: _____

6. Convert the mass of water into volume. (Hint: The density of water is 1.0 g/mL.) Show your work.

Name _____ Section _____ Date _____

7. Calculate the percent error of the P1000 micropipette (see 7. from the graduated cylinder).

8. Dry the weigh boat and weigh it again: _____

9. Measure 150 μL of water using a P200 micropipette.

10. Dispense the 150 μL of water from the micropipette into the weigh boat and weigh the weigh boat with water: _____

11. Compute the mass of the water: _____

12. Convert the mass of water into volume. (Hint: The density of water is 1.0 g/mL.) Show your work.

13. Calculate the percent error of the P200 micropipette (see 7. from the graduated cylinder).

RESULTS AND INTERPRETATIONS

1. Which instrument showed higher accuracy, the graduated cylinder or the pipette?
   _____

2. What do you think is the source of the difference in accuracy?
   _____
   _____

3. Which instrument showed higher accuracy, the P1000 or P200?
   _____

4. What do you think is the source of the difference in accuracy?
   _____

5. If you needed to measure 8 ml of water, What instrument would you use?
   _____

6. If you needed to measure 140 microliters of water, What instrument would you use?
   _____

Name _____ Section _____ Date _____

ACTIVITY 2: MEASUREMENTS OF LENGTHS

The height of all the students that have lab in this room today will be compiled for you to analyze. Make the following hypotheses about what the data will show. **Justify each hypothesis**. You may use resources to develop your hypotheses.

HYPOTHESES

1. Make a hypothesis about the average height.

_____

_____

2. Make a hypothesis about the median height.

_____

_____

3. Make a hypothesis about the mode of the height.

_____

_____

4. Make a hypothesis about the range in height.

_____

_____

5. Make a hypothesis about the standard deviation of the height. It is expected that 68% of students will have a height that is ±1 standard deviation of the mean.

_____

_____

6. From your hypotheses, calculate your expectation for the heights one standard deviation below the mean and one standard deviation above the mean.

_____

_____

If you made your hypotheses in U.S. Common units, now convert them to metric, in centimeters.

1. _____

2. _____

3. _____

4. _____

5. _____

6. _____

Name _____ Section _____ Date _____

DATA COLLECTION

Height

- Measure your height, in feet and inches:

- Convert your height from feet and inches to inches:

- Convert your height to cm (show work):

- Convert your height to meters (show work):

Hand Span

Splay your hand as far as you can and measure the distance from your thumb to pinkie in cm. Rest your hand and repeat to get three measurements.

- Hand span measurement 1:

- Hand span measurement 2:

- Hand span measurement 3:

Calculate your average hand span:

Round your height and your average hand span to the *nearest* **0.1 cm** and record your results, along with your sex, on the class Excel list.

Name _____ Section _____ Date _____

ACTIVITY 2: HEIGHT EXTENDED ANALYSIS

Data Analysis

1. Open the student height data in Excel.

2. Sort the height data from smallest to largest.

3. Look for any data that shows human error. List the entries and justify why you believe they are due to human error. Then remove these entries from the data set.

_____

_____

_____

_____

4. What is the sample size? _____ # women? _____ # men? _____

5. Calculate the mean, median, mode, and range of the height data.

6. Calculate the standard deviation.

7. Calculate the heights one standard deviation below the mean and one standard deviation above the mean.

8. Calculate the percentage of students who have a height within this range (± 1 standard deviation).

9. Fill in the table below with your hypotheses and calculated values. Don't forget units.

Data Analysis Method	Hypothesized Value	Calculated Value
Mean		
Median		
Mode		
Range		
Standard deviation		
± 1 Standard deviation range		
% Students within ± 1 st dev	68%	

10. Create two histograms on one axis, one with the heights of men and one with the heights of women. Use a bin size of 5 cm. (Refer to the directions in the Data Analysis with Excel lab). Give the histogram a title and label the axes.

11. Create a scatter plot of hand span (*y*-axis) versus height (*x*-axis). Include a title, axis titles, a linear trendline, and an R-squared value.

Data Interpretation

Answer each question fully, in complete sentences. Answers submitted should represent your own, independent interpretation of the experimental data.

1. a. Compare your hypothesized values with your calculated values for mean, median, and mode.
   b. By how much do the calculated mean, median, and mode differ from each other?
   c. By looking at the data and histogram, can you account for differences or sameness between these three measures of centrality? Reference the method of finding each of these three values in your discussion.

2. a. What was your hypothesized range? What was the real range from the class data? How did they differ?
   b. Did you expect the shortest person to be taller or shorter? The tallest person to be taller or shorter?

3. a. What was your hypothesized standard deviation? What was the real standard deviation from the class data? How much do they differ?
   b. Is the student population's height more spread out or more concentrated around the mean than you expected?

4. a. Look at the histogram you created. From the graph, what is the most common height range for women? What is the most common height range for men? What heights do both men and women reach? What heights do only women have? What heights do only men have?
   b. Does the height distribution for women and/or for men show an approximate Gaussian distribution (bell curve)? Explain your answer.
   c. Which population (males or females) would you expect to have a larger standard deviation? Why? Reference the appearance of the histograms in your answer.

5. Is there a direct correlation between hand span and height? Explain your answer by referencing the appearance of the graph and the R-squared value.

6. List your three measurements of your own hand span and your average from Activity 2. How was your accuracy and precision at measuring your hand span? Include the meaning of each term in your discussion.

Submit your typed, numbered responses and two graphs to Blackboard.

Name _____ Section _____ Date _____

ACTIVITY 3: MEASUREMENTS OF TEMPERATURE

The temperature measurements taken by all of the students in lab will be compiled for you to analyze. Make the following hypotheses about what the data will show.

HYPOTHESES

1. Make hypotheses about the (a) mean, (b) range, and (c) standard deviation of the body temperature of lab students.

   a. _____

   b. _____

   c. _____

2. What observations have you made, in life or lab, that inform your hypotheses?

   _____

   _____

3. Make hypotheses about the (a) mean, (b) range, and (c) standard deviation of readings of the laboratory's temperature made by lab students.

   a. _____

   b. _____

   c. _____

4. Explain why you picked your hypotheses.

   a. _____

   _____

   b. _____

   _____

   c. _____

   _____

5. Make hypotheses about the (a) mean, (b) range, and (c) standard deviation of readings of the 37°C water bath's temperature made by lab students.

   a. _____

   b. _____

   c. _____

6. Explain why you picked your hypotheses.

a. _____

_____

b. _____

_____

c. _____

_____

7. Make a hypothesis about which temperature measurement will have more variation: student temperature, room temperature, or water bath temperature.

_____

8. Explain your reasoning.

_____

_____

_____

Name _____ Section _____ Date _____

DATA COLLECTION

Body Temperature

1. Place the thermometer against your temple and measure your body temperature in degrees Fahrenheit (°F) three times.

   • Temperature 1:

   • Temperature 2:

   • Temperature 3:

Calculate your average temperature:

Convert your average body temperature to °C:

Room Temperature Water

2. Read the thermometer in the flask of water and record your reading in °C:

Water Bath Water

3. Read the thermometer in the water bath and record your reading in °C:

4. Record your temperature measurements, in °C, for the three locations on the class list.

Name _____ Section _____ Date _____

ACTIVITY 3: TEMPERATURES EXTENDED ANALYSIS

Data Analysis

1. Open the temperature data from lab in Excel.

2. Sort each column of data from smallest to largest.

3. Look for any data that shows human error. List the entries and justify why you believe they are due to human error. Then remove these entries from the data set.

_____

_____

_____

_____

4. Calculate the mean, range, and standard deviation for each temperature's data.

5. Fill in the table below with your hypothesized and calculated values. Don't forget units.

	Mean	**Range**	**Standard Deviation**
Hypothesized Body Temperature			
Calculated Body Temperature			
Hypothesized Room Temperature			
Calculated Room Temperature			
Hypothesized Water Bath Temperature			
Calculated Water Bath Temperature			

6. Create a histogram for each temperature data set, using a bin size of 0.5°C for each one.

Data Interpretation

Answer each question fully, in complete sentences. Answers submitted should represent your own, independent interpretation of the experimental data.

1. a. Compare your hypothesized means to your calculated means for each location.
   b. Can you account for the differences?

2. a. Compare your hypothesized ranges with your calculated ranges for each location.
   b. Was there more or less variation than you anticipated?
   c. What do you think is the source of the variation? Is the variation a reflection of the true state of the environments measured or due to error?
   d. If you think it's due to error, what kind?

3. a. Compare your hypothesized standard deviations with your calculated standard deviations for each location.
   b. What do the standard deviations tell you about the "trueness" of the calculated averages? (Refer back to Lab B if necessary.)

4. a. Describe the appearance of each of the histograms you created.
   b. Do the graphs look approximately like bell curves?
   c. Should they?

Submit your typed, numbered responses and three graphs to Blackboard.

Name _____ Section _____ Date _____

ACTIVITY 4: BOX MEASUREMENTS AND CALCULATIONS

1. Identify the three sides of the box provided. Measure each side in inches, being as precise as possible. List the sides from smallest to largest.

   a. _____

   b. _____

   c. _____

2. Convert your measurements for the box's sides from inches to centimeters. Show your work.

   a.

   b.

   c.

3. Convert your calculated side lengths from centimeters to millimeters. Show your work.

   a.

   b.

   c.

4. Calculate surface area in **cm²** of the smallest face (which has sides a and b). (Hint: Area is equal to length times width.) Show your work.

5. Calculate the volume of the box **cm³**. (Hint: Area is equal to length times width times length.) Show your work.

6. Convert your measurement for volume from cm³ to milliliters and then to liters. Show your work. (See tables D1 and D3 for conversion factors.)

Name _____ Section _____ Date _____

METRIC SYSTEM & SCIENTIFIC METHOD COMPREHENSION

Do the following conversions. Show your work.

1. Convert 40 cm to m.

$$40 \text{ cm} \times \frac{m}{cm} = \quad m$$

2. Convert 60 kg to g.

$$60 \text{ kg} \times \frac{g}{kg} = \quad g$$

3. Convert _____ pL to mL.

4. Convert _____ °F to °C.

5. Convert _____ g of water to cm³.

6. Convert _____ mm to inches.

7. Convert _____ µg to ng.

8. Convert _____ inches to km.

9. Convert _____ ms to ns.

10. Convert _____ °C to °F.

11. Define each part of the Scientific Method.
    a. Hypothesis: _____
       _____
    b. Experiment: _____
       _____
    c. Results: _____
       _____

    d. Interpretation: _____

_____

    e. Conclusion: _____

_____

    f. Communication: _____

_____

12. The word "diffusion" is flashed on a screen three times and the viewers have to report the number of letters in the word. Describe the accuracy and precision of each viewer.
    a. Viewer A reports the number of letters as 5, 7, 6.
          accuracy: precision:
    b. Viewer B reports the number of letters as 9, 9, 9.
          accuracy: precision:
    c. Viewer C reports the number of letters as 6, 6, 6.
          accuracy: precision:
    d. Viewer D reports the number of letters as 10, 8, 9.
          accuracy: precision:

13. A person uses a P1000 micropipette to measure 1.00 mL of water. This water weighs 0.95 g. What is their percent error? Show your work.

14. You want to test your balance and hypothesize that focusing on a spot in the distance will improve how long you can stand on one foot. You do trials with your eyes closed, your eyes open and roaming, and with your eyes fixed on one spot.
    a. What is the independent variable in this experiment?

_____

    b. What is the dependent variable in this experiment?

_____

    c. What are some variables that should be controlled during this experiment?

_____

15. For each scenario, say what kind of error is causing variations in measurements.
    a. I use a stopwatch to measure how long it takes a ball to fall 1 m and get 0.45 s, 0.48 s, and 0.42 s. _____
    b. I find the stopwatch is sticky and it takes me two pushes to get it to start and stop.

_____

Name _____ Section _____ Date _____

METRIC SYSTEM REVIEW QUESTIONS

1. Which of the following is a hypothesis?
    a.   Why are some plants tall and some short?
    b.   Nitrogen fixation is important for plant height.
    c.   Plants are pretty.
    d.   I think that the height of a plant is directly proportional to the number of hours of direct sunlight it receives each day.

2. Which of the following is a conclusion?
    a.   55 g
    b.   I hypothesize that plants require sunlight for growth.
    c.   Keep 5 plants under a box and 5 plants on a windowsill for 1 month, watering once daily.
    d.   Photosynthetic plants cannot grow in absolute dark.

3. Give the accuracy and precision for each set of repeated measurements. Explain your answers.
    a.   Length of an inchworm: 2.54 cm, 2.53 cm, 2.56 cm, 2.52 cm
    b.   Height of a door: 107 cm, 98 cm, 112 cm, 123 cm
    c.   Temperature of a room: 64.0°C, 63.7°C, 64.2°C, 63.8°C
    d.   Weight of a sugar packet: 2.08 kg, 4.80 kg, 8.02 kg, 0.82 kg
    e.   Volume of soda in a 0.5 L bottle: 525 mL, 506 mL, 539 mL, 517 mL

4. Write each value correctly, using the rules for the metric system.
    a.   .99g/ml
    b.   8 kilos
    c.   25 mill
    d.   .032 ug

5. In lab you observe that the reaction product is dark and shiny. Is this result quantitative or qualitative?

6. In lab you observe that the reaction produces 30 mL^3 of 90°C gas. Is this result quantitative or qualitative?

7. You wish to measure 75 mL of fluid. What would you use?

8. You wish to measure 75 µL of fluid. What would you use?

9. You wish to measure 4 mL of fluid. Which would you use: a 1-mL, 5-mL, or 10-mL pipette? Why is your choice the best option?

10. Why did we switch from a beaker to a weigh boat when weighing the water measured by the micropipette? (Hint: Think about the mass of the beaker versus the weigh boat and the mass of the water.)

11. The window of a P200 shows the volume setting to be 167. What is this volume (including units)?

12. The window of a P200 shows the volume setting to be 034. What is this volume (including units)?

13. Some P1000 micropipettes actually reads in mL. There is a line in the window for the decimal place. A reading of 1|00 is 1 mL or 1000 µL. A reading of 0|80 is 0.80 mL or 800 µL. If you used one of these micropipettes and the window read 0|25, what is the volume setting in mL? in µL?

14. A P20 micropipette can measure 2.0 to 20.0 µL. Some P20 micropipettes underline tenth's place decimal. A reading of 20$\underline{0}$ would be 20.0 µL and a reading of 02$\underline{0}$ would be 2.0 µL. What volume would a micropipette that read 09$\underline{8}$ dispense? (Don't forget units.)

15. You wish to measure 50 µL. Would you use a P200 or a P1000? Explain your reasoning.

16. You wish to measure 100 µL. Would you use a P200 or a P1000? Explain your reasoning.

17. The smallest micropipettes can accurately measure 0.1 µL. Convert this to milliliters. Convert this to liters. Show your work.

18. Transmission Electron Microscopes have a resolution of about 0.2 nm. What is this resolution in micrometers? What is this resolution in picometers?

19. A thermometer is miscalibrated, so it reads 2°C in ice water. What kind of error is this? You have used this thermometer to make many measurements. How should you correct your recorded measurements?

20. A student always reads the volume of a graduated cylinder from the topmost point the liquid touches, instead of the bottom of the meniscus. What kind of error is this?

21. A research site is so cold that all the laboratory equipment has shrunk. What kind of error is this?

22. A student measures an object to the greatest precision possible. She measures three times and gets slightly different lengths each time. What kind of error is this?

23. A student collects data on the same sample from an automated instrument three times and gets slightly different values each time. What kind of error is this?

24. A student measures their height as 166 cm but records it as 1166 cm. What kind of error is this?

25. A student measures their temperature and records it as 98.6°C. What kind of error is this?

26. Activity 2 asked you to collect data on the height of the students in lab. Activity 3 asked you to collect their temperature. Which set of data would you expect to show a Gaussian distribution? Which would you expect not to show a Gaussian distribution? Explain your answers.

27. Write the following numbers in scientific notation:
    a. 1234   c. 10.68   e. 150
    b. 0.0037   d. 0.12   f. 17.3

28. Write the following numbers in common notation.
    a. 1.00×10^2 c. 1.5×10^6 e. 3.14159×10^3
    b. 1.25×10^{-1} d. 1.1×10^{-4} f. 4.12×10^0

29. For each conversion, say if the numerical value of the answer is greater than one or less than one. Do not work the conversion.
    a. 1 km → m   d. 1 mm → cm   g. 1 pm → fm
    b. 1 mm → m   e. 1 cm → μm   h. 1 nm → mm
    c. 1 m → cm   f. 1 nm → μm   i. 1 mm → km

30. Do the following conversions. Show your work.
    a. 9 m → cm   c. 7 m → μm   e. 5 m → pm
    b. 8 m → mm   d. 6 m → nm

31. Do the following conversions. Show your work.
    a. 4 pm → m   c. 2 μm → m   e. 0.5 cm → m
    b. 3 nm → m   d. 1 mm → m

32. Do the following conversions. Show your work.

    a. 9.5 mL → cL
    b. 1.5 cL → mL
    c. 8.5 µL → mL

    d. 2.5 mL → µL
    e. 7.5 pL → nL
    f. 3.5 nL → pL

    g. 6.5 pL → µL
    h. 4.5 µL → pL

33. Do the following conversions. Show your work.

    a. 2 kg → g
    b. 3 kg → cg
    c. 4 kg → mg
    d. 5 kg → µg

    e. 6 kg → ng
    f. 7 kg → pg
    g. 8 pg → kg
    h. 9 ng → kg

    i. 10 µg → kg
    j. 11 mg → kg
    k. 12 cg → kg

34. Do the following conversions. Show your work.

    a. 20 in → cm
    b. 20 in → mm

    c. 60 cm → in
    d. 70 mm → in

35. Do the following conversions. Show your work

    a. 30°C → °F
    b. 20°C → °F

    c. 10°C → °F
    d. 0°F → °C

    e. 40°F → °C
    f. 100°F → °C

36. Do the following conversions. Show your work.

    a. 100 mL of water → g
    b. 90 g water → mL

    c. 80 mL of water → cm^3
    d. 70 cm^3 of water → mL

    e. 60 cm^3 of water → g
    f. 50 g of water → cm^3

37. Do the following conversions. Show your work.

    a. 0.5 kg → pg
    b. 0.6 cg → pg
    c. 0.7 mg → pg
    d. 0.8 µg → pg
    e. 0.9 ng → pg
    f. 0.5 kL → nL
    g. 0.6 cL → nL
    h. 0.7 mL → nL
    i. 0.8 µL → nL
    j. 0.9 pL → nL

    k. 0.5 km → µm
    l. 0.6 cm → µm
    m. 0.7 mm → µm
    n. 0.8 nm → µm
    o. 0.9 pm → µm
    p. 0.5 kg → mg
    q. 0.6 cg → mg
    r. 0.7 µg → mg
    s. 0.8 ng → mg
    t. 0.9 pg → mg

    u. 0.5 km → cm
    v. 0.6 mm → cm
    w. 0.7 µm → cm
    x. 0.8 nm → cm
    y. 0.9 pm → cm
    z. 0.5 cg → kg
    aa. 0.6 mg → kg
    bb. 0.7 µg → kg
    cc. 0.8 ng → kg
    dd. 0.9 pg → kg

38. Do the following conversions. Show your work.

    a. 720 in → km
    b. 0.012 in → µm
    c. 0.013 in → nm

    d. 0.014 in → pm
    e. 500 pm → in
    f. 400 nm → in

    g. 300 µm → in
    h. 0.025 km → in

39. Do the following conversions. Show your work.
    a. 4°C → °F
    b. 98.6°F → °C
    c. 60°C → °F
    d. −40°F → °C
    e. 100°C → °F
    f. 32°F → °C
    g. −10°C → °F
    h. 350°F → °C
    i. 50°C → °F

40. Do the following conversions. Show your work.
    a. 300 mL mercury → cm^3
    b. 50 cm^3 liquid helium → mL

41. You measure 115 mL in a 1-L graduated cylinder. When you weigh the water, you get 121 g. What is the percent error for the measurement?

42. You measure 24.0 mL of water with a 25-mL graduated cylinder. When you weigh the water, you get 22.98 g. What is the percent error for the measurement?

43. You measure 500 µL of water with a micropipette. When you weigh the water, you get 0.486 g. What is the percent error for the measurement?

44. You measure 125 µL of water with a micropipette. When you weigh the water, you get 0.129 g. What is the percent error for the measurement?

LABORATORY
E

Cell Biology

OBJECTIVES
- Learn about cell organelles.
- Learn about diffusion and variables that affect the rate of diffusion.
- Learn about cell membranes and variables that affect diffusion through the membrane.
- Learn about tonicity.

VOCABULARY

eukaryote	prokaryote	cell membrane	phospholipid
phospholipid bilayer	hydrophilic	hydrophobic	diffusion
passive transport	active transport	organelle	nucleus
endoplasmic reticulum	Golgi apparatus	peroxisome	lysosome
mitochondrion	flagellum	cilia	diffuse
equilibrium	osmosis	solute	solvent
concentration	semi-permeable	permeable	impermeable
hypertonic	isotonic	hypotonic	positive control
negative control	colorimetric reagent	Benedict's reagent	silver nitrate

Lugol's solution (KI)

SKILLS

Create a dialysis membrane cell.
Use colorimetric reagents to determine the presence or absence of a substance.

INTRODUCTION

The cell is the smallest unit of life. All living things are composed of one or more cells. All cells come from pre-existing cells. The cell carries out the necessary chemical reactions for life and contains the genetic information that encodes the information necessary for conducting these biochemical processes. This genetic information is passed on to the next generation during cell division. These are the tenets of Cell Theory.

Cells are prokaryotic or eukaryotic. Animals, plants, fungi, and protists are eukaryotes. **Eukaryotes** have their genetic material—DNA—enclosed in a nucleus and other organelles where distinct chemical reactions take place. Bacteria and Archaea are prokaryotes. **Prokaryotes** don't have organelles. In this lab we'll focus on eukaryotes; we'll cover prokaryotes in Microbiology Lab F.

ACTIVITY 1: CELL ORGANELLES

INTRODUCTION

Cells are enclosed in a **cell membrane**, or **plasma membrane**. The membrane is composed of a **phospholipid bilayer**, which is made up of two layers of phospholipids. A **phospholipid** is made up of a **hydrophilic** ("water-loving") phosphate group "head" and two **hydrophobic** ("water-fearing") fatty acid "tails." In the cell membrane, the two layers of phospholipids are arranged "tail-to-tail," so that the hydrophobic tails are sandwiched together and the hydrophilic heads of one layer are facing the water outside the cell and the phosphate heads of the other layer are facing the water inside the cell. This is a stable configuration because hydrophilic molecules or moieties mix readily with water whereas hydrophobic molecules or moieties are not soluble in water and separate from water.

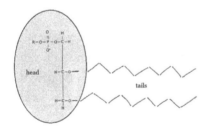

Figure E1   A phospholipid with two fatty acid "tails" and a phosphate "head."

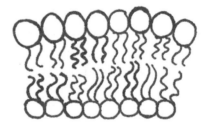

Figure E2   A section of the phospholipid bilayer of the cell membrane, with the fatty acid tails in and the phosphate heads out.

Molecules can move into and out of a cell by several methods. Small, uncharged molecules, such as water, oxygen, and carbon dioxide, can move down their concentration gradient by **passive diffusion** right through the phospholipid bilayer of the cell membrane. Large or charged molecules cannot cross by themselves through the lipid membrane, so they need to be moved by a **transport protein** that spans the membrane. If a molecule is moving down its concentration gradient, moving it doesn't require energy, so it can be moved by **facilitated diffusion** or **passive transport** ("facilitated" because the molecule needs help from a transport protein and "passive" because transport doesn't require energy). Molecules moving up their concentration gradient require the use of energy, in the form of ATP, for transport, in addition to a transport protein. This process is called **active transport**.

Organelles and Structures

Organelles are small "organs" inside the cell that are enclosed in phospholipid bilayer membranes and do specific jobs for the cell. The cell organelles are the nucleus, endoplasmic reticulum (ER), Golgi apparatus, peroxisomes, lysosomes, and mitochondria. The organelles are located in the **cytosol**, the thick liquid of the cell.

The **nucleus**, where the DNA is stored, is enclosed in a double phospholipid bilayer. Here the DNA is stored wrapped around proteins called **histones**, a complex called **chromatin**. Storing DNA as chromatin makes it more compact and stronger.

The **endoplasmic reticulum** (ER) is where secreted proteins and lipids (fats) are synthesized. It is composed of a convoluted series of sacs or tubes of membrane. The area where proteins are synthesized is studded with ribosomes, giving it a rough appearance by electron microscopy, hence the name **rough ER**. The area in which lipids are synthesized lacks ribosomes, and is called the **smooth ER**.

The **Golgi apparatus**, or Golgi body, is a series of flattened sacs of membrane through which proteins and lipids are transported and sent to their final destination, such as outside the cell.

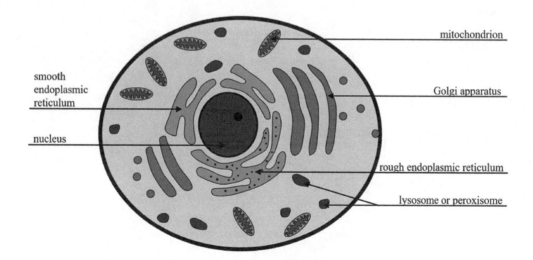

Figure E3 Cartoon diagram of a eukaryotic cell.

Peroxisomes and **lysosomes** are disposal organelles that contain digestive enzymes and molecules, separated from the rest of the cell by a phospholipid bilayer.

Mitochondria (singular: mitochondrion) produce energy, in the form of ATP, for the cell. This is the site of aerobic cellular respiration. Mitochondria are enclosed in a double phospholipid bilayer; the inner membrane has folds, so it has more surface area than the outer membrane.

The plasma membrane covers the surface of the cell, including any projections from the cell, such as flagella or cilia. These structures provide motion. Sperm are the only human cells that have a **flagellum**. **Cilia** in humans are used to move stuff across the surface of the tissue, such as moving mucus in the respiratory tract. Cells with cilia are often covered with these short projections, having hundreds of them, whereas cells with flagella have one or a few long projections. Cilia move with a straight power stroke and a bent recovery stroke, moving liquid over the surface of the cell. Flagella create a wave down their length, propelling the cell forward.

☑   Compare and contrast flagella and cilia.

	Flagella	Cilia
Typical number per cell		
Role in human biology		
Relative length		
Movement of projection		
Direction of propulsion		

Name _____ Section _____ Date _____

ACTIVITY 1: CELL ORGANELLES AND STRUCTURES COMPLETION

Label the parts of the cell.

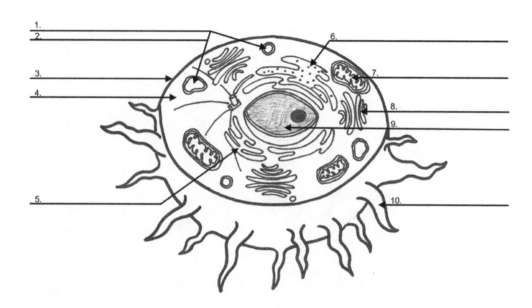

Write what kind of molecules are found inside each cell part and what the part does.

1. and 2. _____

3. _____

4. _____

5. _____

6. _____

7. _____

8. _____

9. _____

10. _____

Name _____ Section _____ Date _____

ACTIVITY 2: DIFFUSION THROUGH A SEMI-SOLID

INTRODUCTION

In this activity we are going to calculate diffusion rates of dye in different conditions.

Molecules **diffuse** (move) down their concentration gradient, from places of high concentration to places of low concentration, to reach **equilibrium**, at which the concentration is equal everywhere. **Concentration** is the amount of substance per space. Because of this, concentration is size-independent. We may see concentration expressed in units such as moles per liter, milligrams per milliliter, grams per cubic centimeter, etc. **Osmosis** is a special word for the diffusion of a liquid, usually water. It may seem funny to think of water as having a concentration, but it does. There are 55.5 moles of water per liter of water. In a solution containing other molecules, water concentration decreases as solute concentration increases. Thus, two locations can have differing concentrations of water, causing osmosis.

EXPERIMENTAL PROCEDURE

Three tubes contain 1.5% agar, a semisolid. A drop of food coloring was added to the top of the agar in each tube. One tube was then put in the refrigerator at 4°C. Another tube was left at room temperature, 20°C. And the third tube was put in the incubator at 37°C. Today you are going to measure the distance (in mm) the dye has diffused into the agar.

In this lab you are also going to time how long it takes for a drop of food coloring to travel through 10 cm of water and calculate the diffusion rate.

Name _____ Section _____ Date _____

HYPOTHESES

1. What do you already know, from life experience or other classes, about the relationship between the density (thickness) or state (e.g., solid, liquid, gas) of a substance and the rate (speed) of diffusion through it?

   _____

   _____

2. What do you already know, from life experience or other classes, about the relationship between the temperature of a substance and the rate (speed) of diffusion through it?

   _____

   _____

3. Based on your knowledge, make a hypothesis about which agar tube will have the fastest diffusion and which agar tube will have the slowest diffusion.

   _____

   _____

4. What will you see that will allow you to compare the rate of diffusion through the different temperature agar tubes?

   _____

   _____

5. Based on your knowledge, make a hypothesis about the relative rate of diffusion through water and through agar.

   _____

   _____

Name _____ Section _____ Date _____

RESULTS

1. Agar diffusion start date and time (from tube) _____

2. Agar diffusion stop date and time (now) _____

3. Elapsed time for agar diffusion (in hours) _____

4. Liquid diffusion time in seconds _____

5. Convert liquid diffusion time to hours _____

6. Complete the following table:

Medium	Distance Traveled (mm)	Diffusion Time (hr)	Diffusion Rate (mm/hr)
Semisolid @ 4°C			
Semisolid @ 20°C			
Semisolid @ 37°C			
Liquid			

7. Is the rate of diffusion through the semisolid fast or slow? _____

8. Should your diffusion rate be a big number or a small number? _____
   If it's not, go back and check your work.

9. Is the rate of diffusion through the liquid water fast or slow? _____

10. Should your diffusion rate be a big number or a small number? _____
    If it's not, go back and check your work.

Name _____ Section _____ Date _____

CONCLUSIONS

1. Based on these experiments, draw a conclusion about the relationship between the temperature of a medium and the rate of diffusion through it.

_____

_____

_____

2. Based on these experiments, draw a conclusion about the relationship between the state of a medium (solid, liquid, gas) and the rate of diffusion through it.

_____

_____

_____

3. If a 5% agar semisolid were used instead of the 1.5% agar, would you expect the rate of diffusion to be faster or slower? Why?

_____

_____

ACTIVITY 3: DIFFUSION THROUGH A SEMI-PERMEABLE MEMBRANE

INTRODUCTION

The purpose of this activity is to learn about diffusion of molecules through a semi-permeable membrane. A **semipermeable** (or **selectively permeable**) membrane is **permeable** to (allows through) some molecules and **impermeable** to (blocks) others, based on some characteristic of the molecule. The plasma membrane of a living cell is permeable or impermeable to molecules based on the molecule's charge, size, and concentration inside the cell. The phospholipid bilayer of a cell is permeable to small, uncharged molecules going down their concentration gradient and impermeable to large molecules, polar or charged molecules, and molecules going up their concentration gradient. In this lab we are going to model a living cell using dialysis membrane, which is porous plastic tubing with uniformly-sized holes.

☑ Based on the description of dialysis tubing, what do you think is the characteristic of molecules that determines if the tubing is permeable or impermeable?

_____

☑ Living cells have several means of moving molecules across their membranes because they have transport proteins. What is the only way molecules can move across the dialysis tubing membrane?

_____

☑ Technically, a "semipermeable" membrane allows or blocks diffusion based on a characteristic whereas a "selectively permeable" membrane can "choose" what to allow or block. Which is the dialysis membrane? Which is a living cell's membrane?

_____

Molecules **diffuse** (spread out) down their concentration gradient to achieve **equilibrium**, the state of uniform concentration. Molecules that are capable of crossing the cell membrane will diffuse through it to achieve equilibrium. If the concentration of a molecule in the solution outside a cell is higher than inside the cell, the solution is said to be **hypertonic**. If the concentration of a molecule in the solution outside a cell is lower than inside the cell, the solution is **hypotonic**. If the concentrations of the molecule inside and outside the cell are the same, then the surrounding solution is **isotonic**.

If the membrane is impermeable to a molecule that has a different concentration outside the cell than in, then water will osmose to try to create equilibrium: The water will move to dilute the molecule. Water will move down its concentration gradient from the area with higher water concentration to the area of lower water concentration.

A hypertonic solution has a relatively high concentration of **solute** (the molecule of interest), which means the solution has a relatively low concentration of water (the **solvent**). In a hypertonic solution, the solute takes up space where water could be, so there is less water in the solution. A cell in a hypertonic solution has relatively low solute and therefore relatively high water concentration, relative to the surrounding solution. So if the membrane is impermeable to the solute, the water will osmose out of the cell, causing the cell to lose volume and shrivel.

A hypotonic solution has a relatively low solute concentration and therefore a relatively high water concentration. A cell in a hypotonic solution has a relatively high solute concentration and a relatively low water concentration, so water from the solution will osmose into the cell, causing it to gain volume and expand, perhaps causing it to pop.

In an isotonic solution, the solute concentration is the same inside and outside the cell, and therefore the water concentration is also equal. In this scenario, movement of water into and out of the cell is balanced and the cell does not change volume.

In this lab we'll create dialysis membrane "cells" with salt (sodium chloride), sugar (glucose), or starch on one side of the membrane and pure water on the other. A molecule of water is composed of one oxygen and two hydrogen atoms. Table salt, NaCl, is composed of two atoms that dissociate (separate) in water. Glucose is made up of twenty-four small atoms. Starch is a large, long polymer of hundreds or thousands of connected glucose molecules. After an incubation time to allow diffusion, we'll test both sides of the membrane for the molecule of interest to see if diffusion occurred.

To detect diffusion we will mix the fluid from the dialysis membrane and the incubation dish bath with a **colorimetric reagent**. The color the colorimetric reagent turns the solution will indicate the presence or absence of the molecule of interest.

To visualize the color change and check for contamination we will also test a positive and a negative control. A **positive control** is something we know contains the molecule of interest, so we know the test should give us a positive result. The positive control tests whether the test is working. A **negative control** does not contain the molecule of interest, so we should see a negative result. The negative control checks for contamination.

HYPOTHESIS

Make a hypothesis about which of these substances will be able to diffuse through the dialysis tubing membrane and which won't. _____
_____
_____

GENERAL EXPERIMENTAL PROTOCOL

Supplies: dialysis tubing, clips, 10% glucose stock solution, 10% sodium chloride stock solution, 1% starch stock solution, pure water stock solution, glass dishes, 10-mL graduated cylinders, funnels.

Safety: Wear goggles when using colorimetric reagents and boiling water.

1. Soak a segment of dialysis tubing in water to soften it.
2. Seal one end of the tubing by folding the bottom sides to the middle to create a point and then folding the point up and securing the folded membrane with a clip, as demonstrated by your lab instructor.
3. Gently rub the top end of the dialysis tubing to open it.
4. Measure out 10 mL of the correct solution and carefully pour it into the dialysis tubing.
5. Fold over the dialysis tubing as you did at the bottom and seal the end with a clip.
6. Rinse and blot dry the filled dialysis tubing "cell" and weigh it. Record the mass.
7. Fill the glass dish with the appropriate fluid and add the dialysis tubing cell.
8. Incubate the cell (leave in the solution) for thirty minutes.
9. Rinse and blot dry the dialysis tubing "cell" and weigh it. Record the mass.
10. Transfer 2 mL of the solution from inside the dialysis tubing into tube 1.
11. Transfer 2 mL of the solution from the incubation dish bath into tube 2.
12. Add 2 mL of the positive control into tube 3.
13. Add 2 mL of the negative control into tube 4.
14. Test the four tubes with the appropriate colorimetric reagent to determine presence or absence of the molecule of interest.

Cleanup

- Thoroughly rinse dishes and clips
- Throw away used tubing
- Throw away plastic pipettes

Figure E4 Dialysis tubing "cell" sealed with clips in bath.

☑ Does the image show a hypertonic, isotonic, or hypotonic solution? _____

Name _____ Section _____ Date _____

EXPERIMENT 1: GLUCOSE IN CELL, WATER IN BATH

A 10% glucose solution is placed inside the dialysis tubing "cell" and incubated in pure water for thirty minutes at room temperature. Afterward, the solution from inside the cell (tube 1) and from the water bath (tube 2) are tested with Benedict's reagent, along with a positive control for the presence of glucose (tube 3) and a negative control for the absence of glucose (tube 4).

Purpose

1. What do you aim to discover with this experiment? (What are you testing?)

_____

_____

2. What data will you collect from this experiment?

_____

_____

Experimental Plan

1. What would you use for the positive control for the presence of glucose?

_____

2. What would you use for the negative control for the absence of glucose?

_____

Hint: What supplies are available to use?

The colorimetric reagent that we use to detect glucose is **Benedict's reagent**. To each tube add 0.5 mL (10 drops) of Benedict's reagent and then heat all the tubes for five minutes in boiling water. The color of the solution after being boiled indicates of the amount of glucose present:

Color	Glucose Concentration
Blue	No glucose
Green	Very low
Yellow	Low
Orange	High
Red	Very high

Name _____ Section _____ Date _____

Hypotheses

1. What colors do you expect your positive and negative controls will turn after the addition of the colorimetric reagent?

positive _____ negative _____

2. Hypothesize what colors the solutions from inside and outside the "cell," after incubation, will turn after the addition of the colorimetric reagent. Explain your hypotheses.

_____

_____

_____

3. If there were a positive change in weight of the cell (final weight – initial weight), what would you think happened during the incubation?_____

_____

4. If there were a negative change in weight of the cell (final weight – initial weight), what would you think happened during the incubation?_____

_____

5. What kind of weight change do you hypothesize will occur for this experiment (positive, negative, none)? Why? _____

_____

_____

☑ In this Experiment, is the bath solution hypertonic, isotonic, or hypotonic to the cell solution?

_____

Name _____ Section _____ Date _____

Results & Conclusions

1. Record the mass of the cell:

   Cell initial mass (g) _____   Initial mass (mg) _____

   Cell final mass (g) _____   Final mass (mg) _____

                                               Change in mass (mg) _____

2. Was there a gain or loss of mass? _____

3. Complete the table with your observations.

Tube	Color	Glucose Concentration
1. Cell		
2. Bath		
3. Positive control		
4. Negative control		

4. Did diffusion occur between the cell and the bath? How can you tell? _____
_____
_____

5. What molecule caused the change in mass? _____

Name _____ Section _____ Date _____

EXPERIMENT 2: WATER IN CELL, GLUCOSE IN BATH

Pure water is placed inside the dialysis tubing "cell" and incubated in a 10% glucose solution for thirty minutes at room temperature. Afterward, the solution from inside the cell (tube 1) and from the incubation dish (tube 2) are tested with Benedict's reagent, along with a positive control for the presence of glucose (tube 3) and a negative control for the absence of glucose (tube 4).

Purpose

1. What do you aim to discover with this experiment? (What are you testing?)

_____

_____

2. What data will you collect from this experiment?

_____

_____

Experimental Plan

1. What would you use for the positive control for the presence of glucose?

_____

2. What would you use for the negative control, for the absence of glucose?

_____

Hint: What supplies are available to use?

The colorimetric reagent that we use to detect glucose is **Benedict's reagent**. To each tube add 0.5 mL (10 drops) of Benedict's reagent and then heat all the tubes for five minutes in boiling water. The color of the solution after being boiled indicates of the amount of glucose present:

Color	Glucose Concentration
Blue	No glucose
Green	Very low
Yellow	Low
Orange	High
Red	Very high

Name _____ Section _____ Date _____

Hypotheses

1. What colors do you expect your positive and negative controls will turn after the addition of the colorimetric reagent?

positive _____ negative _____

2. Hypothesize what colors the solutions from inside and outside the "cell," after incubation, will turn after the addition of the colorimetric reagent. Explain your hypotheses._____
   _____
   _____
   _____

3. If there were a positive change in weight of the cell (final weight—initial weight), what would you think happened during the incubation?_____
   _____

4. If there were a negative change in weight of the cell (final weight—initial weight), what would you think happened during the incubation?_____
   _____

5. What kind of weight change do you hypothesize will occur for this experiment (positive, negative, none)? Why? _____
   _____
   _____

☑   In this Experiment, is the bath solution hypertonic, isotonic, or hypotonic to the cell solution?

   _____

Name _____ Section _____ Date _____

Results & Conclusions

1. Record the mass of the cell:

   Cell initial mass (g) _____   Initial mass (mg)   _____

   Cell final mass (g) _____   Final mass (mg)   _____

                                                 Change in mass (mg) _____

2. Was there a gain or loss of mass? _____

3. Complete the table with your observations.

Tube	Color	Glucose Concentration
1. Cell		
2. Bath		
3. Positive control		
4. Negative control		

4. Did diffusion occur between the cell and the bath? How can you tell? _____
   _____
   _____

5. What molecule caused the change in mass? _____

Name _____ Section _____ Date _____

EXPERIMENT 3: STARCH IN CELL, WATER IN BATH

A 1% starch solution is placed inside the dialysis tubing "cell" and incubated in pure water for thirty minutes at room temperature. Afterward, the solution from inside the cell (tube 1) and from the water bath (tube 2) are tested, along with a positive control for the presence of starch (tube 3) and a negative control for the absence of starch (tube 4).

Purpose

1. What do you aim to discover with this experiment? (What are you testing?)

_____

_____

2. What data will you collect from this experiment?

_____

_____

Experimental Plan

1. What would you use for the positive control?

_____

2. What would you use for the negative control?

_____

Hint: What supplies are available to use?

The colorimetric reagent that we use to detect starch is **potassium iodide (KI),** also known as **Lugol's solution.** Add 2 drops to each tube. If starch is present, the solution will turn purple to black and/or dark precipitate (specks) will form. If no starch is present, the solution will appear yellow (from the iodide).

Name _____ Section _____ Date _____

Hypotheses

1. What colors do you expect your positive and negative controls will turn after the addition of the colorimetric reagent?

positive _____ negative _____

2. Hypothesize what colors the solutions from inside and outside the "cell," after incubation, will turn after the addition of the colorimetric reagent. Explain your hypotheses. _____
   _____
   _____
   _____

3. If there were a positive change in weight of the cell (final weight—initial weight), what would you think happened during the incubation? _____
   _____

4. If there were a negative change in weight of the cell (final weight—initial weight), what would you think happened during the incubation? _____
   _____

5. What kind of weight change do you hypothesize will occur for this experiment (positive, negative, none)? Why? _____
   _____
   _____

☑   In this Experiment, is the bath solution hypertonic, isotonic, or hypotonic to the cell solution?
   _____

Name _____ Section _____ Date _____

Results & Conclusions

1. Record the mass of the cell:

   Cell initial mass (g) _____   Initial mass (mg)   _____

   Cell final mass (g) _____   Final mass (mg)   _____

                                              Change in mass (mg) _____

2. Was there a gain or loss of mass? _____

3. Complete the table with your observations.

Tube	Color	Starch?
1. Cell		
2. Bath		
3. Positive control		
4. Negative control		

4. Did diffusion occur between the cell and the bath? How can you tell? _____
   _____
   _____

5. What molecule caused the change in mass? _____

Name _____ Section _____ Date _____

EXPERIMENT 4: SALT IN CELL, WATER IN BATH

A 10% salt (NaCl) solution is placed inside the dialysis tubing "cell" and incubated in pure water for thirty minutes at room temperature. Afterward, the solution from inside the cell (tube 1) and from the water bath (tube 2) are tested, along with a positive control for the presence of NaCl (tube 3) and a negative control for the absence of NaCl (tube 4).

Purpose

1. What do you aim to discover with this experiment? (What are you testing?)

_____

_____

2. What data will you collect from this experiment?

_____

_____

Experimental Plan

1. What would you use for the positive control?

_____

2. What would you use for the negative control?

_____

Hint: What supplies are available to use?

The colorimetric reagent that we use to detect NaCl is **silver nitrate (AgNO$_3$).** Add 2 drops of silver nitrate to each tube. If NaCl is present, a cloudy, white precipitate will form. If NaCl is absent, the solution will be clear.

Name _____ Section _____ Date _____

Hypotheses

1. What colors do you expect your positive and negative controls will turn after the addition of the colorimetric reagent?

positive _____ negative _____

2. Hypothesize what colors the solutions from inside and outside the "cell," after incubation, will turn after the addition of the colorimetric reagent. Explain your hypotheses._____
_____
_____
_____

3. If there were a positive change in weight of the cell (final weight–initial weight), what would you think happened during the incubation?_____
_____

4. If there were a negative change in weight of the cell (final weight–initial weight), what would you think happened during the incubation? _____
_____

5. What kind of weight change do you hypothesize will occur for this experiment (positive, negative, none)? Why? _____
_____
_____

☑ In this Experiment, is the bath solution hypertonic, isotonic, or hypotonic to the cell solution?
_____

Name _____ Section _____ Date _____

Results & Conclusions

1. Record the mass of the cell:

   Cell initial mass (g) _____ Initial mass (mg) _____

   Cell final mass (g) _____ Final mass (mg) _____

   Change in mass (mg) _____

2. Was there a gain or loss of mass? _____

3. Complete the table with your observations.

Tube	Color	NaCl?
1. Cell		
2. Bath		
3. Positive control		
4. Negative control		

4. Did diffusion occur between the cell and the bath? How can you tell? _____
   _____
   _____

5. What molecule caused the change in mass? _____

Name _____ Section _____ Date _____

DIFFUSION THROUGH A SEMI-PERMEABLE MEMBRANE COMPLETION

Experiment 1

Solution in cell: _____

Solution in bath: _____

Colorimetric indicator used: _____

Molecule presence color: _____

Molecule absence color: _____

Change in mass: _____

Tube	Color	Molecule Present?
1. Cell		
2. Bath		
3. Positive control		
4. Negative control		

Experiment 2

Solution in cell: _____

Solution in bath: _____

Colorimetric indicator used: _____

Molecule presence color: _____

Molecule absence color: _____

Change in mass: _____

Tube	Color	Molecule Present?
1. Cell		
2. Bath		
3. Positive control		
4. Negative control		

Experiment 3

Solution in cell: _____

Solution in bath: _____

Colorimetric indicator used: _____

Molecule presence color: _____

Molecule absence color: _____

Change in mass: _____

Tube	Color	Molecule Present?
1. Cell		
2. Bath		
3. Positive control		
4. Negative control		

Experiment 4

Solution in cell: _____

Solution in bath: _____

Colorimetric indicator used: _____

Molecule presence color: _____

Molecule absence color: _____

Change in mass: _____

Tube	Color	Molecule Present?
1. Cell		
2. Bath		
3. Positive control		
4. Negative control		

Name _____ Section _____ Date _____

ACTIVITY 4: THE EFFECTS OF TONICITY ON RED BLOOD CELLS

INTRODUCTION

Cells require an isotonic solution or else they cannot maintain homeostasis.

- In an **isotonic** solution, the solute concentration is the same inside and outside the cell and thus the water concentration is the same on both sides of the cell membrane.

- In a **hypertonic** solution, the solute concentration is higher outside the cell then inside. If the membrane is impermeable to the solute, then water will osmose across the membrane, down its concentration gradient, from inside the cell to outside the cell. This causes the cell to shrink or shrivel. In red blood cells, this state is called **crenation**.

- In a **hypotonic** solution, the solute concentration is lower outside the cell than inside. If the membrane is impermeable to the solute, then water will osmose across the membrane, down its concentration gradient, from outside the cell to inside the cell. This will cause the cell to swell, possibly pop. The breaking open of red blood cells is called **hemolysis**.

In a 0.9% sodium chloride solution, red blood cells neither crenate nor lyse.

☑ In this lab, we will test red blood cells in four solutions. For each one, indicate if the solution is hypotonic, isotonic, or hypertonic to blood.

0.1% NaCl: _____   What will happen to the cells? _____

0.5% NaCl: _____   What will happen to the cells? _____

0.9% NaCl: _____   What will happen to the cells? _____

10.% NaCl: _____   What will happen to the cells? _____

☑ In this lab we'll hold the tubes containing saline solution and blood up against a book and watch for when we can read the text. Which tube will no longer have cells blocking the words the fastest? Why? _____

_____

☑   Draw a cartoon representing a red blood cell in a (a) hypotonic, (b) isotonic, (c) hypertonic sodium chloride solution.

PROTOCOL

Supplies: 0.1%, 0.5%, 0.9%, and 10% sodium chloride solutions; sheep blood; test tubes with screw-on caps; timers.

Safety: Wear goggles and gloves when handling blood.

1. Obtain four test tubes.
2. Label the tubes with the sodium chloride solution percentages.
3. Using a pipette, add 10 mL of the appropriate saline solution to each tube.
4. While wearing gloves, add 100 µL of sheep's blood to each tube using a micropipette. Pipet slowly to prevent breaking the cells. Cap and invert each tube to mix and record the start time.
5. Observe the solutions by placing the lab manual behind them and watch for when you can read the text through the solution. Record this end time for each tube.
6. Calculate the hemolysis time for each tube.

Cleanup: Rinse out tubes and place them in drain rack.

Name _____ Section _____ Date _____

OBSERVATIONS

	0.1% NaCl	0.5% NaCl	0.9% NaCl	10% NaCl
Start Time				
End Time				
Hemolysis Time				

INTERPRETATIONS

1. Could you see through the 0.1% NaCl solution by the end of the experiment?_____

2. Why? _____

3. Could you see through the 0.5% NaCl solution by the end of the experiment? _____

4. Why? _____

5. Could you see through the 0.9% NaCl solution by the end of the experiment? _____

6. Why? _____

7. Could you see through the 10% NaCl solution by the end of the experiment? _____

8. Why? _____

9. Why was there a difference in hemolysis rate (time to see-through) for the two hypotonic solutions? _____

_____

☑   If you were to repeat this experiment with pure water, what do you expect would happen? _____
What do you think the hemolysis time would be? _____

Name _____ Section _____ Date _____

CELL BIOLOGY COMPREHENSION

1. Suppose an experiment like in lab E were conducted with cellulose, a large polymer composed of thousands of molecules of glucose, inside the dialysis membrane, and pure water in the bath.

    a. After incubation, would you expect the mass of the "cell" to have increased or decreased? _____

    b. Why? _____

    c. After incubation, would you expect to detect cellulose in the bath water? _____

    d. Why or why not? _____

2. Suppose an experiment like in lab E were conducted with fructose, a monosaccharide sugar, inside the dialysis membrane, and pure water in the bath.

    a. After incubation, would you expect the mass of the "cell" to have increased or decreased? _____

    b. Why? _____

    c. After incubation, would you expect to detect fructose in the bath water? _____

    d. Why or why not? _____

3. You create a dialysis membrane "cell" containing NaCl and place it in a bath containing pure water. You incubate the cell at room temperature (20°C) and weigh the cell every ten minutes, then return it to the water bath. At ten minutes, you calculate a change of mass of –50 mg. At twenty minutes, you calculate a change (from the original mass) of –100 mg. At thirty minutes, you calculate a change of mass of –150 mg. At forty minutes, you calculate a change of mass of –180 mg. At fifty minutes, you calculate a change of mass of –200 mg. At sixty minutes, you calculate a change of mass of –200 mg. At seventy minutes, you calculate a change of mass of –200 mg.

    a. How long did it take for the cell and bath to reach equilibrium? _____

    b. If this experiment were repeated with the incubation at 37°C, would you expect it to take more or less time to reach equilibrium? _____

    c. Why? _____

4a. Which organelle stores the genetic information of the cell? _____

4b. Where are secreted proteins translated? _____

4c. Where is ATP generated in the cell? _____

4d. What are the two cellular projections that move? _____

5a. Compared to the cell (dark circle), does the surrounding solution have a higher solute (black dots) concentration, a lower solute concentration, or are the two the same?

_____

5b. Compared to the cell, is the surrounding solution hypertonic, hypotonic, or isotonic? _____

5c. Compared to the cell, does the surrounding solution have a higher water concentration, a lower water concentration, or are the two the same? _____

5d. Assume the solute cannot cross the cell membrane. What is going to diffuse in this scenario? _____

5e. What direction will water diffuse? _____

5f. What will happen to the cell's size? _____

6a. Compared to the cell, does the surrounding solution have a higher solute concentration, a lower solute concentration, or are the two the same? _____

6b. Compared to the cell, is the surrounding solution hypertonic, hypotonic, or isotonic? _____

6c. Compared to the cell, does the surrounding solution have a higher water concentration, a lower water concentration, or are the two the same? _____

6d. Assume the solute cannot cross the cell membrane. What is going to diffuse in this scenario? _____

6e. What direction will water diffuse? _____

6f. What will happen to the cell's size? _____

Name _____ Section _____ Date _____

DIFFUSION REVIEW QUESTIONS

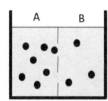

1. a. Two solutions are divided by a semipermeable barrier. Relative to solution A, how would you describe solution B? _____

   b. Once equilibrium is reached, what will the relative concentrations of the solute in the two compartments be? _____

2. a. Compared to the reference sample, which solution is hypotonic?

   _____

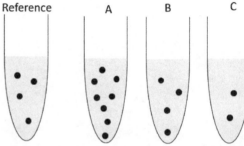

b. hypertonic? _____

c. isotonic? _____

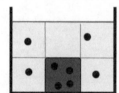

3. A cell (dark gray) is in a beaker of water containing solute (black spots), which is also naturally present inside the cell. The solute cannot diffuse through the cell membrane.

   a. How would you describe the solution, relative to the cell? _____

   b. What will diffuse between the cell and the solution? _____

   c. What will happen to this cell, in this solution? _____

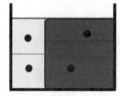

4. A cell (dark gray) is in a beaker of water containing solute (black spots), which is also naturally present inside the cell. The solute cannot diffuse through the cell membrane.

   a. How would you describe the solution, relative to the cell? _____

   b. What will diffuse between the cell and the solution? _____

   c. What will happen to this cell, in this solution? _____

Name _____ Section _____ Date _____

CELL BIOLOGY REVIEW QUESTIONS

1. Why did each experiment in Activity 3 has a positive and a negative control? (i.e., What information do those tests give us?)

2. Explain the results from Activity 3 for Experiment 1: glucose in the cell and water in the bath and Experiment 2: water in the cell and glucose in the bath. What is the effect of switching the locations of the solutions?

3. In the small intestine and the proximal convoluted tubule of the nephrons of the kidney, the epithelial cells have a higher concentration of glucose in them than the fluid around them.

   a. How would you describe the surrounding fluid?

   b. Do you think the plasma membrane of these cells is permeable or impermeable to the extracellular glucose?

4. Table salt, NaCl, dissociates in solution to make charged Na^+ and Cl^- ions. Do you think the phospholipid bilayer is permeable or impermeable to sodium chloride?

5. Proteins are large molecules. Do you think the phospholipid bilayer is permeable or impermeable to proteins?

6. Carbon dioxide is a small, nonpolar molecule. Do you think the phospholipid bilayer is permeable or impermeable to CO_2?

7. List each of the colorimetric reagents used, give what molecule they detect, and state the color they give for the presence and absence of the molecule.

8. Why did we incubate the dialysis membrane "cells" for thirty minutes? How might the results have been different if we had incubated the cell for less time? For more time?

9. Draw a phospholipid; label the "head" and "tails" and identify the hydrophobic and the hydrophilic parts.

10. Draw a small portion of the cell membrane. Label the hydrophobic and hydrophilic parts.

11. What kind of molecules can move through the dialysis membrane? What kind of molecules can't?

12. What kind of molecules can move through a living cell's membrane by passive diffusion? What kind of molecules can't?

13. Cold-blooded animals, such as reptiles, can't regulate their body temperature and have an internal temperature matching their external environment. Inside these organisms' bodies, would diffusion work better on hot or cold days? In summer or winter?

14. A class completes experiments 1–4 of Activity 3 and gets the following results:

Experiment 1	Experiment 2	Experiment 3	Experiment 4
−200 mg	+200 mg	+400 mg	−300 mg
diffusion	diffusion	no diffusion	diffusion

a. Based on their results for Experiments 1 and 2, draw a conclusion about the relationship between the tonicity of the bath solution and the change in mass of the cell.

b. Based on their results for Experiments 1, 3, and 4, draw a conclusion about the relationship between the size of a molecule and the permeability of the dialysis membrane to it.

LABORATORY F

Microbiology

OBJECTIVES

- Learn about types of bacteria.
- Learn about microbiology techniques.

VOCABULARY

prokaryote	gram positive	gram negative	coccus
bacillus	diplo-	strepto-	staphylo-
fastidious	aerobic	anaerobic	facultative
autotroph	heterotroph	aseptic	sterile
autoclave	contamination	media	agar
broth	colony	lawn	turbid
hemolytic	selective	differential	EMB
MAC	CFU	serial dilution	inoculate

SKILLS

Determine if a bacterial colony is gram positive or gram negative.
Determine if a bacterial colony can ferment lactose or not.
Determine if a bacterial colony is hemolytic.
Conduct a serial dilution.
Use aseptic technique.
Inoculate an agar plate.

INTRODUCTION

Microorganisms, or microbes, are microscopic organisms—that is, organisms so small that a microscope is required to see them. Organisms from the domains Bacteria and Archaea are all microscopic. Within the domain Eukarya, mites are an example of microscopic Animalia; kingdom Fungi contains microscopic yeasts; and Protista are almost all microscopic. In this lab we are going to focus on bacteria.

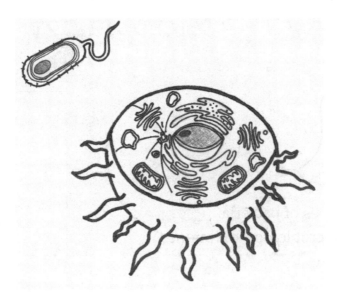

Figure F1   Prokaryotic cell (upper left) and eukaryotic cell (lower right). Prokaryotic cells are smaller and simpler than eukaryotic cells.

Bacteria are **prokaryotes**. Prokaryotes are, on average, smaller than eukaryotes. (Refer to Cell Biology Lab E for more about eukaryotes.) Prokaryotes do not contain membrane-bound organelles. The circular DNA of a prokaryote is sequestered to one area of the cytosol and is not contained in a nucleus. Bacteria are encapsulated by both a cell membrane and a cell wall. The composition of the cell surface of bacteria can be divided into two categories based on how they stain, using a method developed by Hans Christian Gram in 1882.

Gram Stain

The Gram stain procedure is used to give contrast to bacteria on a slide for observation under a microscope. In this procedure, bacteria on a slide are first stained with the dye crystal violet. Then an iodine solution is added to form large, water-insoluble dye complexes. Next the cells are washed with ethanol. Finally, the cells are stained again with a weak, red dye (counterstain). Under the microscope, bacteria are identified based on what color they stain: bacteria that retain the color of crystal violet—appear dark blue or violet—are called gram positive and bacteria colored red by the counterstain are said to be gram negative. Whether or not the bacteria retain the crystal violet dye is due to the structure of the cell surface. **Gram-positive** bacteria have a thick proteoglycan (amino acid–carbohydrate complex) cell wall outside their cell membrane. The water-soluble crystal violet enters the cell, but when the dye reacts with the iodine solution it forms large, insoluble complexes. When the ethanol is added, the ethanol causes osmosis of water out of the cell wall, causing it to shrink, trapping the dye complexes inside the cell. Thus, these cells appear purple. **Gram-negative** cells have an inner cell membrane, a thin proteoglycan cell wall, and a second, outer lipid membrane. When these cells are treated with crystal violet, the dye travels through the outer lipid membrane. When the cells are washed with ethanol, the outer lipid membrane is degraded and removed. The thin cell wall in gram-negative bacteria is insufficient to retain the dye during the ethanol wash. After the wash, these cells are colorless. To visualize them, a red dye is added. This red dye also bathes the gram-positive bacteria, but the first, dark purple stain overwhelms the pale red color in these bacteria. A bacterium's identity as gram positive or gram negative has a number of important implications, such as its susceptibility to different classes of antibiotics.

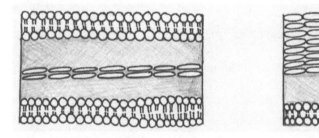

Figure F2   Gram-negative cell envelope with inner and outer phospholipid bilayers and central, thin cell wall (left) and gram-positive cell envelope with cell membrane and thick cell wall (right).

Bacterial Shapes

Bacteria (singular: bacterium) come in different shapes and configurations. Bacteria can be spherical, called **cocci** (singular: coccus); elongated rods, called **bacilli** (singular: bacillus); curved like a comma, called vibrios; or spiral, called spirilla (singular: spirillum) or spirochetes. The bacteria may associate in different arrangements: as pairs (**diplo-**), as groups of four (tetrads), as chains (**strepto-**), or as clusters (**staphylo-**).

Name _____ Section _____ Date _____

ACTIVITY 1: MICROSCOPY
ANABAENA

Anabaena are relatively large bacteria that form filaments. When environmental nitrogen is low, about every tenth bacterium in a filament will stop photosynthesis and instead fix nitrogen, converting N_2 from the air to ammonia, which the cell uses to make nucleic acids and amino acids. These nitrogen-fixing cells are called heterocysts. Photosynthesis is an aerobic process and nitrogen fixation in anaerobic, so a cell cannot do both. The heterocysts receive glucose from neighboring cells and in exchange provide nitrogen-containing organic molecules to those cells.

☑ Explain why, in your own words, a cell cannot do both photosynthesis and nitrogen fixation. _____

_____

Draw a picture of an anabaena filament under the microscope. Note the magnification.

total magnification: ___ x

OTHER BACTERIAL SLIDES

View and draw the other bacterial slides: *Bacillus cereus, Bacillus megaterium, Staphylococcus albus, Micrococcus luteus, spirillum, spirogyra* vegetative.

These bacteria are very small and still hard to distinguish at the highest magnification. If you are having trouble finding them on the slide, try getting a slide with a larger specimen in focus at the highest magnification and then carefully removing the slide and putting the bacterial slide in its place without changing any settings and then using the fine focus knob to find the bacteria. Some slides have faded, so the colors are dim; these are easier to see with lower light.

Name _____ Section _____ Date _____

_____ total magnification: ___ x	_____ total magnification: ___ x	_____ total magnification: ___ x
_____ total magnification: ___ x	_____ total magnification: ___ x	_____ total magnification: ___ x

ACTIVITY 2: COLLECTION, IDENTIFICATION, AND SERIAL DILUTION OF ENVIRONMENTAL MICROBES

INTRODUCTION

Bacterial Growth

Bacteria grow and divide quickly, with a doubling rate as fast as twenty minutes. Environmental conditions play a significant role in the rate of bacterial reproduction. Bacteria will achieve their maximum rate of cell division under ideal conditions for temperature, food, salt, humidity, light, pH, O_2 and CO_2 partial pressures. Bacteria that live in and on humans prefer our body temperature, 37°C, and grow optimally at this temperature. They grow more slowly at a higher or lower temperature. **Fastidious** bacteria require a special food source to grow. Without the special nutrient, like blood, these bacteria cannot grow. **Aerobic** bacteria require the presence of oxygen for growth. **Anaerobic** bacteria require the absence of oxygen for growth. **Facultative** bacteria can grow in either the presence or absence of oxygen. Bacterial growth is exponential, as modeled by this equation:

$$\# \, bacteria_{final \, time} = \# \, bacteria_{start \, time} \times 2^{elapsed \, time \, / \, doubling \, time}$$

☑   If you start with one bacterium in ideal conditions, after three hours (180 minutes) you would have $1 \times 2^{180/20} = 512$ bacteria. How many bacteria would you have after the same period of time under nonideal conditions, when the doubling time is one hour?

Bacteria get their energy from different sources. **Autotrophic** bacteria can produce their own energy, either by photosynthetic conversion of sunlight, water, and carbon dioxide into sugar (**photoautotrophs**) or by doing chemical reactions (**chemoautotrophs**). **Heterotrophic** bacteria absorb nutrients from the environment or a host organism.

Bacteria divide to form identical progeny cells—*clones*. These clones pile up and will eventually form a visible pile, called a **colony**, if grown on a solid medium. As a rule of thumb, a colony must contain a million cells to be visible. If a plate is inoculated (infused) with too many bacteria, bacterial growth will completely cover the plate and you will not see individual colonies. This growth is called a **lawn**. In solution (broth), the presence of lots of bacteria makes the liquid cloudy or *turbid*.

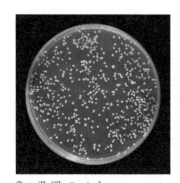

© sruilk/Shutterstock.com

Figure F3   Plate with white colonies.

© Alexander Gold/Shutterstock.com

Figure F4   Plate with bacterial lawn.

Figure F5   Clear (left) and turbid (right) liquid broth.

Selective and Differential Media

Microorganisms are grown in labs in artificial environments that best mimic their ideal conditions. Microbes are grown in or on **media**, which provides nutrients and is pH-buffered. Liquid media is called **broth**. Liquid media is converted to solid media by the addition of **agar**, a polysaccharide extracted from seaweed. After sterilization in an autoclave, hot media is poured into Petri dishes to make agar plates for colony growth. Bacteria are cultured in incubators that maintain the ideal temperature, humidity, and carbon dioxide partial pressure. Many different types of media are available to allow selection of certain types of bacteria and differentiation of bacteria based on specific traits.

Selective media inhibits the growth of some types of bacteria and permits the growth of other types. Therefore, you know something about a bacterium based on whether it's alive and growing or dead and not present.

Differential media provides a visual contrast between bacteria. You know something about a bacterial colony based on what color it is.

Nutrient Agar (NA) is a very commonly used medium for growing bacteria. This is a general-purpose growth media on which most microorganisms can grow. It is neither selective nor differential. It contains carbohydrates, amino acids, vitamins, a nitrogen source, and salts—all the nutrients most microorganisms need to grow.

MacConkey (MAC) agar is both selective and differential. Only gram-negative bacteria can grow on MAC agar. MAC agar contains bile salts and crystal violet, both of which can inhibit the growth of gram-positive bacteria. MAC agar contains a neutral red pH indicator. Bacteria that can ferment lactose produce acid, which lowers the pH of the area around the bacteria, causing the color of the pH indicator to change. Colonies that are on red or pink areas can ferment lactose (such as *Escherichia coli*, *Enterobacter*, and *Klebsiella*).

☑ *Lactobacillus* is a genus of gram-positive, "friendly," lactose-fermenting bacteria. If you swabbed a *Lactobacillus* strain on a MAC plate, what would you see?

_____

Eosin Methylene Blue (EMB) agar selects for gram-negative bacteria. EMB agar contains the dyes eosin and methylene blue, which inhibit the growth of gram-positive bacteria. These dyes are also pH-sensitive. Bacterial colonies that can ferment lactose produce acid, changing the local environment's pH, changing the color of the dyes in the EMB agar. *E. coli* looks metallic green. Other lactose-fermenting bacteria may appear purple for vigorous fermenters, pink for slow fermenters (such as *Klebsiella* and *Enterobacter*), or brown. Bacteria that cannot ferment lactose are not colored (such as *Pseudomonas aeruginosa*) and may show the color of the plate through the colonies. EMB plates are often used to isolate fecal coliforms, bacteria from the colon.

☑ You may see different results on MacConkey agar and EMB agar, even though they are selective and differential for the same traits. Hypothesize why this could be.

_____

_____

Blood agar (BA) is made by adding 5% sheep blood to nutrient agar. Thus, blood agar is not selective—it doesn't inhibit the growth of any type of microorganism. The presence of blood allows fastidious bacteria that require blood to grow on it as well. Blood agar is differential. Bacteria that require blood for growth break down red blood cells, producing various waste products, which have different colors. **Alpha-hemolytic** bacteria produce a green waste product. *Streptococcus pneumoniae*, which causes pneumococcal pneumonia and other diseases, is an example of an alpha-hemolytic bacterium. **Beta-hemolytic** bacteria completely digest red blood cells, causing the media around these colonies to appear clear—all of the red blood cells in their vicinity are gone. *Streptococcus pyogenes*, the bacteria that causes strep throat, is beta-hemolytic. *Enterococcus*, which causes UTIs and other infections, is also beta-hemolytic. **Gamma-hemolytic** bacteria are not hemolytic at all. Colonies that are not colored do not use the red blood cells for growth. If you have bacteria with hemolytic activity on your blood agar plate, please keep it closed!!

☑ *S. pyogenes* is a gram-positive bacterium that ferments lactose to lactic acid. If you streaked nutrient agar, EMB, and blood agar plates with *S. pyogenes,* what would you expect to see on each plate?

_____

_____

_____

Serial dilution

Serial dilutions are performed to reduce the number of cells in a culture. Bacteria can be grown to concentrations as high as a billion (10^9) cells per milliliter of media.

☑ If you were to plate 1 mL of this 10^9 cells/mL solution, would you be able to count the colonies on the plate? _____

☑ What if you plated 100 µL? _____

☑ What if you plated 10 µL? _____

A **serial dilution** is a repeated mixing of a culture with a fluid to reduce the number of cells. If we dilute a culture a known amount and then count the number of colonies produced by the diluted product, we can calculate the number of bacteria in the original culture. We will express the number of bacteria as the number of colony-forming units (CFU) and the concentration of bacteria as CFU/mL. A **colony-forming unit (CFU)** is a bacterium: Each bacterium has the capacity to divide to create a colony of clones.

A series of dilutions is used to create less concentrated cultures with a known relationship to the original culture. The series is constructed so that the same dilution is conducted each time. In this lab we will use a 1:10 dilution, which means each new tube has 1/10th the concentration of the previous tube. This is done by mixing a small volume of the previous culture into a volume of fluid $10\times$ as large.

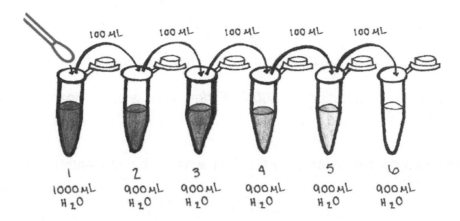

Figure F6 Schematic of setting up a 1:10 serial dilution.

☑ If 1×10^6 cells are placed into tube 1, what would the concentration of that culture be?

_____

If a 1:10 serial dilution is done, as shown in Figure F6, what would the concentration of: Tube 2 be? _____   of Tube 3? _____

Tube 4? _____   Tube 5? _____

Tube 6? _____

How many times more dilute is the culture in tube 6 compared to the culture in tube 1?

_____

We can calculate the concentration of the culture in a tube by inoculating a plate with a small amount of the culture and counting the number of colonies that grows.

$$Concentration\ (CFU/mL) = \frac{\#\ colonies}{inoculation\ volume\ (mL)}$$

☑ If a plate is inoculated with 100 μL of culture and 24 colonies grow, what is the concentration of the culture? _____

☑ If 50 μL of culture is plated and 60 colonies grow, what is the concentration of the culture? _____

Once you know the culture concentration of one of the tubes in the dilution series, you can calculate the concentration of any of the other tubes in the series.

$$Concentration\ (CFU/mL)\ of\ Tube_y = concentration\ Tube_x \times dilution\ factor^{(x-y)}$$

☑ If tube 2 has a concentration of 30000 CFU/ml, what is the concentration of tube 4 in a 1:10 dilution? _____

☑ If tube 6 has a concentration of 12 CFU/ml, what is the concentration of tube 2 in a 1:10 dilution? _____

☑ If 100 μL of culture from tube 3 was plated and grew 56 colonies, what is the concentration of the culture in tube 1 from a 1:10 dilution?

_____

In this activity, your group of four students will swab a location and culture the microbes collected. You will inoculate nutrient agar, EMB, and blood agar plates and do a serial dilution. Once colonies grow, you should be able to determine how many bacteria were picked up from the environment and learn about the characteristics of the bacteria: namely, if they are gram positive, gram negative, or both; whether or not they can ferment lactose; and whether or not they are hemolytic.

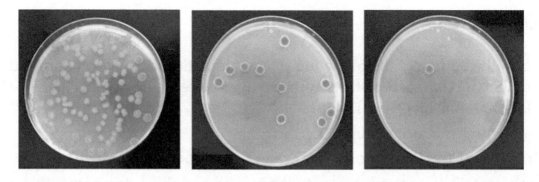

Figure F7 Three plates from a serial dilution.

☑ The plate on the left in figure F7 contains 100 colonies, the middle plate contains 10 colonies, and the last plate contains 1 colony. What is the dilution factor for this serial dilution? _____

☑ Which plate came from the culture that was most concentrated? The most dilute?
   _____

☑ If, for each of these plates, 100 μL of culture from the dilution tube was plated, what is the concentration (in CFU/mL) of the culture in the corresponding tube?
   _____
   _____
   _____

☑ This serial dilution is of bacteria collected from an environment and mixed with 1 mL of water (tube 1). If these plates came from tubes 1, 2, and 3 of a serial dilution, calculate the number of bacteria collected from the environment. Explain why you should get the same result regardless of which plate you use for the calculation.
   _____
   _____
   _____

PROTOCOL

1. Label the bottom of the following plates, along the edge, with your group number and lab section: three nutrient agar plates (also number), one EMB plate, and one blood agar plate.
2. Label three microcentrifuge tubes 1 to 3.
3. Transfer 1000 μL (1 mL) of sterile water to the first microcentrifuge tube.
4. Transfer 900 μL of sterile water to the second and third microcentrifuge tubes.
5. Swab 4 cm^2 of the sample with a sterile cotton swab, then vigorously mix the swab into the sterile water in tube 1.
6. Close and vortex tube 1.
7. Transfer 100 μL of solution from tube 1 into tube 2.
8. Close and vortex tube 2.
9. Transfer 100 μL of solution from tube 2 into tube 3.
10. Vortex tube 1 and transfer 100 μL of solution from tube 1 onto each of the following plates: the first nutrient agar plate, the blood agar plate, and the EMB plate.
11. Vortex tube 2 and transfer 100 μL of solution from tube 2 onto nutrient agar plate 2.
12. Vortex tube 3 and transfer 100 μL of solution from tube 3 onto nutrient agar plate 3.
13. Gently tap out about a dozen glass beads onto each plate. Slide the plates (with their lids on) around on the table to roll the beads across the surface of the plates. The beads spread out the liquid to get even distribution of the bacteria and thus even distribution of the colonies. Keep agitating the plates until all of the liquid is absorbed into the agar.
14. Once the solution has been absorbed by the plates, pour the glass beads from each plate into the jar of ethanol.
15. Give the plates to your instructor to incubate at 37°C for one to two days.
16. Following incubation, the plates will be stored in the cold room (4°C) until the next class period.
17. During the next lab period, record the number, size, and appearance of colonies on each plate. If there are lots (hundreds or thousands) of colonies, you can divide the plate into equal segments, count the number of colonies in one segment, then multiply that colony count by the number of segments on the plate to get an estimate of the total number of colonies on the plate. When analyzing the blood agar plate, hold it up to the light to look for cleared zones around colonies where the blood cells in the media have been lysed.

Name _____ Section _____ Date _____

PURPOSE

1. What do you aim to learn from this experiment?

_____

_____

2. What data will you collect from this experiment?

_____

_____

Complete this image illustrating the protocol by filling in the appropriate volumes:

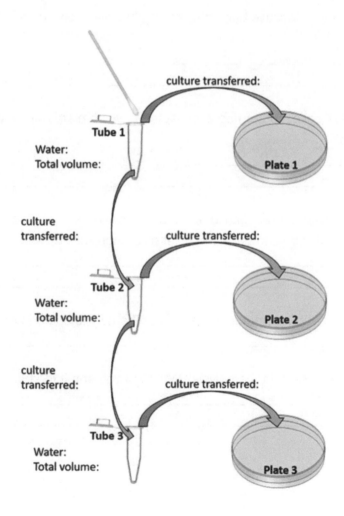

Name _____ Section _____ Date _____

HYPOTHESES

1. Make a hypothesis about the number (order of magnitude) of bacteria picked up in the 4 cm^2 area you swabbed.

_____

2. Make a hypothesis about whether you picked up gram-positive, gram-negative, or both types of bacteria. Note that gram-positive bacteria tend to be benign and pathogenic bacteria tend to be gram-negative.

_____

3. a. If you collect gram-negative bacteria, which plate will show you this? What will you see?

_____

_____

   b. If you do NOT collect gram-negative bacteria, which plate will show you this? What will you see?

_____

_____

   c. If you collect both gram-negative and gram-positive bacteria, how will you know? Which plates will you compare and what difference will you see?

_____

_____

4. Make a hypothesis about whether you picked up hemolytic bacteria or not.

_____

5. Which plate will you check for hemolysis? What will you see if the bacteria are hemolytic?

_____

_____

Name _____ Section _____ Date _____

OBSERVATIONS AND INTERPRETATIONS

EMB Observations	**EMB Interpretation**
Growth?	Gram-_____
# colonies: _____ color: _____	_____ ferment lactose
# colonies: _____ color: _____	_____ ferment lactose
# colonies: _____ color: _____	_____ ferment lactose
Other observations:	
Blood Agar Observations	**Blood Agar Interpretation**
# colonies: _____ color: _____	_____ hemolytic
# colonies: _____ color: _____	_____ hemolytic
# colonies: _____ color: _____	_____ hemolytic
Other observations:	

Nutrient Agar Plate 1 Observations	Nutrient Agar Plate 2 Observations	Nutrient Agar Plate 3 Observations
# colonies:	# colonies:	# colonies:

1. Calculate the ratio of colonies between plates 3 and 2:

   _____

2. Calculate the ratio of colonies between plates 2 and 1:

   _____

3. What was the expected colony ratio between these plates?

   _____

4. If your ratio is not what was expected, can you provide an explanation for what affected your ratio?
   If your ratio was what was expected, what does this say about your technique and accuracy?

   _____

   _____

5. What fraction of the culture from a tube did you spread on the corresponding NA plate?

   _____

6. If you use plate 1 to calculate the number of bacteria you collected from your environmental source, how many bacteria did you collect?

   _____

work:

7. If you use plate 2 to calculate the number of bacteria you collected from your environmental source, how many bacteria did you collect?

_____

work:

8. If you use plate 3 to calculate the number of bacteria you collected from your environmental source, how many bacteria did you collect?

_____

work:

9. What is the mean value for the number of bacteria collected?

_____

10. What is the standard deviation of the number of bacteria collected? (Use Excel, see Lab B.) _____

11. Express the mean in scientific notation (see Lab D) and express the standard deviation to the same power as the mean, using the form: mean ± standard deviation.

_____

12. How does the order of magnitude of your standard deviation compare to the number of bacteria collected? _____

_____

13. What does the relative order of magnitude tell you about your certainty about the number of bacteria collected? _____

_____

14. What does the relative order of magnitude tell you about your accuracy in setting up the serial dilution? (Refer to Lab B to review meaning of standard deviation.)

_____

_____

15. Were the bacteria from the source gram positive, gram negative, or both?

_____

_____

16. How can you tell? _____

_____

17. Could any of the bacteria from this source ferment lactose?

_____

18. How can you tell? _____

_____

19. Were any of the bacteria from this source hemolytic?

_____

20. How can you tell? _____

_____

MICROBIOLOGY EXTENDED ANALYSIS

Submit your typed observations and interpretations from this activity to Blackboard. In your observations, include a description of the growth on each of the plates you inoculated in full sentences. Include the numbers and colors of colonies. For each interpretation, explicitly state your observation and link your observation to your interpretation to support your assertion.

ACTIVITY 3: VISUALIZING CONTAMINATION
INTRODUCTION
Sterilization and Aseptic Technique

We want to grow only the microorganism(s) we **inoculate**, or add, to the media and not any others, so we need to prevent **contamination** by unwanted microorganisms. Microorganisms are everywhere. There are thousands of species of bacteria in and on us, microorganisms floating in the air, and microbes coating surfaces of objects. To minimize the risk of contamination, we must use aseptic technique with sterile equipment.

Aseptic technique minimizes contact of the growth media with possible contaminants, such as our hands and the air. Keep lids on as much as possible, and when opening containers, keep the lid over them. For liquid broth in tubes, hold the tube at an angle to minimize the profile of the opening to limit contaminants falling in from the air. When using a micropipette, use sterile tips and change them frequently. If possible, work near a flame (Bunsen burner); the updraft from the flame carries contaminants away. Wearing gloves can minimize contamination from the hands. Lab equipment, such as pipette tips, test tubes, swabs, and Petri dishes, as well as media, are sterilized before use. **Sterile** supplies have no living

Figure F8   Inoculation of a plate. Note that the scientist is using aseptic technique: the lid is only open as far as it has to be and that it is covering the media.

bacteria on them. Sterilization is performed with an **autoclave**, which heats to high temperature (121°C) and elevated pressure for fifteen to thirty minutes to sterilize lab materials.

☑   Convert 121°C to °F. _____

In this activity, we will inoculate tubes of broth and look for the growth of contamination.

PROTOCOL

1. Each group should collect three tubes of broth and a sterile loop.
2. Number each tube and label each with your section, group, and initials.
3. Inoculation of tube 1: Using your best sterile technique, unwrap the sterile loop, uncap tube 1, swish the sterile loop in the broth, and recap the tube.
4. Inoculation of tube 2: Wipe the loop around on the desktop (both sides). Uncap tube 2 and swish the sterile loop around in the broth, then recap the tube.
5. Inoculation of tube 3: Uncap tube 3 for 15 minutes, then recap.
6. Give the inoculated tubes to your instructor. Tubes will be incubated at 37°C overnight, preferably with shaking to aerate samples.

Name _____ Section _____ Date _____

HYPOTHESES

1. Do you expect bacterial growth in tube 1? Why? _____

_____

2. Do you expect bacterial growth in tube 2? Why? _____

_____

3. Do you expect bacterial growth in tube 3? Why? _____

_____

OBSERVATIONS

Tube 1	Tube 2	Tube 3

INTERPRETATION

1. In which tube(s) did contaminating bacteria grow? How can you tell? _____

_____

2. Which tube(s) had no contamination? How can you tell? _____

_____

CONCLUSION

1. How successful was your aseptic technique? Explain your reasoning. _____

_____

2. What things in lab are contaminated with bacteria? _____

_____

Name _____ Section _____ Date _____

MICROBIOLOGY COMPREHENSION A

1. Complete the image below for the serial dilution completed in lab, indicating the dilution factor at each step.

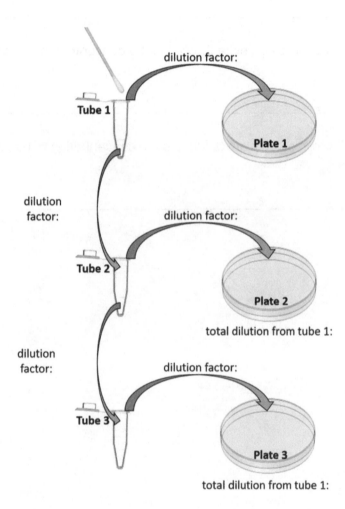

2. If you counted 2189 colonies on plate 1, how many bacteria were collected on the cotton swab?

_____

3. If you counted 364 colonies on plate 2, how many bacteria were collected on the cotton swab?

_____

4. If you counted 28 colonies on plate 3, how many bacteria were collected on the cotton swab?

_____

5. If you counted 1345 colonies on plate 1, what is the concentration of bacteria, in CFU/mL, in tube 1?

_____

6. If you counted 216 colonies on plate 2, what is the concentration of bacteria, in CFU/mL, in tube 1?

_____

7. If you counted 47 colonies on plate 3, what is the concentration of bacteria, in CFU/mL, in tube 1?

_____

Name _____ Section _____ Date _____

MICROBIOLOGY COMPREHENSION B

1. You do a 1:10 serial dilution and count 2812 colonies on plate 1.

   a. How many colonies would you expect of plate 2? _____

   b. How many colonies would you expect of plate 3? _____

2. You do a 1:10 serial dilution and count 12 colonies on plate 3.

   a. Approximately how many colonies would you expect of plate 2? _____

   b. Approximately how many colonies would you expect of plate 1? _____

3. You do a 1:10 serial dilution and count 281 colonies on plate 2.

   a. How many colonies would you expect of plate 1? _____

   b. How many colonies would you expect of plate 3? _____

4. You do a 1:10 serial dilution and count 149 colonies on plate 2.

   a. How many colonies would you expect of plate 3? _____

   b. How many colonies would you expect of plate 1? _____

5. a. You transfer 100 μL of culture onto a plate and count 26 colonies. What is the concentration of bacteria in the culture tube, in CFU/mL? _____

   b. You transfer 100 μL of culture onto a plate and count 37 colonies. What is the concentration of bacteria in the culture tube, in CFU/mL? _____

   c. You transfer 50 μL of culture onto a plate and count 4 colonies. What is the concentration of bacteria in the culture tube, in CFU/mL? _____

   d. You transfer 125 μL of culture onto a plate and count 201 colonies. What is the concentration of bacteria in the culture tube, in CFU/mL? _____

6. a. You have a culture with a bacterial concentration of 50 CFU/mL and you inoculate a nutrient agar plate with 100 μL of it. How many colonies would you expect to grow?

   _____

b. You have a culture with a bacterial concentration of 70 CFU/mL and you inoculate a nutrient agar plate with 100 μL of it. How many colonies would you expect to grow?

_____

c. You have a culture with a bacterial concentration of 180 CFU/mL and you inoculate a nutrient agar plate with 25 μL of it. How many colonies would you expect to grow?

_____

d. You have a culture with a bacterial concentration of 240 CFU/mL and you inoculate a nutrient agar plate with 250 μL of it. How many colonies would you expect to grow?

_____

7. You make a 1:10 serial dilution and transfer 100 μL of culture onto each corresponding plate. You count 176 colonies on plate 3.

a. How many colonies would you expect of plate 2? _____

b. How many colonies would you expect of plate 1? _____

c. What is the concentration of bacteria in the culture tube 3? _____

d. What is the concentration of bacteria in the culture tube 2? _____

e. What is the concentration of bacteria in the culture tube 1? _____

8. You make a 1:10 serial dilution and transfer 100 μL of culture onto each corresponding plate. You count 4729 colonies on plate 1.

a. How many colonies would you expect of plate 2? _____

b. How many colonies would you expect of plate 3? _____

c. What is the concentration of bacteria in the culture tube 1? _____

d. What is the concentration of bacteria in the culture tube 2? _____

e. What is the concentration of bacteria in the culture tube 3? _____

9. You make a 1:10 serial dilution and transfer 100 μL of culture onto each corresponding plate. You count 146 colonies on plate 3.

a. What is the concentration of bacteria in the culture tube 3? _____

b. What is the concentration of bacteria in the culture tube 2? _____

c. How many colonies would you expect of plate 2? _____

d. What is the concentration of bacteria in the culture tube 1? _____

e. How many colonies would you expect of plate 1? _____

10. You make a 1:10 serial dilution and transfer 100 μL of culture onto each corresponding plate. You count 3329 colonies on plate 1.

   a. What is the concentration of bacteria in the culture tube 1? _____

   b. What is the concentration of bacteria in the culture tube 2? _____

   c. How many colonies would you expect of plate 2? _____

   d. What is the concentration of bacteria in the culture tube 3? _____

   e. How many colonies would you expect of plate 3? _____

11. You streak an environmental swab on an EMB plate and incubate it overnight at 37°C. The next day you see pink colonies on the plate.

   a. Are the bacteria gram positive or gram negative? _____

   b. Can they ferment lactose? _____

12. You inoculate an EMB plate with bacteria and grow colorless colonies.

   a. Can the bacteria ferment lactose? _____

   b. Are they gram positive or gram negative? _____

13. You find metallic green colonies on an EMB plate.

   a. What kind of bacteria have you grown? _____

   b. What is their Gram state? _____

   c. Can they ferment lactose? _____

14. You streak bacteria on an EMB plate and after three days of incubation there are still no colonies. What do you know about the bacteria from this?

   _____

15. You streak some bacteria on a nutrient agar plate and a blood agar plate. You get no growth on the NA plate and greenish colonies on the BA plate. Explain why you got no growth on the NA plate. Explain what the greenish color on the BA plate means.

   _____

   _____

16. You streak some bacteria on a nutrient agar plate and an EMB plate. You get lots of colonies on the nutrient agar plate and none on the EMB plate. Explain why you got no growth on the EMB plate.

   _____

   _____

17. You swab an environmental source for bacteria and then inoculate a nutrient agar plate, an EMB agar plate, and a blood agar plate. After incubation at 37°C for two days, you observe 40 white colonies on the nutrient agar plate, 10 white colonies on the EMB plate, and 30 white colonies and 10 green on the blood agar plate.

   a. Did you collect gram-positive, gram-negative, or both types of bacteria from the environmental source? Explain your answer by referencing the growth on the pertinent plates.

   _____

   _____

   b. Did you collect lactose-fermenting bacteria from the environmental source? Explain your answer by referencing the growth on the pertinent plate.

   _____

   _____

   c. Did you collect hemolytic bacteria from the environmental source? Explain your answer by referencing the growth on the pertinent plate.

   _____

   _____

   d. What is the minimum number of bacterial cells that were picked up from the environment? _____

18. You do an environmental swab and inoculate a nutrient agar plate, an EMB agar plate, and a blood agar plate. After incubation at 37°C for two days, you observe 80 beige colonies on the nutrient agar plate, 80 pink colonies on the EMB plate, and 80 green colonies on the blood agar plate.

   a. Are the bacteria on the nutrient agar plate gram positive or gram negative? Explain your reasoning._____

   _____

   b. Are the bacteria on the blood agar plate gram positive or gram negative? Explain your reasoning._____

   _____

   c. Are the bacteria on the blood agar plate hemolytic? Explain your reasoning.

   _____

   d. Are the bacteria on the nutrient agar plate hemolytic? Explain your reasoning.

   _____

e. Can the bacteria on the EMB plate ferment lactose? Explain your reasoning.

_____

f. Do the bacteria on the nutrient agar plate have the ability to ferment lactose? Explain your reasoning.

_____

_____

g. Do the bacteria on the blood agar plate have the ability to ferment lactose? Explain your reasoning.

_____

_____

19. a. What is it called when you heat up something to kill the bacteria? _____

b. What is the machine called where this is done? _____

c. Introduction of unwanted microbes is called what? _____

d. What is a cloudy liquid culture called? _____

e. What is bacterial growth on a plate that is so thick there are no individual colonies called?

_____

20. a. What is a CFU? What is a lay term for a CFU?

_____

b. Explain how a bacterial colony is formed. Include the word "clones."

_____

_____

_____

Name _____ Section _____ Date _____

MICROBIOLOGY COMPREHENSION C

1. Answer each of the questions below using the plate images provided.

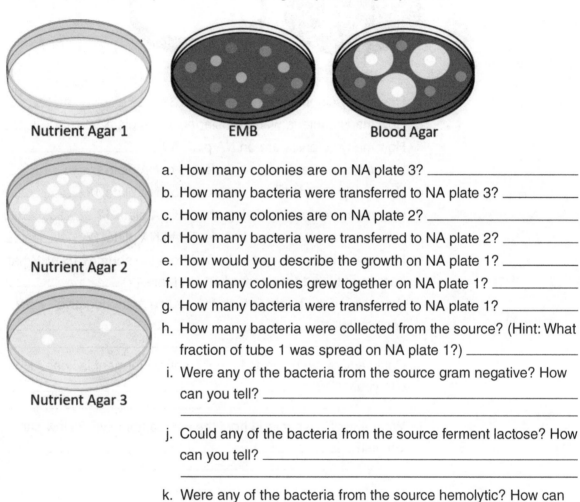

Nutrient Agar 1   EMB   Blood Agar

Nutrient Agar 2

Nutrient Agar 3

a. How many colonies are on NA plate 3? _____

b. How many bacteria were transferred to NA plate 3? _____

c. How many colonies are on NA plate 2? _____

d. How many bacteria were transferred to NA plate 2? _____

e. How would you describe the growth on NA plate 1? _____

f. How many colonies grew together on NA plate 1? _____

g. How many bacteria were transferred to NA plate 1? _____

h. How many bacteria were collected from the source? (Hint: What fraction of tube 1 was spread on NA plate 1?) _____

i. Were any of the bacteria from the source gram negative? How can you tell? _____

_____

j. Could any of the bacteria from the source ferment lactose? How can you tell? _____

_____

k. Were any of the bacteria from the source hemolytic? How can you tell? _____

_____

Name _____ Section _____ Date _____

2. Answer each of the questions below using the plate images provided.

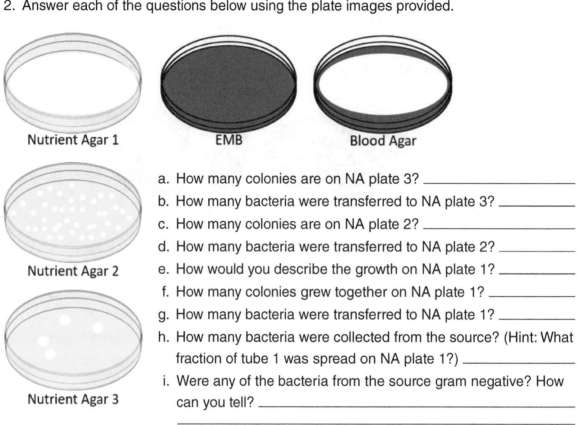

Nutrient Agar 1   EMB   Blood Agar

Nutrient Agar 2

Nutrient Agar 3

a. How many colonies are on NA plate 3? _____

b. How many bacteria were transferred to NA plate 3? _____

c. How many colonies are on NA plate 2? _____

d. How many bacteria were transferred to NA plate 2? _____

e. How would you describe the growth on NA plate 1? _____

f. How many colonies grew together on NA plate 1? _____

g. How many bacteria were transferred to NA plate 1? _____

h. How many bacteria were collected from the source? (Hint: What fraction of tube 1 was spread on NA plate 1?) _____

i. Were any of the bacteria from the source gram negative? How can you tell? _____
_____

j. Could any of the bacteria from the source ferment lactose? How can you tell? _____
_____

k. Were any of the bacteria from the source hemolytic? How can you tell? _____
_____

Name _____ Section _____ Date _____

3. Answer each of the questions below using the plate images provided.

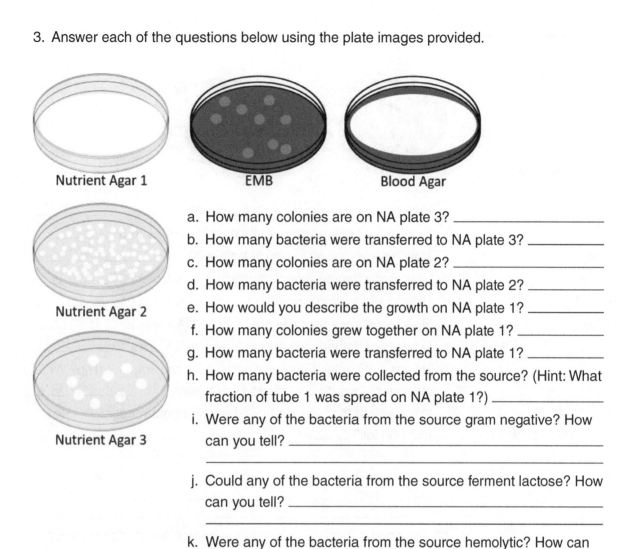

Nutrient Agar 1   EMB   Blood Agar

Nutrient Agar 2

Nutrient Agar 3

a. How many colonies are on NA plate 3? _____

b. How many bacteria were transferred to NA plate 3? _____

c. How many colonies are on NA plate 2? _____

d. How many bacteria were transferred to NA plate 2? _____

e. How would you describe the growth on NA plate 1? _____

f. How many colonies grew together on NA plate 1? _____

g. How many bacteria were transferred to NA plate 1? _____

h. How many bacteria were collected from the source? (Hint: What fraction of tube 1 was spread on NA plate 1?) _____

i. Were any of the bacteria from the source gram negative? How can you tell? _____

_____

j. Could any of the bacteria from the source ferment lactose? How can you tell? _____

_____

k. Were any of the bacteria from the source hemolytic? How can you tell? _____

_____

Name _____ Section _____ Date _____

4. Answer each of the questions below using the plate images provided.

Nutrient Agar 1   EMB   Blood Agar

Nutrient Agar 2

Nutrient Agar 3

a. How many colonies are on NA plate 3? _____

b. How many bacteria were transferred to NA plate 3? _____

c. How many colonies are on NA plate 2? _____

d. How many bacteria were transferred to NA plate 2? _____

e. How would you describe the growth on NA plate 1? _____

f. How many colonies grew together on NA plate 1? _____

g. How many bacteria were transferred to NA plate 1? _____

h. How many bacteria were collected from the source? (Hint: What fraction of tube 1 was spread on NA plate 1?) _____

i. Were any of the bacteria from the source gram negative? How can you tell? _____

_____

j. Could any of the bacteria from the source ferment lactose? How can you tell? _____

_____

k. Were any of the bacteria from the source hemolytic? How can you tell? _____

_____

Name _____ Section _____ Date _____

5. Answer each of the questions below using the plate images provided.

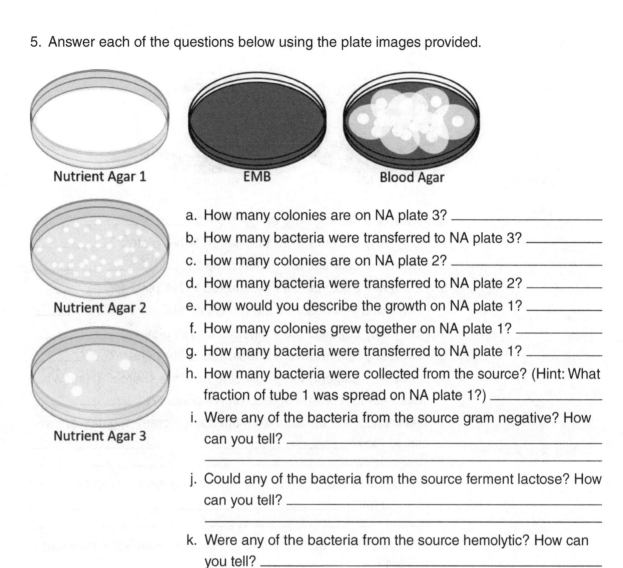

Nutrient Agar 1   EMB   Blood Agar

Nutrient Agar 2

Nutrient Agar 3

a. How many colonies are on NA plate 3? _____
b. How many bacteria were transferred to NA plate 3? _____
c. How many colonies are on NA plate 2? _____
d. How many bacteria were transferred to NA plate 2? _____
e. How would you describe the growth on NA plate 1? _____
f. How many colonies grew together on NA plate 1? _____
g. How many bacteria were transferred to NA plate 1? _____
h. How many bacteria were collected from the source? (Hint: What fraction of tube 1 was spread on NA plate 1?) _____
i. Were any of the bacteria from the source gram negative? How can you tell? _____
_____
j. Could any of the bacteria from the source ferment lactose? How can you tell? _____
_____
k. Were any of the bacteria from the source hemolytic? How can you tell? _____
_____

Name _____ Section _____ Date _____

6. Answer each of the questions below using the plate images provided.

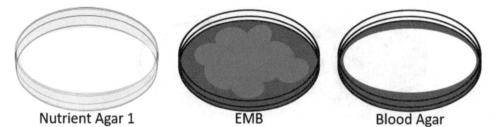

Nutrient Agar 1   EMB   Blood Agar

Nutrient Agar 2

Nutrient Agar 3

a. How many colonies are on NA plate 3? _____

b. How many bacteria were transferred to NA plate 3? _____

c. How many colonies are on NA plate 2? _____

d. How many bacteria were transferred to NA plate 2? _____

e. How would you describe the growth on NA plate 1? _____

f. How many colonies grew together on NA plate 1? _____

g. How many bacteria were transferred to NA plate 1? _____

h. How many bacteria were collected from the source? (Hint: What fraction of tube 1 was spread on NA plate 1?) _____

i. Were any of the bacteria from the source gram negative? How can you tell? _____

_____

j. Could any of the bacteria from the source ferment lactose? How can you tell? _____

_____

k. Were any of the bacteria from the source hemolytic? How can you tell? _____

_____

Name _____ Section _____ Date _____

MICROBIOLOGY REVIEW QUESTIONS

1. You do a 1:10 serial dilution and count 2 colonies on plate 6.

   a. How many colonies would you expect of plate 5?

   b. How many colonies would you expect of plate 4?

   c. How many colonies would you expect of plate 3?

   d. How many colonies would you expect of plate 2?

   e. How many colonies would you expect of plate 1?

2. You do a 1:10 serial dilution and count 281 colonies on plate 1.

   a. How many colonies would you expect of plate 2?

   b. How many colonies would you expect of plate 3?

3. You do a 1:10 serial dilution and count 397 colonies on plate 2.

   a. How many colonies would you expect of plate 1?

   b. How many colonies would you expect of plate 3?

4. You do a 1:2 serial dilution and count 8 colonies on plate 2.

   a. How many colonies would you expect of plate 1?

   b. How many colonies would you expect of plate 3?

5. a. You transfer 100 μL of culture onto a plate and count 26 colonies. What is the concentration of bacteria in the culture tube?

   b. You transfer 100 μL of culture onto a plate and count 37 colonies. What is the concentration of bacteria in the culture tube?

   c. You transfer 500 μl of culture onto a plate and count 194 colonies. What is the concentration of bacteria in the culture tube?

   d. You transfer 75 μL of culture onto a plate and count 41 colonies. What is the concentration of bacteria in the culture tube?

6. You make a 1:10 serial dilution and transfer 100 μL of culture from tube 3 onto plate 3. You see 13 colonies grow.

   a. What is the concentration of bacteria in tube 3?

   b. What is the concentration of bacteria in tube 2?

   c. What is the concentration of bacteria in tube 1?

   d. How many colonies would you expect of plate 2?

   e. How many colonies would you expect of plate 1?

7. You make a 1:15 serial dilution and transfer 250 μL of culture from tube 3 onto plate 3. You count 17 colonies on plate 3.

   a. What is the concentration of bacteria in the culture tube 3?

   b. What is the concentration of bacteria in the culture tube 2?

   c. How many colonies would you expect of plate 2?

   d. What is the concentration of bacteria in the culture tube 1?

   e. How many colonies would you expect of plate 1?

8. You make a 1:25 serial dilution and transfer 75 μL of culture from tube 1 onto plate 1. You count 6,362 colonies on plate 1.

   a. How many colonies would you expect of plate 2?

   b. How many colonies would you expect of plate 3?

   c. What is the concentration of bacteria in the culture tube 1?

   d. What is the concentration of bacteria in the culture tube 2?

   e. What is the concentration of bacteria in the culture tube 3?

9. A serial dilution is created by repeatedly transferring 100 μL of the previous culture to the next tube containing 900 μL of water. 100 μL of the culture from tube 4 was spread on a plate and 21 colonies grew.

   a. What is the dilution factor used in this serial dilution?

   b. How many bacteria were present in the 100 μL of culture used from tube 4?

   c. How many milliliters were plated from tube 4?

   d. What is the CFU/mL concentration of tube 4?

   e. What is the CFU/mL concentration of tube 5?

   f. What is the CFU/mL concentration of the tube 1?

g. How many colonies would you expect to see on a plate that had 100 μL of culture from tube 3 spread on it?

h. How many colonies would you expect to see on a plate that had 100 μL of culture from tube 5 spread on it?

10. A serial dilution is created by repeatedly transferring 100 μL of the previous culture to the next tube containing 400 μL of water. 250 μL of the culture from tube 5 was spread on a plate and 55 colonies grew.

a. What is the dilution factor used in this serial dilution?

b. How many bacteria were present in the 250 μL of culture used from tube 5?

c. How many milliliters were plated from tube 5?

d. What is the CFU/mL concentration of tube 5?

e. What is the CFU/mL concentration of tube 4?

f. What is the CFU/mL concentration of tube 1?

g. How many colonies would you expect to see on a plate that had 250 μL of culture from tube 6 spread on it?

h. How many colonies would you expect to see on a plate that had 250 μL of culture from tube 4 spread on it?

11. a. You do a serial dilution and count 189 colonies on plate 4, 19 colonies on plate 5, and 2 colonies on plate 6. What was your dilution factor?

b. You do a serial dilution and count 1875 colonies on plate 4, 75 colonies on plate 5, and 3 colonies on plate 6. What was your dilution factor?

c. You do a serial dilution and count 1008 colonies on plate 4, 84 colonies on plate 5, and 7 colonies on plate 6. What was your dilution factor?

d. You do a serial dilution and count 256 colonies on plate 4, 32 colonies on plate 5, and 4 colonies on plate 6. What was your dilution factor?

12. a. You have a bacterial culture with a concentration of 60 CFU/ml and inoculate a plate with it and grow 3 colonies. How much of the culture did you transfer to the plate? Give your answer in microliters.

b. You have a bacterial culture with a concentration of 80 CFU/mL and inoculate a plate with it and grow 40 colonies. How much of the culture did you transfer to the plate? Give your answer in microliters.

c. You have a bacterial culture with a concentration of 160 CFU/mL and inoculate a plate with it and grow 24 colonies. How much of the culture did you transfer to the plate? Give your answer in microliters.

13. Nutrient Agar contains all the nutrients most microorganisms need to grow. What kind of bacteria are the exception?

14. You streak an environmental swab on a MAC plate and incubate it overnight at 37°C. The next day you see pink colonies on the plate. What type of organism have you grown? Is it gram positive or gram negative? Can it ferment lactose?

15. You inoculate an EMB plate with bacteria and grow colorless colonies. Can the bacteria ferment lactose? Are they gram positive or gram negative?

16. You find metallic green colonies on an EMB plate. What kind of bacteria have you grown?

17. You streak bacteria on a MAC plate and after three days of incubation there are still no colonies. What do you know about the bacteria from this?

18. You streak some bacteria on a nutrient agar plate and a blood agar plate. You get no growth on the NA plate and greenish colonies on the BA plate. Explain why you got no growth on the NA plate. Explain what the greenish color on the BA plate means.

19. You streak some bacteria on a nutrient agar plate and an EMB plate. You get lots of colonies on the nutrient agar plate and none on the EMB plate. Explain why you got no growth on the EMB plate.

20. You swab an environmental source for bacteria and then inoculate a nutrient agar plate, an EMB agar plate, and a blood agar plate. After incubation at 37°C for two days, you observe 40 white colonies on the nutrient agar plate; 6 white and 4 purple colonies on the EMB plate; and 30 white colonies, 6 green colonies, and 4 colonies will clear halos around them on the blood agar plate.

    a. Did you collect gram positive, gram negative, or both types of bacteria from the environmental source? Explain your answer by referencing the growth on the pertinent plates.

    b. Assuming that the same numbers and types of bacteria were swabbed on all plates, what percentage of the bacteria collected from the environmental source were gram positive? Gram negative?

    c. Did you collect lactose-fermenting bacteria from the environmental source? Explain your answer by referencing the growth on the pertinent plate.

    d. Assuming that the same numbers and types of bacteria were swabbed on all plates, what percentage of the bacteria collected from the environmental source had the ability to ferment lactose?

e. Did you collect hemolytic bacteria from the environmental source? Explain your answer by referencing the growth on the pertinent plate.

f. Assuming that the same numbers and types of bacteria were swabbed on all plates, what percentage of the bacteria collected from the environmental source were hemolytic?

g. Do you think the hemolytic bacteria are gram positive or gram negative? Why?

h. What is the minimum number of bacterial cells that were picked up from the environment?

21. You do an environmental swab and inoculate a nutrient agar plate, an EMB agar plate, and a blood agar plate. After incubation at 37°C for two days, you observe 80 beige colonies on the nutrient agar plate, 80 pink colonies on the EMB plate, and 80 white colonies and 20 green colonies on the blood agar plate.

a. Why does the blood agar plate have more colonies than the other plates?

b. Which color colonies are hemolytic?

c. Can you learn anything about the Gram state of the hemolytic bacteria from this experiment? Explain.

d. Are the bacteria on the nutrient agar plate gram positive, gram negative, or both? Explain your reasoning.

e. Do the bacteria on the nutrient agar plate have the ability to ferment lactose? Explain your reasoning.

f. Are the bacteria on the nutrient agar plate hemolytic? Explain your reasoning.

22. We use a machine that heats and pressurizes samples. What is this machine called? What is this machine doing?

23. An unused tube of broth is cloudy. Why? (What happened to it?) What's the term for cloudy liquid?

24. In microbiology, what is a "clone"?

25. Describe in your own words how a colony is formed.

26. Bacterial growth that covers a plate—instead of having individual colonies—is called what?

27. a. If you start with one bacterium with a doubling time of twenty minutes, how many bacteria will you have in one hour? After four hours? After twelve hours?

    b. What if you started with two bacteria?

    c. With 10 bacteria?

28. Refrigeration slows, but does not stop, bacterial growth. People suggest you throw out leftovers after three days. Explain why this advice helps prevent food poisoning.

29. a. *Salmonella* has a doubling time of about ten hours at 10°C. It takes about thirty hours to thaw a chicken in the refrigerator. How many times more bacteria are on the thawed chicken than on the frozen chicken?

    b. *Salmonella* has a doubling time of about one hour at 25°C. It takes about five hours to thaw a chicken in a warm kitchen. How many times more bacteria are on the thawed chicken than on the frozen chicken?

30. Describe how *Anabaena* look under the microscope. What do the larger, different-looking cells do?

31. In each box, name and sketch the type of bacterium indicated by the column and row.

	Round	Rod-Shaped
Pairs		
Chains		
Clusters		

32. Compare and contrast prokaryotes and eukaryotes.

	Prokaryotes	Eukaryotes
Nucleus?		
Organelles?		
Cell size?		
Multicellular?		
Organism types?		

33. Compare and contrast the types of agar used in this lab.

	NA	EMB	MAC	BA
Full name				
Composition				
Differential?				
Selective?				
Grows				
Color of colonies and meaning				

LABORATORY
G

Molecular Biology

VOCABULARY

DNA	genome	nucleotide	adenine
guanine	cytosine	thymine	phosphodiester bond
polynucleotide	antiparallel	hydrogen bond	double helix
alleles	SNPs	restriction enzyme	restriction site
palindrome	RFLP	electrophoresis	plasmid
comb	well	gel	buffer
lane	band	ethidium bromide	intercalate
loading dye	DNA ladder	reference band	base pair (bp, kb)

SKILLS

Digest DNA with a restriction enzyme.
Pour, load, run, and analyze a gel.

INTRODUCTION

DNA (deoxyribose nucleic acid) encodes the genetic information for life. The **genome** (full set of DNA) of eukaryotic cells is packaged into chromosomes that are stored in the nucleus. DNA is composed of nucleotides. Each **nucleotide** consists of a deoxyribose sugar, a nitrogenous base, and phosphate group(s). There are four types of nucleotides in DNA: **adenine** (**A**), **guanine** (**G**), **cytosine** (**C**), and **thymine** (**T**). Nucleotides are linked together by **phosphodiester bonds**, linking the phosphate of one nucleotide to the sugar of the next, creating the phosphate-sugar backbone of the DNA. A strand of linked nucleotides is called a

polynucleotide. DNA is composed of two **antiparallel** polynucleotide strands held together by **hydrogen bonds** between the bases of the two strands. Guanine (G) base pairs to cytosine (C), forming three hydrogen bonds. Adenine (A) and thymine (T) base pair to form two hydrogen bonds. The two DNA strands twist together to form a **double helix**.

☑ Write the complementary DNA sequence and draw in the hydrogen bonds between bases. The first few are done for you: 5'–G C A T C T G A C A G T–3'

||| ||| || ||

3'–C G T A   –5'

Single Nucleotide Polymorphisms (SNPs)

The human genome contains approximately three billion base pairs. Overall, each person's DNA is very similar—about 98.4%[1]—to every other person's DNA. This 1.6% difference includes deletions, duplications, and insertions, and these can range in size from a single nucleotide to thousands of bases. Some changes cause different **alleles**, or gene variants; some cause genetic disorders and diseases; and some have no known effect. The type of genetic variation we're interested in in this lab is **single nucleotide polymorphisms**, or **SNPs** (*poly-* many, *morph-* appearance). These affect a single nucleotide—one base—and is a spot where several different bases are possible in different genomes. SNPs are the most common kind of genetic change, appearing about every 1,000 bases. This means each person has approximately three million places where their DNA is potentially distinguishable from another person's DNA due to SNPs. The chance of two people having all the same SNPs is infinitesimally small ($1/4^{3,000,000}$). Therefore, SNPs can be used as forensic evidence to match a suspect to a crime scene DNA sample. Testing 20 SNPs would provide a unique genetic profile of the perpetrator and exonerate other suspects.

Restriction Enzymes

Restriction endonucleases are enzymes that break the phosphodiester bonds of both DNA strands at specific DNA sequences. Each endonuclease recognizes a specific DNA sequence, a **restriction site**, and cleaves, or "cuts," the DNA at a specific site in each strand at that sequence. Many restriction sites are **palindromes**. In DNA, a palindrome is a DNA sequence that is the same 5' → 3' in the top strand and 5' → 3' in the bottom strand (remember, the two strands are antiparallel, so

[1]Naidoo, N., Y. Pawitan, R. Soong, D. N. Cooper, and C. S. Ku. Human genetics and genomics a decade after the release of the draft sequence of the human genome. *Hum Genomics* 5, no. 6 (2011): 577–622. doi:10.1186/1479-7364-5-6-577.

they are read in opposite directions). Below are some examples of DNA palindromes of different lengths.

5′–AT-3′   5′–GGCC-3′   5′–TACGTA-3′   5′–GCATATGC-3′
3′–TA-5′   3′–CCGG-5′   3′–ATGCAT-5′   3′–CGTATACG-5′

Figure G1   Examples of DNA palindromes of different lengths.

☑   Which of these is a palindrome? Circle it and cross out the rest.

5′–ATTTA–3′   5′–CGTT–3′   5′–CGCG–3′   5′-ATCAT-3′
3′–TAAAT–5′   3′–TTGC–5′   3′–GCGC–5′   3′–TAGTA–5′

A restriction enzyme cuts the DNA backbone phosphodiester bond. The place where the bond is broken can be at the same site on both strands (leaving "blunt" ends) or in staggered positions (leaving "sticky" ends). Cutting by a restriction enzyme separates the double-stranded DNA into fragments.

☑   The restriction enzyme DpnI cuts between the A and T in the sequence 5'-GATC-3'. First, identify the palindrome that DpnI recognizes in the DNA sequence below. Next, indicate where the cut will be made in the top strand and in the bottom strand. Then draw (write out) the two double-stranded DNA fragments resulting from digestion with DpnI. Do the fragments have blunt ends or sticky ends?

5'-GCATCTGATCAGT-3'
3'-CGTAGACTAGTCA-5'

☑   The restriction enzyme SacI cuts between the T and 3'C in the sequence 5'-GAGCTC-3'. Identify the palindrome that SacI recognizes in the DNA sequence below, indicate where the cut will be made in the top strand and in the bottom strand, then draw (write out) the fragments resulting from digestion with SacI. Do the fragments have blunt ends or sticky ends?

5'-TACGAGCTCATCATT-3'
3'-ATGCTCGAGTAGTAA-5'

☑   Restriction enzymes are said to "cut" DNA. What other ways to describe it can you think of? List as many synonyms as you can. _____
_____

Restriction endonucleases, like all enzymes, have conditions at which they work best. Most restriction enzymes work best at 37°C. They also need the right buffer, providing the right salt concentration, to work efficiently. And like all enzymes, they need time to work, so longer incubations result in a higher cutting efficiency.

Restriction enzymes come from bacteria, which have restriction endonucleases to work as their "immune system" to protect them from infection by viruses (bacteriophages). Viruses replicate by injecting their DNA (or RNA) into a host organism, whose cellular machinery replicates, transcribes, and translates the viral DNA to make more viruses. To prevent this, bacterial restriction enzymes chop up foreign DNA. By having a restriction enzyme that recognizes a sequence that is not present in the bacterial genome, the cell can identify and cleave foreign DNA, protecting the cell.

The naming convention for restriction enzymes is to use the first letter of the bacterial genus name and two letters from the species name, followed by strain designation, followed by a roman numeral for order of discovery. The letters from the genus and species should be italicized. For example, *Eco*RI was the first enzyme isolated from *Escherichia coli* strain RY13 and *Hin*d III was the third restriction enzyme isolated from *Haemophilus influenzae* strain Rd.

☑   If you isolated the first restriction enzyme from *Bacillus circulans* strain B, what would it be named? _____

Restriction Fragment Length Polymorphism (RFLP)

Restriction fragment length polymorphism (RFLP) is a technique that takes advantage of SNPs and restriction enzymes to generate distinct DNA fragments for genetic profiling. Recall that genomes vary because of the presence of SNPs, single nucleotides that differ between people. If a SNP falls in a restriction site, the site will no longer be recognized by the restriction enzyme and the DNA will not be cut. Different combinations of SNPs will result in the addition or loss of restrictions sites, resulting in different-sized fragments from different genomes cut by the same restriction enzyme. Figure G2 is an example of four genomes with different SNPs in two locations. Some of the genomes contain *Eco*RI restriction enzyme sites and some do not, resulting in different numbers and sizes of DNA fragments.

With RFLP analysis, DNA is digested with a restriction enzyme to create fragments and then the fragments are separated by size and visualized using DNA gel electrophoresis.

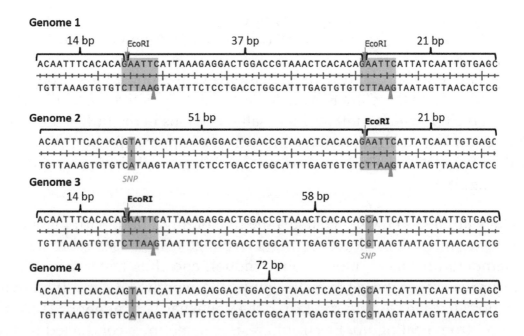

Figure G2 Example of different SNPs resulting in the presence or absence of restriction sites, resulting in different numbers and sizes of DNA fragments for each genome.

DNA Gel Electrophoresis

DNA gel electrophoresis is a technique used to separate DNA fragments by size. It utilizes the negative charge of DNA to draw DNA fragments through a semisolid gel in an electric field. A mixture of DNA fragments is loaded at the top of the gel and then the electric field is turned on. Smaller fragments "migrate" or "run" faster through the gel and thus travel farther than larger fragments, resulting in size separation. Bands of DNA fragments are visualized using ethidium bromide (EtBr) and ultraviolet (UV) radiation.

Figure G3 Rate of DNA migration is dependent on size.

DNA gel electrophoresis is conducted using a gel matrix composed of agarose. Agarose is a purified carbohydrate polymer extracted from seaweed. The molecules of agarose in the gel are cross-linked, created a matrix of holes and tunnels. Higher concentrations of agarose result in more cross-links and smaller holes. Different types of agarose also result in different amounts of cross-linking.

DNA is loaded into the gel and the DNA must physically migrate through the holes in the gel to move toward the anode. Small pieces of DNA can navigate the labyrinth of the gel and move relatively quickly, but large pieces of DNA get tangled and move slowly. Thus DNA can be separated by its length (number of nucleotides).

DNA is negatively charged (the oxygen atoms of the phosphate groups carry a negative charge) and therefore is attracted toward the positive electrode. The gel is bathed in a **buffer**, which contains ionic salts. The ions in the buffer provide moving charges and make the solution conductive. Changing the buffer changes the migration of the DNA. Using purified water in place of the buffer would result in no DNA migration.

The voltage applied to the gel changes the rate of migration, with higher voltage causing faster migration. However, higher voltage also causes more heat. While higher temperatures mean more atomic motion and thus faster migration, high temperature can cause the gel to melt, ruining the experiment. So, although higher voltages do cause the DNA to run faster, the voltage is kept at about **110 V** to prevent the gel from heating up. Electrophoresis is sometimes conducted in a refrigerated room to allow the application of higher voltage without damaging the experiment.

DNA from humans and many other organisms is linear, but DNA from bacteria is in closed circles. Molecular biologists often use bacterial DNA units called **plasmids** to produce DNA because plasmids are easy to manipulate and easy to amplify inside bacteria. A plasmid of a given length can be supercoiled (the circular DNA is twisted); relaxed, as a floppy circle; or linearized (by a restriction enzyme). These different forms have different shapes, so they migrate at different rates through a gel.

☑   List six things that affect how far a DNA fragment runs in a gel.

To prepare a gel for electrophoresis, the gel is liquefied and poured into a casting tray to mold it. A **comb** is inserted into the liquid gel to create depressions, or **wells**, into which the DNA is loaded. The wells get the DNA inside the gel so that it can migrate through the gel. The vertical strip of gel below a well is called a **lane**. One DNA sample is loaded per well and the DNA fragments from that sample appear as bright **bands** within the lane. The vertical position of a band in a lane is due to the size (length) of the DNA fragment. The brightness of a band is due to the number of fragments at that location—the more pieces of DNA of a particular size, the brighter the band.

The agarose gel is prepared with EtBr mixed into it. **Ethidium bromide** (EtBr) **intercalates** (inserts) between the base pairs of DNA. EtBr is fluorescent: It absorbs UV light and emits orange light. EtBr is much brighter intercalated into DNA than it is free, so DNA is present where a bright band of EtBr is visible.

EtBr is a mutagen and potential carcinogen: It can pass through the skin and intercalate into your DNA. Therefore it is important to wear gloves when handling gels and to protect against cross-contamination. (For instance, remove gloves before touching surfaces people without gloves will touch.) UV light is used to excite the EtBr in the gel to visualize the location of the DNA bands. UV radiation is a carcinogen. Protect yourself from exposure to the UV light by using a protective shield when visualizing directly and closing the door on the transilluminator when imaging.

After digestion we will mix loading dye into the DNA samples. **Loading dye** contains glycerol, which makes the solution thick and heavy, and bromophenol blue and xylene cyanol (or other dye(s)), to color it. The glycerol weighs down the DNA sample so that it settles into the gel well instead of floating away. The dye allows us to visualize the location of the DNA sample when loading it into the wells. The dyes are also negatively charged, like DNA, so they migrate toward the positive electrode. Thus, the position of the dye on the gel during electrophoresis is a proxy for the location of the DNA (because the DNA cannot be seen). Xylene cyanol has a molecular weight similar to a double-stranded DNA 3500 bp long and bromophenol blue runs at about the same rate as a 300 bp DNA fragment. Electrophoresis should be stopped before the bromophenol blue dye runs off the end of the gel.

We will use a solution of DNA fragments of known length as a standard. This "ladder" or "marker" is produced commercially. We will use a ladder called the "1 kb ladder" produced by the company Invitrogen (1 mL of ladder costs more than $500), shown in Figure G4. It contains fragments of DNA with lengths of 10000, 8000, 6000, 5000, 4000, 3000, 2000, 1500, 1000, and 500 base pairs (**bp**). 1 kilobase (**kb**) equals 1,000 bp, so the fragments can also be written as 10, 8, 6, 5, 4, 3, 2, 1.5, and 0.5 kb. Like any other DNA fragments, the longer the gel is run, the farther the DNA fragments in the ladder will migrate, so your ladder may have the bands clumped closer together and closer to the top of the gel if you run it for less time and farther apart and farther from the top of the gel if you run it for more time than the gel from Figure G4.

This ladder contains a **reference band** at 3,000 bp (3 kb). The reference band contains twice as many DNA fragments as the other bands, so it is twice as bright. Why is this useful? What if a person runs the gel so long the bottom bands run off the gel? Or a person runs the gel for such a short amount of time that the high molecular weight bands don't separate? How would you know which bands are which? Because the reference band is brighter, you can identify it for sure, and then can label the other bands in the ladder up and down from there, instead of starting at the top or bottom of the ladder.

Why do we use a ladder? First, so we can *estimate* the size of the fragments in other lanes by eye. DNA fragments with the same size (length, molecular weight) will travel at the same rate through the gel. By comparing the horizontal position of a band of unknown size to the bands in the ladder, you can make a guess about the length of the unknown band. Furthermore, we can use the ladder to create a standard curve for *calculating* the size of the fragments in the sample lanes.

DNA runs logarithmically, not linearly. This means that the spacing between bands in the ladder is not even. There will be more space between the 1,000 bp and 2,000 bp bands than there will be between the 5,000 bp and 6,000 bp bands, even though both sets differ by 1,000 bp. This makes estimation of the experimental bands' sizes difficult.

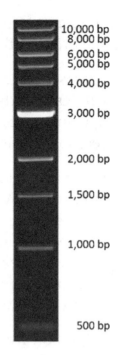

Figure G4   Bands from the 1 kb DNA ladder.

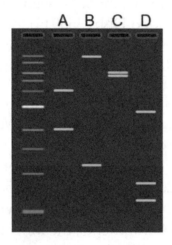

☑   Identify the molecular weight of each band in the ladder in the gel shown and circle the reference band. Estimate the size of each of the unknown bands in the gel.

_____

_____

_____

_____

Name _____ Section _____ Date _____

ACTIVITY 1: RFLP SIMULATION

1. Below is a DNA sequence. The blanks are the **SNPs** in this DNA sequence. Each is a spot where different people may have a different nucleotide present. Choose which nucleotide you have at each of the two blank spots (your choices are A, C, T, or G for each). Fill in the complementary base in the bottom strand.

   5'–ACGTGA_TTCGACGAATGCTATGAATT_CAGCGATCTAACGATGTA–3'

   3'–TGCACT_AAGCTGCTTACGATACTTAA_GTCGCTAGATTGCTACAT–5'

2. Your DNA sequence, and the corresponding DNA sequence for each person in your lab, is digested by the restriction enzyme *Eco*RI. *Eco*RI recognizes the palindromic sequence 5'-GAATTC-3'. *Eco*RI cuts between the G and A in this sequence. Does this produce sticky or blunt ends?

   Why is this a **palindrome**? Write out the complementary sequence.

   5'–GAATTC–3'

3. Look for this sequence in your DNA strand. How many DNA fragments will your DNA generate?

4. We are now going to do **RFLP** Analysis of the digested DNA from the people in your lab. We will run the digested DNA on a gel using electrophoresis to separate the bands by size.

5. Which lane of the gel best matches the fragments you would see from your DNA sequence?

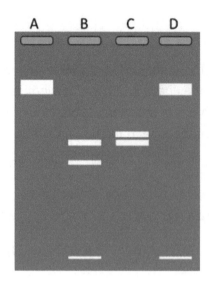

6. Find one person in your lab section with the SNPs that correspond to the fragments in each lane.

A.

B.

C.

D.

7. Measure the distance each band migrated by measuring from the bottom of the well to the top of the band, in millimeters.

	Lane A	Lane B	Lane C	Lane D
Band 1				
Band 2				
Band 3				

8. The equation for the standard curve for this gel (ladder not shown) is $y = 59.436e^{-0.039x}$, where y is the band size, in bp, and x is the distance the band migrated, in mm. Calculate the size of each band in each lane.

	Lane A	Lane B	Lane C	Lane D
Band 1				
Band 2				
Band 3				

9. How do your calculated band lengths compare to the real band lengths?

_____

_____

_____

ACTIVITY 2: RFLP EXPERIMENT

Now we are going to carry out all the parts to RFLP analysis: We will pour a gel, digest DNA, run a gel, and evaluate the results to determine identity.

(FICTIONAL) BACKSTORY

Randy and his identical twin were separated at birth. Randy is trying to find his lost brother and has been communicating with three people who may possibly be his twin. Each man has submitted a sample of his DNA to be analyzed.

You will conduct an RFLP analysis of the four men's DNA: You will digest each piece of DNA with a restriction enzyme and compare the resulting DNA fragments to determine if one of the men is Randy's brother.

☑ How will you be able to tell if an individual is Randy's twin? (What will you see on a gel? Why would that happen?) _____
_____
_____

☑ How will you be able to tell if a person is *not* Randy's twin? _____
_____

PROTOCOLS

To prepare an agarose gel:

Each table of eight will pour one gel.

1. Heat a tube of 1% agarose gel with EtBr in boiling water. Loosen the cap before placing it in the boiling water.
2. Once the gel is completely melted, remove it from the water bath using a test tube clamp or a studded silicone rubber mitt. Tighten the lid and very gently invert the tube several times to evenly mix the gel (avoid bubble formation).
3. Set up the gel apparatus as in Figure G5 with the casting tray turned parallel to the reservoirs of the gel apparatus so that the sides of the gel rig and the casting tray makes a mold for forming the gel. Make sure the rubber end gaskets are smooth. If you are having trouble sliding the casting tray into place without disrupting the end gaskets, try wetting them.

4. Carefully pour the liquefied gel into the casting tray, avoiding forming bubbles. You can use a micropipette tip to pop or move any bubbles that are present in the gel.

5. Insert the comb into the grooves toward the top of the casting tray.

6. Allow the gel to harden on a level surface without being disturbed. It can be moved into the refrigerator as soon as it is poured and the comb is added to speed up solidification.

7. Once the gel has solidified, carefully lift the casting tray up and rotate it so the comb-side of the gel is toward the side of the gel apparatus that connects to the black lead.

8. Fill the buffer reservoirs and cover the gel with 1x buffer. The gel should have a thin layer of buffer over it.

9. Carefully remove the comb by grasping it with both hands and pulling straight up.

10. Check the wells for bubbles. Bubbles can be removed by pipetting buffer into the well. Please ask your lab instructor for assistance.

☑   Why do you not want bubbles in the gel? _____
_____

☑   Why should the comb be near the black lead? _____
_____

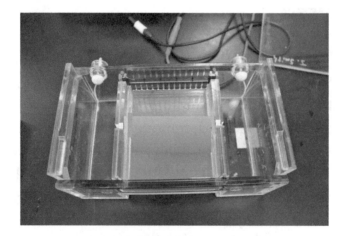

Figure G5   Setup for forming the gel. Note the position of the casting tray and comb relative to the gel rig.

To digest DNA:

1. Collect your sample of DNA from your lab instructor and label it with the sample ID and your initials.

2. Briefly spin the tube in a (balanced) microcentrifuge to collect the DNA at the bottom of the tube. Make sure you can see the 2 μL drops of DNA at the bottom of the tube.

3. Add 18 μL enzyme mix to the DNA and pipet up and down to mix. The enzyme mix contains the restriction enzyme and a buffer that is optimal for digestion. Remember, the tip on the micropipette must be changed between tubes.

4. Briefly spin the tube in a balanced microcentrifuge to collect the mixture at the bottom of the tube.

5. Place the tube in a floater in the 37°C water bath for 15 to 30 minutes (the longer the digest, the better).

6. After digestion is complete, remove your sample from the water bath.

7. Collect a tube containing loading dye from your lab instructor. Label the tube with the sample ID, your initials, and your group ID.

8. Briefly mix the tube by inverting and concentrate the solution at the bottom of the tube with a short spin in the microcentrifuge.

9. Transfer all of the solution from the digestion tube to the tube containing the loading dye. Pipet up and down to mix.

10. Give the tube to the lab instructor to freeze until the next lab period, or proceed to gel loading.

☑ Why is it important to balance the microcentrifuge? _____
    _____

☑ List three things important to good micropipette technique. (Refer to Lab D if necessary.)
    _____
    _____
    _____

☑ Why must the micropipette tip be changed between DNA samples?
    _____

☑ Why must the micropipette tip be changed between introductions into the enzyme
    mix?_____

☑   What enzyme are you using? _____

☑   What enzyme mix are you using? _____

☑   Why is a longer digestion incubation time better? _____
_____

| Balanced with 2 tubes | Balanced with 3 tubes | UNBALANCED |

Figure G6   Balanced and unbalanced tube positions in a micro-centrifuge. Always balance the tubes before spinning.

To load the agarose gel:

- If your DNA sample was frozen, thaw it completely before proceeding. It will thaw more quickly if you hold it and roll it in your hands.
- Each person is responsible for loading the DNA sample they digested.
- Please practice pipetting into a well on the practice gel before loading your sample into your group's gel.
- There are two groups of four at each table. One group will load their samples on the left side of the gel and the other group on the right side of the gel, with the ladder in the middle.
- Samples should be loaded in the following order: R, M1, M2, M3, ladder, R, M1, M2, M3.

1. The gel should be turned, the comb removed, and buffer added before loading the gel (see earlier protocol).
2. Briefly spin your sample in a balanced microcentrifuge to concentrate the solution at the bottom of the tube.
3. Suck all of the solution from your tube into the micropipette tip. If the volume of fluid is less than 20 µL, carefully depress and hold the plunger of the micropipette to remove the air (do this over the open tube so if you lose liquid you can suck it back up. You want to have only liquid and no air in the tip of the pipette).
4. Maintaining the plunger position, move the micropipette over the gel.

5. Steady yourself and place the tip of the pipette tip into the well. The tip should be inside the well in the gel, but not very deep.

6. Slowly depress the micropipette plunger to release the fluid into the well. If the solution is not going into the well, stop, and ask your lab instructor for help.

7. Stop pipetting when all of your sample has left the tip. Avoid using the blow-out function on the pipette, because you could blow your sample out of the well.

☑ Why do you not want air in the gel well? _____

_____

Figure G7 Loading a gel.

To run the gel:

1. Once all of the wells are loaded, firmly attach the lid of the gel apparatus to the electrodes.

2. Make sure the leads are connected to the correct, color-coded positions on the power supply.

3. Turn on the power supply with the switch at the back of the unit then press the power button on the front of the unit. To set the power supply, press the K (constant) button to get Volts, then press the Set button to get Volts and use the up/down arrows to reach 110. Then press Run.

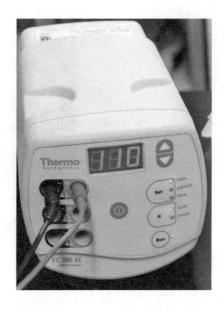

Figure G8 Power box for electrophoresis with proper settings.

4. Check that your gel is running properly. If it is, you will see bubbles forming from the wires in the buffer reservoirs and the DNA samples migrating in the correct direction.

5. Run the gel at 110 volts for 20 to 30 minutes.

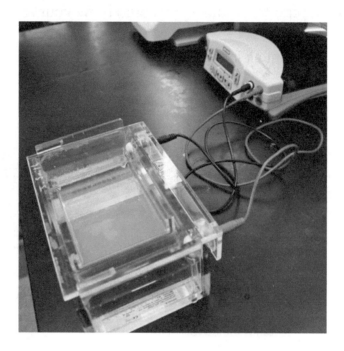

Figure G9   Gel ready to run.

Figure G10 Bubbles formed during electrophoresis.

To analyze the bands on the agarose gel:

1. Once the dye has run at least halfway down the gel, turn off the power supply and remove the lid.

2. Carefully lift the gel and casting tray out of the buffer, holding onto the top and bottom sides of the casting tray and carrying it level to prevent the gel from slipping out.

3. Gently tip the gel from the casting tray onto the tray of the transilluminator.

4. Using white light, position the gel inside the viewing area.

5. Using UV light, image the gel. Your lab instructor will do this for you. Do not touch the buttons or screen of the transilluminator with gloves!

6. Use the gel image to determine if there is a DNA match.

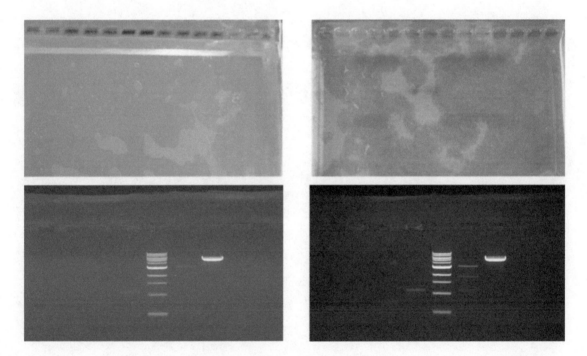

Figure G11 Upper left: Loaded gel. Upper right: Gel after run (white light). Lower left: Gel under UV radiation. Lower right: Black-and-white image of gel under UV radiation.

Clean-up:

- Throw away gel and gloves in appropriate biosafety hazard area.
- Pour running buffer into proper receptacle.
- Throw microcentrifuge tubes in trash.
- Eject micropipette tips into provided receptacle.

Name _____ Section _____ Date _____

RESULTS

1. Print out your gel image as large as possible.

2. Measure the distance each band in the ladder ran, in millimeters. To do this, measure from the bottom of the well to the top of the band for each of the bands in the ladder in your gel picture. Record the values in the table below.

DNA Fragment Size (bp)	Distance Migrated (mm)
10,000	
8,000	
6,000	
5,000	
4,000	
3,000	
2,000	
1,500	
1,000	
500	

3. Measure the distance each band in each experimental lane ran, in millimeters, and record the values in the table below.

4. Using the ladder, estimate the size of each fragment and record it in the tables.

5. Use Excel to calculate the size of the DNA in each band as described in the direction for the extended analysis, and add the values to the tables below.

Randy			
	Distance Migrated (mm)	Estimated Fragment Size (bp)	Calculated Fragment Size (bp)
Band 1			
Band 2			
Band 3			

Man 1			
	Distance Migrated (mm)	Estimated Fragment Size (bp)	Calculated Fragment Size (bp)
Band 1			
Band 2			
Band 3			

Man 2			
	Distance Migrated (mm)	Estimated Fragment Size (bp)	Calculated Fragment Size (bp)
Band 1			
Band 2			
Band 3			

Man 3			
	Distance Migrated (mm)	Estimated Fragment Size (bp)	Calculated Fragment Size (bp)
Band 1			
Band 2			
Band 3			

MOLECULAR BIOLOGY EXTENDED ANALYSIS

Directions

1. Open the Standard Curve.xlsx file in Excel.
2. Enter the distances you measured for the migration of the standard curve bands into the appropriate cells in the Excel file (blue font). (Make sure the Excel file has the correct band sizes for the ladder you used.)
3. View the standard curve generated from the ladder. When you entered the distance for the ladder into the Excel file, a graph should have been generated. The graph should show a blue line of your data and a black line that is the fit of your data. If the blue line doesn't show, change the x-axis to a more appropriate range. (Click on the x-axis, then right-click. Chose "format axis" from the menu that appears. A menu should open on the right-hand side of your screen. Change the minimum and maximum values to fit the distances you measured for the ladder.) The equation for the fit should appear in the upper right-hand corner of the graph. The equation is an exponential function, in the form $y = \text{number } e^{-0.0??x}$.
4. Record the equation of the standard curve and the R^2 value from the graph on the Extended Analysis page.
5. Use Excel to calculate the size (in bp) of each of the DNA bands in each of your samples. In the right-hand column (red font), a "dummy" equation has already been entered. *You must modify it* to match the equation for the standard curve from the graph (see step 3 above). You will need to change the coefficient and the decay constant (the two parts of the equation that are numbers), but leave the rest of the equation the same. (Excel uses the function EXP() to denote the natural exponential function e. The x value for the function is the distance in mm the band ran, so x is the Excel cell containing the distance the band ran).
6. Complete the Extended Analysis.
7. Upload your Excel file to Blackboard.

Name _____ Section _____ Date _____

MOLECULAR BIOLOGY EXTENDED ANALYSIS

Record the values generated by Excel.

Standard curve equation: _____

R^2 value of fit: _____

1. What does R^2 value tell you about the goodness of fit of your data?
_____

2. Are there any ladder data points that do not conform to the standard curve?
_____

3. Remove any outliers and record your new R^2 value: _____

   Did this improve the fit? _____

4. Use your standard curve equation to calculate the size in bp of the following bands.
   Show your work!

   a. band that ran 20.8 mm

   b. band that ran 30.4 mm

5. a. How well do your estimates for the band sizes and calculated band sizes compare?
      By how much do your estimated and calculated sizes differ?

   b. Explain why there is a difference between the estimated and calculated sizes.

   c. Which way of determining band size—estimating or calculating—is more precise?

   d. Explain the origin of any discrepancies between the estimated and calculated band
      sizes.

_____
_____
_____
_____
_____
_____
_____
_____
_____

6. a. According to your RFLP data, does one of the men match Randy?

   b. Explain your choice.

   c. By how much do the band sizes for that man's sample and the corresponding bands in Randy's sample differ in size, by your calculation?

   _____

   _____

   _____

   _____

   _____

ACTIVITY 3: ISOLATION OF DNA FROM CHEEK CELLS

We viewed the cells from inside our mouth, stained with methylene blue, in Lab A, and could see the nucleus inside the stained cell. In this activity, we are going to extract DNA from these cells.

PROTOCOL

1. Pour 5 mL of 25% dish detergent solution in a large test tube with a cap.
2. Pour ~10 mL of 0.9% NaCl salt solution into a cup.
3. Swish the salt solution around in your mouth for about 30 seconds.
4. Spit the solution back into the cup.
5. Pour the solution into the large test tube and screw on the cap.
6. Slowly tip the tube back and forth for 2 to 3 minutes.
7. *Optional*: Add a pinch of meat tenderizer, a squirt of fresh pineapple juice, a squirt of contact lens cleaner, **OR** 1 mL of proteinase K solution to the tube and gently tip tube back and forth for 5 more minutes.
8. Get 5 mL of 95% ethanol from the instructor in a clean graduated cylinder.
9. Slightly tilt the test tube and slowly and gently pour the ethanol down the side of the tube.
10. The DNA should form white strands in the middle (interface) between the two layers of solution. This will take 1 minute or more.
11. Add 1 mL (20 drops) of pure water into a clean microcentrifuge tube.
12. Swirl a glass stir rod or wooden stir stick around in the solution to wind the DNA strands around the rod.
13. Transfer the DNA from the rod to the water in the microcentrifuge tube.

☑ What is the role of the detergent in this protocol? _____
_____

☑ The ethanol precipitates the DNA, causing it to come out of solution and separating it from the cellular debris that is soluble in both layers. What is in the cellular debris?
_____

☑ The optional additions in step 7 all contain enzymes that digest proteins. What protein do we need to separate the DNA from to get pure DNA? _____

Name _____ Section _____ Date _____

ACTIVITY 4: QUANTIFICATION OF DNA

Now we're going to quantify (measure) the amount of DNA we extracted in Activity 3.

PROTOCOL

1. Your lab instructor will turn on the NanoDrop, set it to detect nucleic acids, initialize, and blank the NanoDrop with 2 µL of water.

2. Wipe the water off the analyzer with a Kimwipe.

3. Place a 2 µL drop of your DNA sample on the analyzer, gently lower the pedestal arm, and measure the absorbance of your sample.

4. Repeat the measurement of your DNA concentration three times using three 2 µL drops of DNA and record the NanoDrop readings, with units.

5. When finished, wipe the analyzer and pedestal arm with a Kimwipe dampened with pure water.

RESULTS

	Drop 1	Drop 2	Drop 3	Average
Concentration				
Abs @ 260 nm				
Abs @ 280 nm				
Abs @ 230 nm				

6. Convert your average concentration from ng/µL to µg/µL. Show your work.

7. Convert your average concentration from ng/µL to g/L. Show your work.

Name _____ Section _____ Date _____

INTERPRETATION

- The nitrogenous bases of nucleic acids absorb UV light, with maximum absorption at 260 nm. The amount of absorption is proportional to the amount of DNA, thus the concentration of the DNA can be calculated based on absorption at 260 nm.

- Aromatic amino acids in proteins absorb UV light, with maximum absorption at 280 nm. Thus the concentration of protein in a solution can be calculated based on absorption at 280 nm.

- Many organic substances, such as some solvents and the peptide bonds in proteins, absorb light in the 200–230 nm range. Absorbance at 230 nm is used as a measure of contamination.

- 260/280 ratio: This ratio compares the absorbance at 260 nm (nucleic acid) and 280 nm (protein) and is used to assess the purity of the nucleic acid. If the ratio is lower than ~1.8 for DNA, it suggests the presence of protein (or other contaminant) in the DNA sample.

- 260/230 ratio: This ratio compares the absorbance at 260 nm (nucleic acid) and 230 nm (organic) and is used to assess the purity of the nucleic acid. If the ratio is lower than ~2, it suggests the presence of contaminant(s) in the DNA sample.

1. Calculate these two ratios for your DNA sample.

260/280 Ratio	260/230 Ratio

2. Interpret your ratios and draw a conclusion about the purity of your DNA sample.

_____

_____

_____

_____

Name _____ Section _____ Date _____

MOLECULAR BIOLOGY COMPREHENSION A

1. a. SNP is the abbreviation for what? _____

   b. In your own words, explain what an SNP is. _____
   _____
   _____

2. a. RFLP is the abbreviation for what? _____
   _____

   b. What is RFLP analysis used for? _____
   _____
   _____

   c. In your own words, describe the procedure for conducting a RFLP analysis.
   _____
   _____
   _____
   _____

   d. Why does RFLP analysis work? (i.e., what is different between different people?)
   _____
   _____

3. a. What kind of molecules recognize DNA palindromes?
   _____

   b. What does this enzyme do at the DNA palindrome sequence it recognizes?
   _____

4. Here is one strand of DNA. Complete the second strand to make a palindrome.
        5'–T A A C G G C C G T T A–3'

5. Here is a linear DNA strand. It is cut with an enzyme that recognizes the sequence
   5'–TTAA–3'. This restriction enzyme cuts at the 3' side of the second adenine of this
   sequence on each strand. How many DNA fragments would result? _____

        5'–AACGTATTAACGAAGCTATAATATTAACCGCGATTAACGATTA–3'
        3'–TTGCATAATTGCTTCGATATTATAATTGGCGCTAATTGCTAAT–5'

6. Within the population, there is an SNP at the underlined position in this genomic sequence (see below). Write out the complementary strand of DNA for part *a,* and then reproduce the genomic sequence (both strands) with the indicated SNP variant for *b—d.*

   a. 25% of the population has this sequence in the top strand: 5'– GAATGC–3'

   b. 25% of the population has a "T" in the top strand at the SNP:

   c. 25% of the population has a "C" in the top strand at the SNP:

   d. 25% of the population has a "G" in the top strand at the SNP:

   e. Which sequence (*a—d*) would be cut by a restriction enzyme? Justify your answer.

   _____

7. a. In this gel image, how many lanes are there? _____

   b. Which lane contains the ladder (marker)? _____

   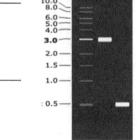

   c. How many bands are in the ladder? _____

   d. How many DNA bands are there that are NOT in the ladder lane?

   _____

   e. Give the size of each of the DNA bands that are NOT in the ladder lane in both base pairs (bp) and kilobases (kb).

   _____

   _____

Name ——————————————— Section ——————— Date ——————

MOLECULAR BIOLOGY COMPREHENSION B

1. Most restriction enzymes work optimally at human body temperature. What temperature is this, in °C? (Hint: What temperature is the water bath in which you incubated your digestions?) ———————————————————————————————

2. a. What is the charge of DNA? ———————————————————————————

   b. Toward which electrode does DNA move?

   ——

3. Here is a lane from a gel that contains nucleotide fragments that are 500 bp, 1000 bp, and 3000 bp long.

   a. Label each band with the appropriate size.

   b. Measure the distance each band ran, in mm.

   c. Which band has the longest DNA fragment?

   d. Which band has the highest concentration (most) DNA fragments?

4. Here is a gel on which digested samples from three suspects and the perpetrator from a crime scene (CSS) have been run. Which suspect's DNA was found at the crime scene?

_____

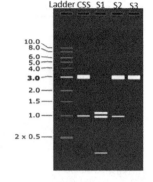

5. Here is a gel on which digested samples from three suspects, the crime scene (CSS), and the victim (V) have been run. Unfortunately, the sample obtained from the crime scene contains both the perpetrator and the victim's DNA. Which suspect's DNA was found at the crime scene?

_____

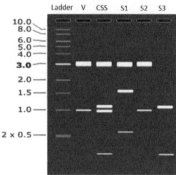

6. **Three samples of one person's DNA were cut with three different enzymes**. Indicate how many different fragments were generated with each enzyme and match each digestion to the correct lane in the gel below.

Sample A: digestion with AccII: cuts at 5'–CG|CG–3'   # Fragments _____

5'–ACCTCGTACGCGTAAAGCTTATTCGCGGTGATTAACACGAC–3'
3'–TGGAGCATGCGCATTTCGAATAAGCGCCACTAATTGTGCTG–5'

Lane _____

Sample B: digestion with AfaI: cuts at 5'–GT|AC–3'   # Fragments _____

5'–ACCTCGTACGCGTAAAGCTTATTCGCGGTGATTAACACGAC–3'
3'–TGGAGCATGCGCATTTCGAATAAGCGCCACTAATTGTGCTG–5'

Lane _____

Sample C: digestion with AluI: cuts at 5'–AG|CT–3'   # Fragments _____

5'–ACCTCGTACGCGTAAAGCTTATTCGCGGTGATTAACACGAC–3'
3'–TGGAGCATGCGCATTTCGAATAAGCGCCACTAATTGTGCTG–5'

Lane _____

7. **Three people's DNA were cut with the same enzyme**. Indicate how many different fragments were generated for each person and match each digestion to the correct lane in the gel.

Person 1: digestion with BamHI: 5'–G|GATCC–3'   # Fragments _____

5'–GGAGGATCCCTTATTCGAGGATCCTGATTAACACGACACTACTT–3'
3'–CCTCCTAGGGAATAAGCTCCTAGGACTAATTGTGCTGTGATGAA–5'

Lane _____

Person 2: digestion with BamHI: 5'–G|GATCC–3'   # Fragments _____

5'–GGAGCATCCCTTATTCGAGGATCCTGATTAACACGACACTACTT–3'
3'–CCTCGTAGGGAATAAGCTCCTAGGACTAATTGTGCTGTGATGAA–5'

Lane _____

Person 3: digestion with BamHI: 5'–G|GATCC–3'   # Fragments _____

5'–GGAGGATCCCTTATTCGAGGATCGTGATTAACACGACACTACTT–3'
3'–CCTCCTAGGGAATAAGCTCCTAGCACTAATTGTGCTGTGATGAA–5'

Lane _____

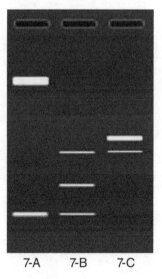

Gel for #6

6-1   6-2   6-3

Gel for #7

7-A   7-B   7-C

8. Describe the RFLP scenario we are doing in lab. Is it like #6 or #7?

Name _____ Section _____ Date _____

MOLECULAR BIOLOGY REVIEW QUESTIONS

1. What is in the DNA ladder mix?

2. Why is a DNA ladder useful?

3. Why is a reference band in a DNA ladder useful?

4. Why is the reference band extra-bright?

5. In your own words, explain what DNA gel electrophoresis does.

6. Why is DNA gel electrophoresis useful?

7. Explain the steps of DNA extraction, restriction digestion, and running a DNA gel.

8. How is DNA separated in gel electrophoresis? What factors affect the rate of DNA travel?

9. What does loading dye do?

10. How do you see the DNA in the gel? What does EtBr do?

11. What safety precautions should a person take when doing gel electrophoresis?

12. Which base pairing, guanine to cytosine or thymine to adenine, is stronger? Why?

    Use this image of DNA to answer questions 13–15:

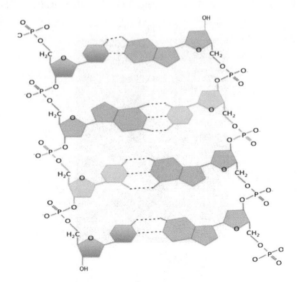

13. Can you identify the A-T base pairs? The G-C base pairs? How can you tell?

14. Can you tell that the two strands have opposite (antiparallel) orientation? How?

15. Locate each of the phosphodiester bonds. Locate all of the hydrogen bonds.

16. This segment of linear DNA, which has a length of 1,040 bp, can be cut by a number of different enzymes. Say how many fragments of DNA you would get and the length of each fragment for a digestion with each enzyme (alone) listed in the table below.

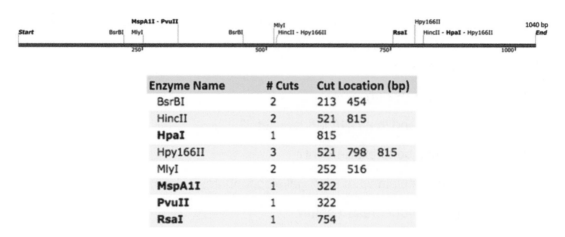

Enzyme Name	# Cuts	Cut Location (bp)		
BsrBI	2	213	454	
HincII	2	521	815	
HpaI	1	815		
Hpy166II	3	521	798	815
MlyI	2	252	516	
MspA1I	1	322		
PvuII	1	322		
RsaI	1	754		

SnapGene software (from GSL Biotech; available at snapgene.com)

17. Explain RFLP analysis.

18. Explain what a restriction enzyme is and what it does.

19. Explain what is seen on a DNA agarose gel and what the distance of the bands from the top of the gel tells you about the size of the DNA fragment in that band.

20. Identify the molecular weight (bp length) of each band in the ladder in the gel and circle the reference band. Estimate the size of each of the unknown bands.

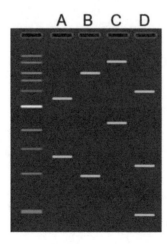

21. Identify the molecular weight of each band in the ladder and estimate the size of each of the unknown bands in the gel.

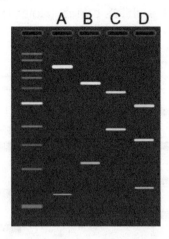

22. Six DNA samples were run on this gel, two of which were loaded twice. Find the two sets of matching lanes.

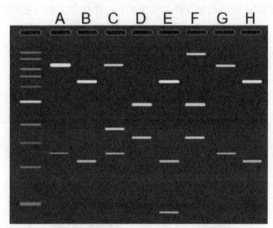

23. Digested DNA samples from ten women were run on this gel, including samples from two sets of identical twins. Can you find the identical twins' DNA?

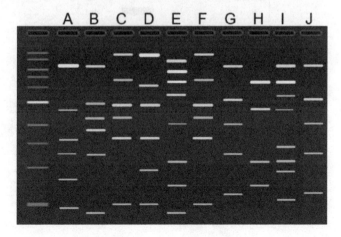

24. Here is a gel for a paternity test. The mother and child's DNA are run along with the DNA from three possible fathers. Which man is the father? Explain how you can tell. Explain the origin of each of the child's bands. (Note: The colors in this gel have been inverted.)

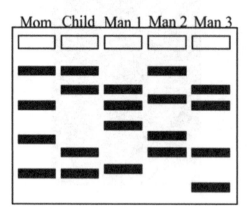

25. Here is a gel for a paternity test. The mother and child's DNA are run along with the DNA from three possible fathers. Which man is the father? Explain how you can tell. Explain the origin of each of the child's bands.

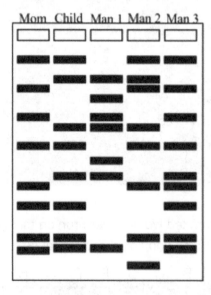

LABORATORY H

Cellular Reproduction

VOCABULARY

mitosis	meiosis	diploid	haploid
gamete	sister chromatids	interphase	prophase
metaphase	anaphase	telophase	cytokinesis
synapsis	tetrads	spermatogenesis	chromosome
seminiferous tubules	crossing-over	oogenesis	spermatozoon
polar bodies	testes	homologous	ovum
homologous chromosomes	gametogenesis	recombination	

SKILLS

Identify stages of cell division under the microscope.
Visualize gametes under the microscope.

INTRODUCTION

Cells need to divide to create new cells for growth and repair and to make gametes for sexual reproduction. Two different types of cell division are used to produce cells for these different purposes. **Mitosis** is the cell division process in eukaryotes that produces two progeny (daughter) cells that are identical to the original dividing cell; the cells produced by mitosis will become part of the organism's body. **Meiosis** is the process that produces four progeny cells that are distinct from the original dividing cell. The cells produced by meiosis are sex cells for possible fusion with sex cells from the opposite sex to create new diploid organisms.

Humans are **diploid**, having pairs of chromosomes. Each **chromosome** is a linear unit of hereditary information, composed of tens to hundreds of millions of nucleotides. Humans have 23 pairs, or 46 chromosomes. Human sex cells, or **gametes**, are **haploid**: They have 23 chromosomes, none of which are paired. When an egg and sperm fuse, they create a new diploid cell with 46 chromosomes. The egg and sperm each donate one of each type of chromosome. These paired chromosomes are called **homologous chromosomes**. We can use a shorthand to indicate whether a cell is haploid or diploid and how many chromosomes it has by writing an equation, such as:

$$2N = 46 \quad \text{or} \quad 1N = 23$$

Here, the 2 stands for two copies of each chromosome, a diploid cell; and 1 stands for one copy of each chromosome, a haploid cell. N stands for the number of different types of chromosomes the cell has. The number is the total number of chromosomes the cell has. Human diploid cells have $2N = 46$ chromosomes, where $N = 23$.

☑ Answer the following question for an organism whose genome is indicated by $2N = 20$.

Is it haploid or diploid? _____

How many different types of chromosomes does it have? _____

How many chromosomes does it have total? _____

How many chromosomes would a gamete from this organism have? _____

Write the equation to indicate a gamete from this organism. _____

Mitosis

The cell cycle for actively dividing cells consists of interphase and mitosis. **Interphase** is divided into three phases: G_1, S, and G_2. During S phase, the chromosomes are duplicated. The duplicated **sister chromatids** (identical, copied chromosomes) remain connected to each other after synthesis and are separated during mitosis. Mitosis is divided into four phases: prophase, metaphase, anaphase, and telophase. The cells that are produced by mitosis may then enter interphase and divide themselves. In higher eukaryotes, the cell cycle is about twenty-four hours. Of this, twenty-three hours are spent in interphase and one hour is spent in mitosis.

☑ When you look at dividing eukaryotic cells, what percentage of cells do you expect to see in mitosis? _____

During mitosis, a diploid cell divides to form two diploid progeny cells that are identical to the original cell. Mitosis is important for increasing the number of cells in the body for growth, replacing old cells, and healing wounds.

☑ Think of the human life cycle. In what stage do you think mitosis occurs most frequently?_____

In **prophase**, the cell prepares for chromosomal separation: The chromosomes condense, the nucleolus disappears, and the nuclear envelope breaks down, allowing microtubules from the mitotic spindle to attach to the sister chromatids. The microtubules push and pull the chromosomes to line them up at the center of the cell during **metaphase**. During **anaphase**, sister chromatids are pulled apart, toward opposite poles of the cell. In **telophase**, the cell prepares to enter interphase: The condensed chromosomes relax and nuclear envelopes form around the chromosomes. Concurrent to late anaphase and telophase, **cytokinesis** occurs to "pinch apart" the cell membrane and separate the cytoplasm of the progeny cells.

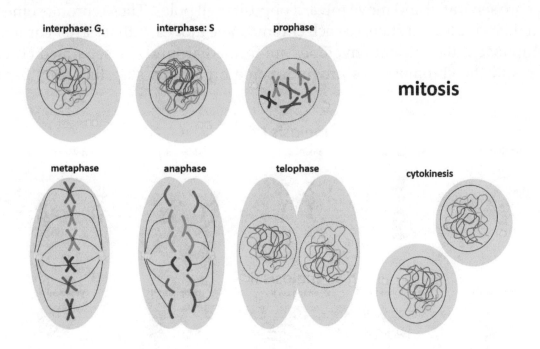

Figure H1 Stages of mitosis for a cell containing 2N=6 chromosomes.

Meiosis

Meiosis is the cell division process that produces gametes for sexual reproduction. Meiosis produces four genetically distinct haploid cells. Meiosis is a dead-end process—the cells produced cannot divide further.

Meiosis is preceded by interphase, during which the chromosomes are duplicated (S phase). Meiosis can be divided into two stages, meiosis I and meiosis II; during each stage there are prophase, metaphase, anaphase, and telophase stages.

During **prophase I**, each of the duplicated chromosomes finds its homologous chromosome in a process called **synapsis**. (Note that synapsis does <u>not</u> occur in mitosis.) The pairs of duplicated homologous chromosomes are called **tetrads**. Once the homologous chromosomes are paired, they exchange DNA segments in a process called **homologous recombination**, also known as **crossing-over**. This increases the genetic diversity of the cells produced by meiosis.

☑   Why does homologous recombination increase genetic diversity? _____

_____

Once homologous recombination is finished, the chromosomes condense further and the nuclear envelope breaks down, completing prophase I. During **metaphase I**, the tetrads are moved to the center of the cell. In **anaphase I**, the homologous chromosomes are separated and move toward opposite cell poles. These chromosomes are still in their duplicated state, so each chromosome moves with its sister chromatid. In **telophase I**, the nuclear envelopes are formed around the separated chromosomes and the chromosomes unwind. Some organisms skip this step, because

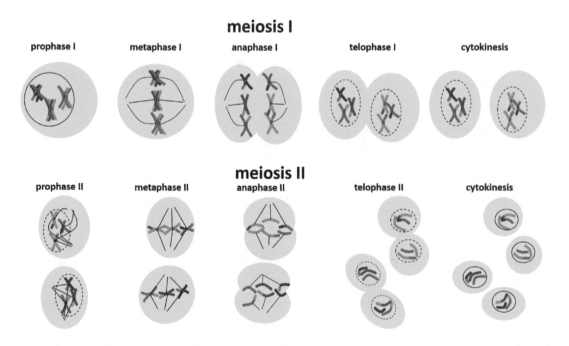

Figure H2   Stages of meiosis for a cell containing $2N = 6$ chromosomes. Note that chromosomes do unwind in the telophase stages.

telophase I is followed by **prophase II**, in which the chromosomes condense and the nuclear envelopes are broken down. During **metaphase II**, sister chromatids align at the center of the cells. The sister chromatids are pulled apart, toward opposite poles, during **anaphase II**. Once sister chromatids are separated, they are called chromosomes. During **telophase II**, nuclear envelopes are formed around the chromosomes and the condensed chromosomes relax. **Cytokinesis** occurs concurrently during each telophase step to separate progeny cells.

Gametogenesis

Gametogenesis is the production of **gametes**, or haploid sex cells, by meiosis. During sexual reproduction, two gametes, from opposite sexes, meet and fuse, forming a zygote, or new diploid cell. (This zygote may then divide by mitosis to create an embryo and develop into a new organism.) Meiosis in males is called **spermatogenesis** and results in the formation of **spermatozoa** (singular: **spermatozoon**), or sperm. In females, **oogenesis** results in the formation of **ova** (singular: **ovum**), or eggs.

Spermatogenesis occurs in the **testes** of males from puberty to death. Spermatozoa are produced in the **seminiferous tubules** of the testes. Each testis contains approximately 400 to 600 tubules, producing over 100 million sperm per day. Spermatogenesis consists of three parts: (1) mitosis of diploid stem cell progenitors; (2) meiosis; (3) spermiogenesis, the formation of the characteristic sperm shape.

Diploid cells line the basement membrane (outer ring) of the seminiferous tubule walls. These stem cells (*spermatogonia*) divide by mitosis, to prevent loss of the stem cells, then diploid progeny starts meiosis. As these cells—*spermatocytes*—undergo first meiosis I and then meiosis II, they migrate away from the basement membrane, through the Sertoli cell epithelium of the tubule, toward the central lumen (inner open space). The products of meiosis are haploid *spermatids*. Spermatids then undergo *spermiogenesis* to get the right shape—small head and long flagellum—to become spermatozoa. The spermatozoa are released from the epithelium of the seminiferous tubule walls into the lumen and are washed away from the testes to the epididymis. In the epididymis, spermatozoa finish maturation, becoming motile and capable of fertilization. The epididymis connects to the vas deferens, from which sperm are ejected from the body. Spermatogenesis takes about two months: rounds of mitosis of the spermatogonia take sixteen to eighteen days; spermatocyte meiosis takes approximately twenty-four days; reaching full maturity in the epididymis requires another twelve to twenty-six days.

Oogenesis, the formation of ova, occurs in the **ovaries**. Oogenesis begins when a female is a fetus. During the fetal period, *oogonia*—diploid stem cell progenitors—develop, divide by mitosis, and (all) enter meiosis. Meiosis progresses part way through prophase I (including homologous recombination) before freezing (as *oocytes*) until the onset of puberty. With each menstrual cycle, the ovulated oocyte progresses through meiosis I and enter meiosis II, stopping at metaphase II. It will only complete meiosis, and become a mature ovum, if it is fertilized (which occurs in the uterine (Fallopian) tube). Females have a finite number of oocytes and oogenesis ends with menopause. Each round of meiosis in females creates only one functional egg. The other three cells are **polar bodies**, which each contain a haploid set of chromosomes and very little cytoplasm and are nonfunctional. The vast majority of cytoplasm is directed to the functional egg, which will be the cytoplasm of the diploid zygote if the egg is fertilized.

ACTIVITY 1: CHROMOSOME PREPARATION FROM ONION ROOT TIP BY SQUASH MOUNT

Read the entire procedure before beginning! Wear goggles during procedure!

1. Turn on the hot plate and set to the highest temperature setting. Fill a 100-mL beaker to the halfway mark with distilled water and place two or three boiling stones in the beaker. Keep extra distilled water nearby so that water in the beaker can be replaced as it evaporates. DO NOT ADD WATER TO A DRY/ HOT BEAKER OR IT MAY EXPLOSIVELY SHATTER!

2. While waiting for the water to boil, carefully use a razor blade to trim a root hair from the main stem. Place the root on a blank slide and trim the root, retaining only the last 2–3 mm at the end of the tip.

3. With the tip of the root in the center of the slide, add 1 drop of 1N HCl. Use care in applying acid to avoid spillage on clothing or tabletops. Place the slide across the mouth of the beaker and heat for 1.5 minutes, adding acid if necessary to prevent boiling dry. The combination of heat and acid fixes, or kills, the meristem tissue and makes it ready to accept a simple stain.

4. Carefully remove the slide from the beaker and place on a paper towel. Using Kimwipes, gently blot away the remaining acid, taking care to avoid removing the root tip from the slide.

5. Add half a drop of TBO (0.5% Toluidine blue O) stain to cover the root tip. Return the slide to the mouth of the beaker and heat for 2 minutes, adding additional stain if necessary to ensure that the root does not evaporate dry.

6. After two minutes, remove the slide from the beaker and use a Kimwipe to blot excess stain from slide. Add several drops of distilled water, blot, and repeat until no more stain is released when water is added. Then add water and blot one more time. Take care to avoid removing the root tip!

7. Add 1 drop of distilled water and place a cover slip over the root tip.

8. In order to make a squash mount, place the slide between paper towels and place it on the floor. Carefully place the heel of your shoe so that it covers the slide and fully apply your weight. Avoid twisting your foot and refrain from using small heels (high heels) when preparing the squash mount. The root tip should appear as a smashed circle by eye after the squash.

9. The TBO stain is a simple stain that attaches to the acid groups of nucleic acids. If you have done your squash mount correctly, any chromosomes present in the meristem should be stained a light purple. Try to find cells that are in each of the four stages of mitosis.

☑ Onions are $2N = 16$. How many chromosomes are present in each stage?

_____

Clean-up:

• Place glass cover slips in sharps container or plastic cover slips in trash
• Wash slides, removing root tip and dye, and place on tray with paper towels by sink

ACTIVITY 2 & 3: MICROSCOPY OF MITOSIS AND MEIOSIS

Mitosis

When you look at actively dividing tissue, most of the cells will be in interphase. In higher eukaryotes, cell division takes about twenty-four hours, twenty-three of which are spent in interphase, with all of mitosis lasting about one hour. Therefore you will have to scan around the slide prepared in Activity 1 to find mitotic cells. Mitotic cells have tightly packed chromosomes, which makes them visible under the microscope. In interphase cells, the chromosomes are not visible because they are loosely packed as chromatin. The chromatin is contained within the nuclear envelope, so the nucleus will be distinct and fairly evenly colored, with perhaps a darker spot for the nucleolus.

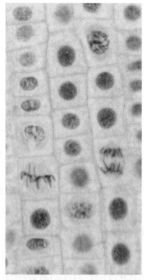

© Rattiya Thongdumhyu/Shutterstock.com

Figure H3 Mitotic cells of onion root tip.

☑ Trace the cell walls of several cells and circle the nucleus in each of those cells in Figure H3. How many stages of cell division can you identify?

☑ Trace the cell membrane of several cells and circle the nucleus in each of those cells in Figure H4. Can you find two examples of each phase of mitosis?

☑ For the Completion, you are asked to look at mitosis in both an onion (and/or broad bean plant) and in a fish blastula. Which type of tissue would you expect your own mitotic cells to most resemble? Why?

_____

Meiosis

Spermatozoa develop from the periphery toward the lumen of the seminiferous tubule, progressing through meiosis as they move. Maturation of a haploid cell to a spermatozoon involves the cell changing shape and composition. The cell loses most of its cytoplasm and grows a flagellum, which extends toward the lumen of the seminiferous tubule.

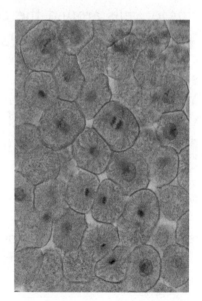

Figure H4 Mitotic cells of white fish blastula.

☑ Trace the boundary (basement membrane) of several seminiferous tubules.

☑ Put an "X" in the lumen of several seminiferous tubules.

☑ Dot several cells along the periphery of a seminiferous tubule.

☑ Trace over several cells in the center of a seminiferous tubule (not all of the tubules show the elongated cells, so find one that does).

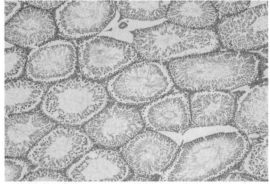

© Choksawatdikorn/Shutterstock.com

Figure H5   Seminiferous tubules of the testis.

The ovary contains *follicles* (fluid-filled sacs), each of which contains an immature oocyte. The follicles differ in the maturity of the oocytes, with primordial follicles that are frozen in early meiosis I; primary follicles that have just restarted meiosis; secondary follicles, which are larger; tertiary follicles; and a Graafian follicle. The primordial and primary follicles are small structures near the surface of the ovary. The Graafian follicle is very large and is the one oocyte that will ovulate with that month's cycle. A Graafian follicle contains an inner egg; the cumulus oophorus, the ring of cells around the oocyte (the innermost ring of cells, touching the oocyte, is the corona radiata); and the antrum, the open space around the corona cumulus oophorus. You will need to use high magnification to view the primordial and primary follicles and low magnification to view the whole Graafian follicle.

☑ Circle several follicles.

☑ Trace the cell membrane of the oocyte inside one of the secondary follicles.

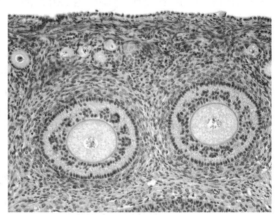

© Jose Luis Calvo/Shutterstock.com

Figure H6   Ovary with primordial and primary follicles and two secondary follicles.

Name _____ Section _____ Date _____

CELLULAR REPRODUCTION MICROSCOPY COMPLETION

Activity 1 & 2: Mitosis

1. Look at the **onion root squash** you made or the prepared slide from the broad bean plant *Vicia faba*. Draw one interphase cell and four cells in mitosis. Try to find a cell in each stage of mitosis. For each cell you find undergoing mitosis, say what stage it is in.

Interphase	Mitosis	Mitosis	Mitosis	Mitosis
	_____phase	_____phase	_____phase	_____phase

total magnification: _____x

2. Look at the slide of the **white fish blastula**. Draw one interphase cell and four cells in mitosis from this animal embryo. Try to find a cell in each stage of mitosis. For each cell you find undergoing mitosis, say what stage it is in.

Interphase	Mitosis	Mitosis	Mitosis	Mitosis
	_____phase	_____phase	_____phase	_____phase

total magnification: _____x

3. Look at the slide of **human chromosomes**. On the slide you may find whole cells and isolated nuclei with different levels of chromatin packing. Move to a high-power objective and search the slide for an area where the nuclear envelope is gone and the fully condensed chromosomes are visible. Describe what the chromosomes look like. Do the chromosomes look like they would fit in a nucleus?

Name _____ Section _____ Date _____

Activity 3: Meiosis

4. Look at the slide of the mammalian **testis** at lowest power. Draw a picture of the arrangement of the seminiferous tubules.

┌──┐
│   │
│   │
│   │
│   │
│   │
│   total magnification: _____x │
└──┘

Focus on one seminiferous tubule and look at the cells in it at the highest magnification. Look at the purple nuclei along the periphery of the tubule and toward the center of the tubule. Describe the shape and size of the nuclei as you move from the outside toward the center of the tubule and draw a picture of each.

Peripheral Cell	**Central Cell**
total magnification: _____x	total magnification: _____x

5. Look at the slide of the mammalian **ovary**. Draw a picture of the Graafian follicle and label the parts. Note the magnification used to view the Graafian follicle.

   Go back to the lowest power and find the edge of the ovary. Increase the magnification and look at the primordial and primary follicles along the side of the ovary. Draw a picture of this region, showing multiple follicles and the texture of the surrounding tissue. Note the magnification used to view the follicles.

Graafian Follicle	Primordial and Primary Follicles
total magnification: _____x	total magnification: _____x

6. Look at the **sperm smear** slide. The sperm are small, so on the lowest power the heads will look like dark dots (if visible at all). Increase magnification as high as possible and find a single sperm with an unbroken flagellum. Draw a single sperm, with the proper proportion between the size of the head size and the length of the flagellum.

total magnification: _____x

7. Now draw a picture of the oocyte from the Graafian follicle and a sperm to scale relative to each other.

Name _____ Section _____ Date _____

CELLULAR REPRODUCTION COMPREHENSION

For each cell division stage, draw in the appropriate chromosomes for a cell that is 2N=4. Use two different colors and color the homologous chromosomes the same color.

Interphase G$_1$

Interphase S

MITOSIS   **MEIOSIS**

Prophase   Prophase I

Metaphase   Metaphase I

Anaphase   Anaphase I

Telophase   Telophase I/
                              Prophase II

                              Metaphase II

                              Anaphase II

Telophase II

For questions 1–7, indicate if the statement is true for *mitosis* or *meiosis*.

_____ 1. This type of cell division results in cells that are different from the parent cell.

_____ 2. One $2N$ cell → two $2N$ cells

_____ 3. This type of cell division results in cells that have half the number of chromosomes as the parent cell.

_____ 4. One $2N$ cell → four $1N$ cells

_____ 5. This type of cell division occurs in all cells of the body except for in the formation of sex cells.

_____ 6. This type of cell division occurs in the formation of sex cells.

_____ 7. This type of cell division produces cells that are identical to each other.

_____ 8. In a particular organism, $2N = 16$. How many chromosomes will be found in each of the body cells of this organism?

_____ 9. In a particular organism, $2N = 16$. How many chromosomes will be found in each of the sex cells of this organism?

_____10. In which phase of meiosis are tetrads formed?

_____11. Prior to mitotic cell division, a cell has 14 chromosomes. How many chromosomes will each of the progeny cells have?

_____12. Crossing-over occurs during: (a) meiosis I (b) meiosis II (c) mitosis (d) cytokinesis (e) in both mitosis and meiosis

_____13. Which of the following events occurs during prophase I of meiosis?

(a) Four sex cells are produced   (b) the DNA is replicated

(c) homologous pairs of chromosomes are pulled apart

(d) homologous pairs of chromosomes are linked together

_____14. The DNA is copied during which one of the following?

(a) the mitotic phase   (b) interphase   (c) prophase

(d) metaphase   (e) cytokinesis

_____15. Which of the following is true of interphase?

(a) It is a time of cell growth and development.

(b) It composes a large part of the life cycle of a cell.

(c) Chromosomes are duplicated during this time.

(d) A cell is preparing for division during this time.

(e) All of the above are true.

_____16. Which of the following is not a stage of mitosis?

(a) interphase   (b) prophase   (c) metaphase

(d) anaphase   (e) telophase

_____17. When are sister chromatids separated?

(a) anaphase I of meiosis   (b) anaphase II of meiosis

(c) anaphase of mitosis   (d) both A and B   (e) both A and C

(f) both B and C   (g) A, B, and C

Name _____ Section _____ Date _____

CELL REPRODUCTION REVIEW QUESTIONS

	Mitosis	**Meiosis**
What is the purpose of this process? (What kind of cells are made from this process?)		
Where does this process occur in humans?		
When in a person's life-time does this process occur?		
Describe the parent cell for this process.		
What happens to the parent cell before this process can occur? (Phase name and what happens.)		
How many cells are produced by this process?		(*eggs =)
Are the cells produced diploid or haploid?		

Describe the chromosomal makeup of the produced cells: Are they identical to or distinct from the parent cell?		
What are the steps of this process?		
Generally, explain the overall procedure and outcome of this process.		meiosis I: meiosis II:
When are sister chromatids separated in this process?		
When are homologous chromosomes separated in this process?		
Does anything special happen in this process that does not happen in the other process?		
Anything else important to remember about this process?		

	Spermatogenesis	Oogenesis
What kind of cell division is this?		
What is the name of the gamete formed?		
In which sex does this process occur?		
Where in the body does the process take place?		
When during a person's life does the process occur?		
How many functional gametes are produced per cell division?		
Describe the appearance of the produced cells.		

LABORATORY I

Genetics

OBJECTIVES

- Learn to set up Punnett Squares and analyze predicted offspring.
- Predict the genotype of an individual based on their phenotype.

VOCABULARY

diploid	gene	allele	genotype
phenotype	dominant	recessive	homozygous
heterozygous	hemizygous	Punnett Square	autosomal
sex-linked	wild-type		

SKILLS

Use Punnett Squares.
Sex and identify traits of fruit flies.
Stain cells from an onion root tip.

INTRODUCTION

Animals are **diploid**: Their chromosomes are paired up, so there are two copies of each gene. The human genome consists of 23 pairs of chromosomes (46 chromosomes total). Each chromosome contains around 1,000 genes. A **gene** is a stretch of DNA that encodes the sequence of a functional molecule (usually a protein). In the population, there are multiple versions of each gene, called **alleles**. These alleles may be dominant or recessive, depending on how the gene product behaves in the organism—how it appears in action. The appearance of a gene in an organism is the **phenotype** of the trait. The phenotype is determined by the combination of the two alleles (from the two copies of the gene from the two homologous chromosomes). A **dominant** allele is seen in the phenotype. A **recessive** allele is masked if a dominant allele is present. Recessive alleles are seen in the phenotype only if both alleles are recessive. The phenotype is the same whether an individual has one dominant allele or two, but the **genotype**, or genetic makeup, is different. Having two of the same allele is called **homozygous** and having two different alleles (on the two chromosomes) is called **heterozygous**. If a person has two dominant alleles, their genotype is **homozygous dominant**. If a person has one dominant and one recessive allele, their genotype is **heterozygous**. If a person has two recessive alleles, their genotype is **homozygous recessive**.

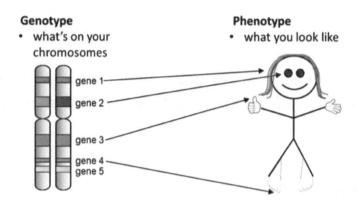

Figure I1   Genotype on chromosomes and phenotype in physical appearance.

When writing genotypes, alleles can be represented with letters. Dominant alleles are represented with capital letters and recessive alleles are represented with lowercase letters. Make sure you choose letters for which you can tell capital and lowercase apart in your handwriting and don't use X or Y—save those for the sex chromosomes.

☑   Represent a heterozygous genotype using the first letter of your first name.

_____

☑   Represent a homozygous recessive genotype using the first letter of your last name.

_____

☑   Represent a homozygous dominant genotype using the last letter of your last name.

_____

In humans, the chromosome pairs are numbered 1–23, with the twenty-third pair being the sex chromosomes. The human species has two types of sex chromosomes, named X and Y. Females have two X chromosomes and males have one X and one Y chromosome. Thus, males only have one copy of each of the genes on the X chromosome and one copy of each of the genes on the Y chromosome—they are **hemizygous** for these genes.

Alleles on the sex chromosomes are represented as superscripts on the chromosome's letter, for example X^A or X^a. Since females have two copies of the X chromosome, alleles on the X chromosome are dominant or recessive.

☑ Explain the relationship between genotype and phenotype of X-chromosome alleles in males. _____

_____

_____

Autosomal traits are determined by genes that are on the autosomal chromosomes, pairs 1–22 in humans, and **sex-linked** traits are controlled by genes on the sex chromosomes.

Punnett Squares

Punnett Squares are used to calculate expected genotype and phenotype ratios for a genetic cross. If one trait is being analyzed, a square with four boxes is used. If inheritance of two traits is being analyzed, a square with sixteen boxes is needed. To use a Punnett Square, the genotypes of both parents must first be determined. Each allele for one parent is written over a column and each allele for the other parent is written beside a row. The alleles are carried into the boxes; the allele over a column is written in the two boxes below and the allele next to a row is written in the two boxes across that row. To simplify reading the offsprings' genotypes, it is recommended that you write any dominant allele first in a box, followed by any recessive allele. The boxes now contain the genotypes of the offspring. The genotype of each box can be analyzed to determine the resulting phenotype. The genotypes and phenotypes can be reported as a ratio, fraction, or a percentage.

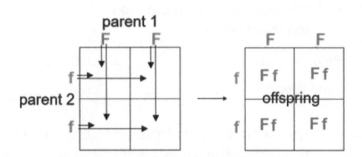

Figure I2   Parent 1 is homozygous dominant, with a genotype represented by FF. Parent 2 is homozygous recessive, with a genotype represented by ff. Their offspring are all heterozygous, with the genotype Ff.

☑   Using the Punnett Square shown in Figure I3, answer the following questions:

	F	f
F	FF	Ff
f	Ff	ff

Figure I3   A Punnett Square produced by a cross of two heterozygous parents.

Describe the parents' genotypes in words. _____

What percentage of the offspring are homozygous dominant? _____

What percentage of the offspring are heterozygous? _____

What percentage of the offspring are homozygous recessive? _____

What percentage of the offspring show the dominant phenotype? _____

What percentage of the offspring show the recessive phenotype? _____

It is standard to report genotype ratios for autosomal traits in the order homozygous dominant : heterozygous : homozygous recessive. For the Punnett Square shown in Figure I3, this ratio would be 1:2:1. Likewise, it is standard to report the phenotypic ratio as dominant: recessive. Figure I3 shows a ratio of 3:1.

	F	f
f		
f		

☑   Complete the Punnett Square to the left. Give the genotypic and phenotypic ratios.

Genotypes: _____

Phenotypes: _____

Figure I4 shows an example of an X-linked Punnett Square. In a sex-linked Punnett Square, not only the genotype but the sex of each individual is important.

	X^f	Y
X^F	$X^F X^f$	$X^F Y$
X^f	$X^f X^f$	$X^f Y$

Figure I4   A sex-linked Punnett Square for a trait on the X-chromosome.

☑ Using the Punnett Square shown in Figure I4, answer the following questions:

Describe the mother's genotypes in words. _____

Describe the father's genotypes in words. _____

What are the genotypes of the female offspring? _____

What is the ratio of the phenotypes of the female offspring? _____

What are the genotypes of the male offspring? _____

What is the ratio of the phenotypes of the male offspring? _____

	X^F	Y
X^f		
X^f		

☑ Complete the Punnett Square to the left.

What is the ratio of the phenotypes of all the offspring? _____

What is the ratio of the phenotypes of the male offspring? _____

What is the ratio of the phenotypes of the female offspring? _____

ACTIVITY 1: FRUIT FLY GENETICS

INTRODUCTION

The fruit fly species *Drosophila melanogaster* is a commonly used model organism for genetics. These flies are diploid with four pairs of chromosomes. Fruit flies have both autosomal and sex-linked traits. Chromosome pair 1 is the sex chromosomes (XX in females and XY in males) and pairs 2–4 are autosomal chromosomes.

☑ How many chromosomes does a fruit fly have? _____

Many inherited traits have been identified in fruit flies. In this lab we will look at traits affecting eye color, body color, and wing morphology (see Figure I6). We will identify flies by their phenotype—wild-type (WT) or mutant—and their sex. **The wild-type (WT)** traits in fruit flies are the common, "normal" phenotypes—red eyes, long wings, brown body (see Figure I5). The tip of the abdomen in male flies is dark, which is best viewed from the ventral side (belly-up).

Figure I5   Wild-type male (top) and female (bottom) fruit flies. Note the dark abdomen in the male fruit fly. Also note the flies' red eyes and long wings.

Figure I6   Male (left) and female (right) fruit flies with each of the mutant traits available in this lab.

a: Dumpy wings: notice the scalloped edges on the short wings.

b: Apterous wings: notice the lack of wings.

c: White eyes: eyes appear white instead of red.

d: Yellow bodies: bodies are lighter in color; may be easier to discern with naked eye than with dissecting microscope.

PROTOCOL

In this activity we are going to count live, unconscious fruit flies. The flies live in vials that contain media at the bottom, which the flies eat and in which the flies lay their eggs and the larvae grow. The vials are stoppered with sponges. We will anesthetize them with carbon dioxide to count them. Please take care when working with the flies to keep them alive and healthy. Protect them from getting squashed, damaged, wet, or stuck in their media.

1. Each group should collect a vial of fruit flies from their lab instructor. The vials are labeled at the top with the parental phenotypes for the cross. Record the abnormal phenotype on the completion page. You will be looking for the parental mutation in the F1 progeny generation. Each vial has one mutation.

2. Fill a dish with ice (pour out any water) and use the tool to pack it down.

3. Anesthetize the fruit flies. This will be done by your instructor. Turn on the CO_2 tank and adjust the knob to a low-pressure flow. Turn the vial containing the flies upside down and insert the needle from the CO_2 tank into the vial. Continue to add CO_2 until all the flies have fallen asleep. Maintain the vials on their side to keep from trapping the unconscious flies in the media.

4. Gently tap the anesthetized fruit flies into a Petri dish.

5. Place the Petri dish on the ice in the dish. The ice will keep the flies asleep. Pay attention to the ice melting and dump it out and pack fresh ice into the dish as needed to prevent the Petri dish from being flooded with water!

6. Place the fruit fly/Petri dish/ice dish setup on the stage of the dissecting microscope and adjust the focus until the flies are in focus.

7. Using a paint brush, gently move the fruit flies around to sort them into four piles: WT males, mutant males, WT females, mutant females. It may be easiest to first sort by sex to make two piles, then sort each of those piles by phenotype. Work quickly so you can return the flies to their vial as soon as possible.

8. Record the number of fruit flies you have for each category on the completion page.

9. When finished, gently sweep the fruit flies onto the folded paper with the paint brush.

10. While holding the vial fairly level, gently tap the flies into the vial.

11. Stopper the vial. Make sure part of the sponge is sticking out of the vial.

12. Keep the vial horizontal until all of the fruit flies wake up.

13. Repeat this process with a vial of flies expressing a different mutant trait.

PURPOSE

1. What do you aim to discover with this experiment?

_____

_____

2. What data will you collect from this experiment?

_____

_____

Name _____ Section _____ Date _____

ACTIVITY 1: FRUIT FLY GENETICS COMPLETION

1. Give the name of the mutant phenotype expressed by one parent of the flies counted.

2. Give the number of flies that you count in each category.

   a. WT males:

   b. Mutant males:

   c. WT females:

   d. Mutant females:

3. Is the ratio for WT to mutant males 100:0 or 50:50?

4. Is the ratio for WT to mutant females 100:0 or 50:50?

5. Is there a difference in this ratio between the sexes?

6. Is this an autosomal or a sex-linked trait?

7. Punnett Squares give ratios of 100:0, 75:25, or 50:50. Which of these ratios is closest to what you saw for your ratio of the WT to mutant phenotypes?

8. Complete the Punnett Square to reflect the (idealized) ratio of offspring you counted.

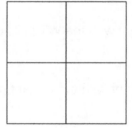

9. What is the genotype of the parent with the WT phenotype? Use the vocabulary terms to describe it.

10. What is the genotype of the parent with the mutant phenotype? Use the vocabulary terms to describe it.

1. Give the name of the mutant phenotype expressed by one parent of the flies counted.

2. Give the number of flies that you count in each category.

   a. WT males:

   b. Mutant males:

   c. WT females:

   d. Mutant females:

3. Is the ratio for WT to mutant males 100:0 or 50:50?

4. Is the ratio for WT to mutant females 100:0 or 50:50?

5. Is there a difference in this ratio between the sexes?

6. Is this an autosomal or a sex-linked trait?

7. Punnett Squares give ratios of 100:0, 75:25, or 50:50. Which of these ratios is closest to what you saw for your ratio of the WT to mutant phenotypes?

8. Complete the Punnett Square to reflect the (idealized) ratio of offspring you counted.

9. What is the genotype of the parent with the WT phenotype? Use the vocabulary terms to describe it.

10. What is the genotype of the parent with the mutant phenotype? Use the vocabulary terms to describe it.

ACTIVITY 2: HUMAN GENETICS

INTRODUCTION

While few traits in humans show simple Mendelian inheritance, we can still trace inheritance of traits through family trees. Some examples of traits that we can treat as if they were Mendelian and follow inheritance from one generation to the next are:

Dimples: When you smile, do you have an indent in your cheek? That is a dimple.

Freckles: Spots of darker color on the face and body are freckles.

Hairline: A pointed hairline on the forehead is called a widow's peak.

Earlobes: May be fused with the side of the face (attached) or the end may hang free (unattached).

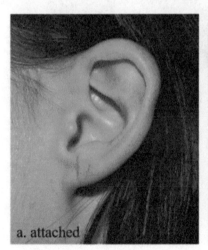 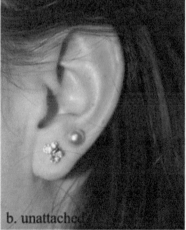

Cleft chin: A dimple in the chin is called a cleft. These vary widely in severity. Any presence counts as a cleft.

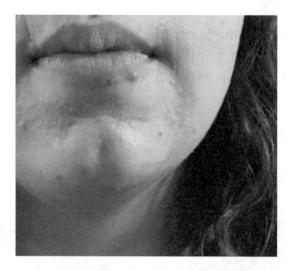

Tongue rolling: The ability to curl the sides of the tongue up.

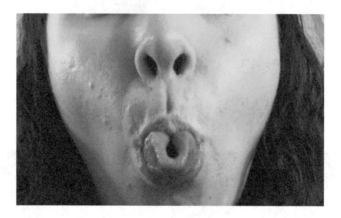

Middle finger hair: The presence of any hair counts.

Toe length: Which toe is longest, the big toe or the second toe?

Name _____ Section _____ Date _____

ACTIVITY 2: HUMAN GENETICS COMPLETION

Instructions: Write your phenotype and the phenotype of each of your family members, if you know them, for each trait. Then pick a letter to stand for each trait's dominant and recessive alleles. Use the appropriate capital and lowercase letters to represent each person in your family's genotype or possible genotypes, given their phenotype and the phenotypes of their relatives.

Example: **Dimples**: Having dimples is dominant and not having dimples is recessive.

PHENOTYPES   mother: no dimples   father: unknown   you: no dimple

others: sister: dimples

GENOTYPES   mother: *dd*   you: *dd*   sister: *Dd:* recessive allele from mom and must have gotten the dominant allele from dad

father: must be *Dd*, since the student doesn't have dimples

1. **Dimples**: Having dimples is dominant and not having dimples is recessive.

PHENOTYPES   mother: father: you:

others:

GENOTYPES   mother: father: you:

others:

2. **Freckles**: Having freckles is dominant and not having freckles is recessive.

PHENOTYPES   mother: father: you:

others:

GENOTYPES   mother: father: you:

others:

3. **Hairline**: Having a widow's peak is dominant and having a straight hairline is recessive.

    PHENOTYPES mother: father: you:

                           others:

    GENOTYPES mother: father: you:

                           others:

4. **Earlobes**: Having unattached earlobes is dominant and having attached earlobes is recessive.

    PHENOTYPES mother: father: you:

                           others:

    GENOTYPES mother: father: you:

                           others:

5. **Cleft chin**: Having a cleft chin is dominant and not having a cleft is recessive.

    PHENOTYPES: mother: father: you:

                           others:

    GENOTYPES mother: father: you:

                           others:

6. **Tongue rolling**: Being able to roll your tongue is dominant and not being able to roll your tongue is recessive.

    PHENOTYPES: mother: father: you:

                           others:

GENOTYPES   mother: father: you:

others:

7. **Middle finger hair**: Having hair on your middle finger is dominant and not having hair on your middle finger is recessive.

PHENOTYPES: mother: father: you:

others:

GENOTYPES   mother: father: you:

others:

8. **Toe length**: Having your first toe be the longest toe is dominant and having your second toe be the longest toe is recessive.

PHENOTYPES: mother: father: you:

others:

GENOTYPES   mother: father: you:

others:

Name _____ Section _____ Date _____

GENETICS COMPREHENSION

1. A female fruit fly with apterous (no) wings mates with a male fly with wild-type (WT) wings. Half of their male offspring have apterous wings and half of their male offspring have WT wings. Half of their female offspring have apterous wings and half of their female offspring have WT wings.

   a. Given the ratio of the offspring's phenotypes, what kind of trait would you expect this to be? (Choices: autosomal or sex-linked) _____

   b. Given your answer for a, does the sex of a fly affect their expected phenotype? _____

   c. Give the genotypes of each parent: (Hint: use letters)
   Male: _____   Female:_____

   d. Create a Punnett Square representing this cross. (Hint: Double-check that the offspring have the phenotype ratios that the problem states they have.)

2. A female fruit fly with apterous wings mates with a male fly with WT wings. All of their offspring have WT wings.

   a. Make a Punnett Square for their offspring.

   b. Give the genotypes of each parent:

   Male: _____   Female:_____

3. A female fruit fly with WT wings mates with a male fly with WT wings. Approximately ¾ of their offspring have WT wings; the remaining ~25% have no (apterous) wings.

   a. Make a Punnett Square for their offspring.

   b. Give the genotypes of each parent:

   Male: _____   Female:_____

4. A female fruit fly with white eyes mates with a male fruit fly with red (wild type) eyes. All of their male offspring have white eyes and all of their female offspring have red eyes.

    a. Given the ratio of the offspring's phenotypes, what kind of trait would you expect this to be? (Choices: autosomal or sex-linked) _____

    b. Given your answer for a, does the sex of a fly affect their expected phenotype? _____

    c. Give the genotypes of each parent: (Hint: use letters)

        Male: _____   Female:_____

    d. Fill in a Punnett Square representing this cross. (Hint: Double-check that the male and female offspring have the phenotypes that the problem states they have.)

5. A male fruit fly with white eyes mates with a female fruit fly with red eyes. All of their offspring have red eyes.

    a. Make a Punnett Square for their offspring. (Hint: The inheritance pattern for white eyes is always the same.)

    b. Give the genotypes of each parent:

        Male: _____   Female:_____

6. A male fruit fly with white eyes mates with a female fruit fly with red eyes. Half of their off-spring have red eyes and half have white eyes.

   a. Make a Punnett Square for their offspring. (Hint: The inheritance pattern for white eyes is always the same.)

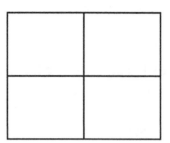

   b. Give the genotypes of each parent:

   Male: _____   Female:_____

Name _____ Section _____ Date _____

GENETICS REVIEW QUESTIONS SET A

1. Dimples are dominant and not having dimples is recessive. A man with dimples has children with a woman who does not have dimples and half of their children have dimples and half don't.

   a. What is the man's genotype?

   b. What is the woman's genotype?

2. Freckles are dominant and not having freckles is recessive. A woman with freckles has children with a man who does not have freckles and all of their children have freckles.

   a. What is the man's genotype?

   b. What is the woman's genotype?

3. Hemophilia is X-linked recessive. A man with hemophilia has children with a woman who is unaffected. None of their children have hemophilia.

   a. What is the man's genotype?

   b. What is the woman's genotype?

4. Hemophilia is X-linked recessive. A couple in which neither parent has hemophilia have children and half of their sons have hemophilia.

   a. What is the man's genotype?

   b. What is the woman's genotype?

5. Having a widow's peak is dominant and having a straight hairline is recessive. Two people who are heterozygous for a widow's peak have children.

   a. What is the man's genotype?

   b. What is the woman's genotype?

   c. Draw the Punnett Square for their children.

d. What percentage of their children would you expect to have a widow's peak?

e. What percentage of their children would you expect to have a straight hairline?

6. Huntington's disease is autosomal dominant. A man with Huntington's disease (who is heterozygous) has children with a woman who is unaffected.

a. What is the man's genotype?

b. What is the woman's genotype?

c. Draw the Punnett Square for their children.

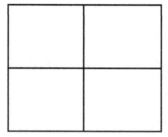

d. What percentage of their children would you expect to be affected?

e. What percentage of their children would you expect to be unaffected?

7. Color blindness is X-linked recessive. A woman who is a carrier for color blindness has children with a man who has normal vision.

a. What is the man's genotype?

b. What is the woman's genotype?

c. Draw the Punnett Square for their children.

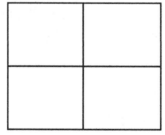

d. What percentage of their sons would you expect to be color blind?

e. What percentage of their daughters would you expect to be color blind?

8. Fragile X syndrome is X-linked dominant. An unaffected woman has children with a man who has Fragile X syndrome.

   a. What is the man's genotype?

   b. What is the woman's genotype?

   c. Draw the Punnett Square for their children.

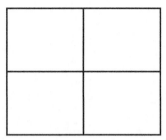

   d. What percentage of their sons would you expect to be affected?

   e. What percentage of their daughters would you expect to be affected?

Name _____ Section _____ Date _____

GENETICS REVIEW QUESTIONS SET B

1. A man with an autosomal recessive disorder has children with a woman without the mutation. Make a Punnett Square for their potential offspring.

<table>
<tr><td></td><td></td></tr>
<tr><td></td><td></td></tr>
</table>

Genotypic Ratio	Phenotypic Ratio
AA =	
Aa =	dominant phenotype =
aa =	recessive phenotype =

Which of the possible genotypes listed above would be affected by the disorder?

2. A man with a genetic disorder and a heterozygous genotype has children with a woman without the mutation. Make a Punnett Square for their potential offspring.

<table>
<tr><td></td><td></td></tr>
<tr><td></td><td></td></tr>
</table>

Genotypic Ratio	Phenotypic Ratio
AA =	
Aa =	dominant phenotype =
aa =	recessive phenotype =

Which of the possible genotypes listed above would be affected by the disorder?

3. A woman who carries an X-linked mutation but has a typical phenotype marries a man with a typical phenotype and they have children. Make a Punnett Square for their potential offspring.

<table>
<tr><td></td><td></td></tr>
<tr><td></td><td></td></tr>
</table>

Genotypic Ratio	Phenotypic Ratio
$X^D X^D$ =	
$X^D X^d$ =	♀ dominant phenotype =
$X^d X^d$ =	♀ recessive phenotype =
$X^D Y$ =	♂ dominant phenotype =
$X^d Y$ =	♂ recessive phenotype =

Which of the possible genotypes listed above would be affected by the mutation?

4. A man with an X-linked dominant disorder has children with a woman with a typical phenotype. Make a Punnett Square for their potential offspring.

Genotypic Ratio

$X^D X^D =$

$X^D X^d =$

$X^d X^d =$

$X^D Y =$

$X^d Y =$

Phenotypic Ratio

♀ dominant phenotype =

♀ recessive phenotype =

♂ dominant phenotype =

♂ recessive phenotype =

Which of the possible genotypes listed above would be affected by the disorder?

5. A man with an autosomal recessive disorder has children with a woman who is a carrier of the same mutation. Make a Punnett Square for their potential offspring.

Genotypic Ratio

AA =

Aa =

aa =

Phenotypic Ratio

dominant phenotype =

recessive phenotype =

Which of the possible phenotypes listed above would be affected by the disorder?

6. Two people who have a shared genetic disorder and heterozygous genotypes have children. Make a Punnett Square for their potential offspring.

Genotypic Ratio

AA =

Aa =

aa =

Phenotypic Ratio

dominant phenotype =

recessive phenotype =

Which of the possible phenotypes listed above would be affected by the disorder?

7. A man who is affected by an X-linked recessive mutation marries a woman who carries the same mutation and they have children. Make a Punnett Square for their potential offspring.

Genotypic Ratio

$X^DX^D =$

$X^DX^d =$

$X^dX^d =$

$X^DY =$

$X^dY =$

Phenotypic Ratio

♀ dominant phenotype =

♀ recessive phenotype =

♂ dominant phenotype =

♂ recessive phenotype =

Which of the possible phenotypes listed above would be affected by the disorder?

8. A man with an X-linked dominant disorder has children with a woman who is heterozygous for the same mutation. Make a Punnett Square for their potential offspring.

Genotypic Ratio

$X^DX^D =$

$X^DX^d =$

$X^dX^d =$

$X^DY =$

$X^dY =$

Phenotypic Ratio

♀ dominant phenotype =

♀ recessive phenotype =

♂ dominant phenotype =

♂ recessive phenotype =

Which of the possible phenotypes listed above would be affected by the disorder?

Name _____ Section _____ Date _____

GENETICS REVIEW QUESTIONS SET C

1. You count 100 fruit flies and find 23 WT males, 26 WT females, 20 mutant males, and 31 mutant females.

   a. What kind of inheritance pattern do you expect this mutant trait has?

   b. What do you think the genotypes and phenotypes of the parents are?

2. You count 100 fruit flies and find 38 WT males, 36 WT females, 14 mutant males, and 12 mutant females.

   a. What kind of inheritance pattern do you expect this mutant trait has?

   b. What do you think the genotypes and phenotypes of the parents are?

3. You cross a mutant female with a WT male and count 100 of their offspring and find 56 WT males and 44 WT females.

   a. What kind of inheritance pattern do you expect this mutant trait has?

   b. What do you think the genotypes and phenotypes of the parents are?

4. You count 100 fruit flies and find 59 mutant males and 41 WT females.

   a. What kind of inheritance pattern do you expect this mutant trait has?

   b. What do you think the genotypes and phenotypes of the parents are?

5. You count 100 fruit flies and find 26 WT males, 20 mutant males, and 54 WT females.

   a. What kind of inheritance pattern do you expect this mutant trait has?

   b. What do you think the genotypes and phenotypes of the parents are?

6. You count 100 fruit flies and find 55 WT males and 47 mutant females.

   a. What kind of inheritance pattern do you expect this mutant trait has?

   b. What do you think the genotypes and phenotypes of the parents are?

7. You count 100 fruit flies and find 12 WT males, 13 WT females, 37 mutant males, and 38 mutant females.

   a. What kind of inheritance pattern do you expect this mutant trait has?

   b. What do you think the genotypes and phenotypes of the parents are?

8. You cross a mutant male with a WT female and count 100 of their offspring and find 58 mutant males and 42 mutant females.

   a. What kind of inheritance pattern do you expect this mutant trait has?

   b. What do you think the genotypes and phenotypes of the parents are?

Histology

OBJECTIVE

• Learn about the tissues of the body.

VOCABULARY

histology	tissue	epithelial tissue	connective tissue
muscle tissue	nervous tissue	squamous	cuboidal
columnar	simple	stratified	pseudostratified
transitional	microvilli	brush border	goblet cell
cilia	keratinized	non-keratinized	matrix (ECM)
ground substance	collagenous fibers	elastic fibers	areolar
loose	dense	regular	irregular
fibroblast	chondrocyte	osteocyte	adipocyte
lacunae	canaliculi	lamellae	central canal
osteon	avascular	cartilage	bone
adipose	blood	skeletal	cardiac
smooth	striation	neuron	neuroglia
axon	dendrites	cell body	

SKILLS

Identify tissues from prepared slides.
Describe different types of body tissues.

INTRODUCTION

Histology is the study of microscopic structures of tissues. A **tissue** is a collection of similar cells that forms a layer that fulfills a certain function for an organ. There are four basic tissue types: epithelial, muscle, connective, and nervous.

EPITHELIAL TISSUE

Epithelial tissues (epithelium) cover the surfaces of the body and serve as barriers between the "inside" and the "outside" on an organ. The outer layer of the skin, the lining of the stomach and intestines, and the diffusive membrane of the lungs are all epithelial tissues. Epithelial tissues are composed of tightly bound cells and very little else. There are no blood vessels in epithelial tissues, - they are **avascular**.

☑   What is present in epithelial tissue besides epithelial cells? Hint: What can you sense with your skin? _____

Epithelial tissues are categorized by their cell shape and the number of layers of cells in the tissue. Epithelial cells are divided into three shapes: squamous, cuboidal, and columnar. **Squamous** cells, when viewed from the side, appear short and wide; the cell is only slightly taller than the nucleus is. When viewed from the top, epithelial cells resemble fried eggs: a round nucleus inside an irregular cell. **Cuboidal** cells are approximately the same dimension in all directions: They are as tall as they are wide as they are long and are not much bigger than their nucleus. **Columnar** cells, when viewed from the side, are much taller than they are wide; they are only slightly wider than their nucleus.

Epithelial tissues are composed either of a single layer of cells or of multiple layers of cells. **Simple** tissues are composed of one layer and **stratified** tissues have more than one layer. One way to determine if a tissue is simple or stratified is to look at the stained nuclei in a cross-sectional slide. Usually the nuclei of the cells in a layer are all lined up; if there's one row of nuclei, the tissue is simple; if there are multiple layers of nuclei, the tissue is most likely stratified.

Putting the two ways of describing tissues together, we get six possibilities: simple squamous, simple cuboidal, simple columnar, stratified squamous, stratified cuboidal, stratified columnar. All of these possible tissue types are present in human biology.

Figure J1   Squamous cells viewed from above.

☑ Trace each squamous cell (note, the cells overlap) and circle each nucleus in Figure J1.

Simple squamous epithelium is the thinnest epithelial tissue possible: a single layer of thin cells. Diffusion works best over short distances, so this tissue forms the barrier in many places where diffusion takes place. Structures composed of simple squamous epithelium include the alveoli of the lungs (gas exchange between blood and lungs, see Lab L), capillaries (exchange of molecules between blood and tissue, see Lab K), and the glomerular capsules of the kidneys (fluid exchange between blood and nephron, see Lab M).

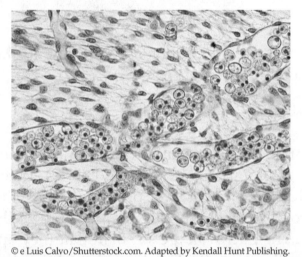

© e Luis Calvo/Shutterstock.com. Adapted by Kendall Hunt Publishing.

Figure J2 Capillaries containing embryonic, nucleated, red blood cells.

☑ Locate the nucleus of each of the cells making up the wall of one of the capillaries in Figure J2.

Simple cuboidal epithelium is found in the proximal and distal convoluted tubules of the nephron and part of the nephron loop (see Lab M) and in small ducts of exocrine glands. This tissue provides a barrier that also allows absorption and secretion.

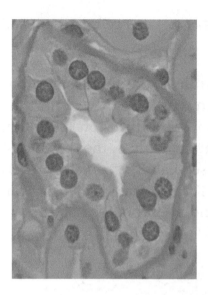

Figure J3   Simple cuboidal cells lining the lumen of a nephron.

☑   Outline each cell in Figure J3.

Absorption and secretion can also occur across **simple columnar epithelium**, such as the organs of the gastrointestinal tract (see Lab N). When viewing the small intestine, look for **microvilli**, microscopic projections from the apical (top) surface of the cells. The microvilli increase the surface area of the cells, improving the efficiency of absorption. The microvilli are so small that they appear as a dark band across the top of the cells, called the **brush border**. These structures do not move. These cellular projections are supported by actin microfilaments. Also look for **goblet cells** in the tissue, which produce mucus. These cells stain differently from the surrounding cells and often have a "wine glass" shape.

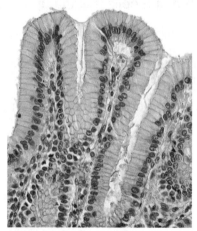

Figure J4   Simple columnar epithelium lining the gastric pits of the stomach.

☑ Draw in the boundary between the epithelium and the connective tissue below and trace a few of the epithelial cells in Figure J4.

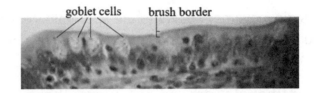

Figure J5 Simple columnar epithelium of the small intestine with goblet cells and microvilli brush border.

Ciliated pseudostratified columnar epithelium is found in the respiratory tract. This tissue is a single layer of cells, because all of the cells touch the basal (bottom) surface, but not all of the cells reach the apical (top) surface. Since the cells in the tissue are different heights, their nuclei appear at different levels in the tissue, giving it the appearance of a stratified tissue. The **cilia**—hair-like structures—on the apical surface on the tissue move and beat together to move mucus across the surface of the tissue. Tubulin microtubules provide the structure for cilia. Mucus is made by **goblet cells** in the tissue. Mucus traps particulate matter and germs and the beating of the cilia moves the mucus up and out of the respiratory tract.

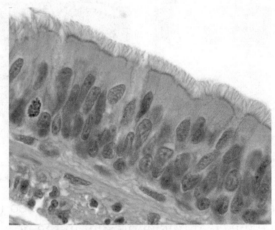

© Jose Luis Calvo/Shutterstock.com

Figure J6 Ciliated pseudostratified columnar epithelium of the trachea.

☑ Circle the cilia and locate and trace three goblet cells in Figure J6.

☑ What is the purpose of making and moving mucus through the respiratory tract?

☑ Compare and contrast the microvilli of simple columnar epithelium and cilia of pseudostratified epithelium. _____

_____

☑ Cellular projections aid movement of immature spermatozoa and ova through their respective reproductive tracts. Which kind of structure—cilia or microvilli—do you think are present? Why? _____

Stratified squamous epithelial is present on surfaces that get abraded, such as the skin, mouth, pharynx, esophagus, rectum, anus, and vagina. Stratified squamous epithelium can be keratinized or nonkeratinized. **Keratinized** epithelium is essentially dead cells that have degraded organelles and a high concentration of **keratin**, a tough protein that makes the cells water-resistant. Keratinized epithelium does not have to be kept wet, so this is what our body surface is coated with. When you look at the slide of skin, look for the outermost layer of wavy strands—that's the layer of dead, keratinized cells. **Non-keratinized** cells are alive and thus must be kept moist. Stratified squamous epithelium found in internal locations and at mucous membranes is non-keratinized.

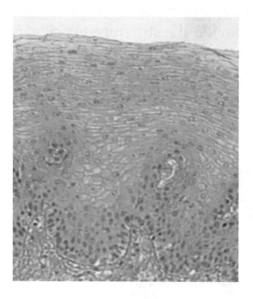 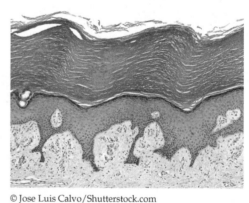

© Jose Luis Calvo/Shutterstock.com

Figures J7 and J8   Nonkeratinized (left) and keratinized (right) stratified squamous epithelium. Notice the clear nuclei present in the nonkeratinized tissue and the thick layer of dry material in the keratinized tissue.

☑ For Figures J7 and J8, identify where the epithelium ends and the connective tissue begins.

☑ Explain why stratified tissue, not simple tissue, is present in locations that get abraded. _____

☑ Of the locations listed as having stratified squamous epithelium, which do you think are keratinized? Which do you think are non-keratinized? _____

_____

☑ Reflect back to Lab A and the appearance of the skin cells and cheek cells stained in that lab. Explain the appearance of those cells in light of what you learned here.

_____

_____

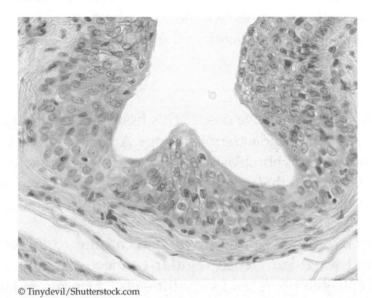

© Tinydevil/Shutterstock.com

Figure J9 Transitional epithelium facing the lumen of the ureter.

Transitional epithelium is found lining organs that distend (stretch): the ureters, bladder, urethra, and prostate gland ducts. When this tissue is relaxed, the cells appear cuboidal and the tissue appears thick; when the tissue is distended, the cells appear squamous and the tissue appears thin. Some of the cells in transitional epithelium have two nuclei (binucleated).

CONNECTIVE TISSUE

Connective tissue is the most diverse category of tissue. Connective tissue is found in all parts of the body. Connective tissues are different from other tissue types because they have relatively low cell concentrations; the majority of the tissue is composed of matrix. The **extracellular matrix** (or extracellular material, **ECM**) contains protein fibers and **ground substance**—water with dissolved salts, carbohydrates, and glycosylated proteins (proteins with carbohydrates attached). The ground substance can vary from being liquid to solid. The matrix fibers are collagenous fibers and elastic fibers. **Collagenous fibers**, composed of the protein collagen, provide strength to the tissue. Because of its ubiquity in connective tissues, collagen is the most abundant protein in animals. Collagenous fibers are tough, thick, and do not branch. **Elastic fibers** are composed of the protein elastin and give tissues flexibility and stretchiness. Elastic fibers are thin, small, and branched.

The cells of the connective tissue include **fibroblasts**, which produce fibers; macrophages, immune cells that engulf foreign entities and old cells; and specialized cells that are tissue-specific.

Connective tissue can be divided into **fibrous connective tissues** and **specialized connective tissues**. Fibrous connective tissue can be divided into **loose** and **dense** based on the concentration of collagen in the tissue.

Fibrous Connective Tissue

Areolar tissue is a loose connective tissue. This tissue has a lot of ground substance, which appears as open space under the microscope. Areolar tissue contains nonoriented fibers. Areolar tissue contains fibroblasts, adipocytes (fat cells), macrophages, and other cells. Areolar tissue is found throughout the body. It is found under almost all epithelial tissues, provides cushioning, support, and blood supply to the epithelial tissue.

The dense connective tissue can be divided according to the orientation of the fibers: regular and irregular. **Dense regular** connective tissue contains densely packed, parallel collagen fibers, and very little else. Dense regular connective tissue is very strong in the direction the fibers run. Dense regular connective tissue contains fibroblasts that produce the collagen and a few blood vessels and sensory nerve fibers. You will be able to see the stained nuclei of the fibroblasts under the microscope. Tendons (attach muscle to bone) and ligaments (connect bone to bone) are composed of dense regular connective tissue.

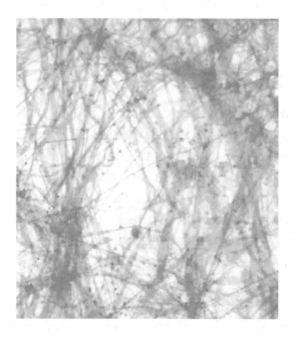

Figure J10   Fibers in areolar loose connective tissue.

☑ Dense regular connective tissue has a low concentration of blood vessels. What does this mean for the rate of healing of tendons and ligaments? _____

_____

☑ An ankle sprain occurs when the ankle turns one way and the foot twists the other, overstretching or tearing a ligament. Explain why this kind of composite movement would injure dense regular connective tissue. _____

_____

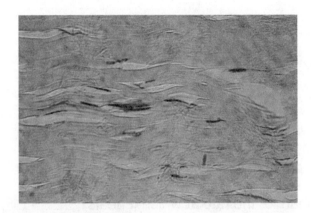 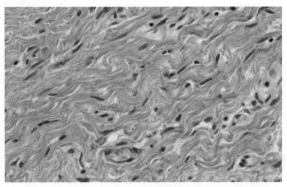

© e Luis Calvo/Shutterstock.com. Adapted by Kendall Hunt Publishing.

Figures J11 and J12 Dense regular connective tissue from tendon on left and dense irregular connective tissue from the dermis on right.

Dense irregular connective tissue is densely packed with randomly oriented collagen fibers. This makes the tissue strong in all directions. Dense irregular connective tissue is present in the skin, under the epithelium, and around organs, bones, nerves, and cartilage.

☑ For Figures J11 and J12, draw in arrows indicating the direction(s) the fibers run in the tissue.

☑ A layer of dense irregular connective tissue protects many of the body's organs. Explain why it's protective. _____

_____

☑ What is the most common type of cell in dense irregular connective tissue? Why?

_____

Specialized Connective Tissue

The specialized connective tissues are cartilage, bone, adipose tissue, and blood.

There are three types of cartilage, the most common type being hyaline cartilage. Hyaline **cartilage** is a firm, rubbery connective tissue that gives structure to the nose, ears, respiratory pathway, etc. Its matrix, which is thick and rich in collagen fibers, is secreted by **chondrocytes**. Cells need to be bathed in fluid, so the chondrocytes live in liquid-filled pits in the matrix called **lacunae** (singular: lacuna). Cartilage is **avascular**—there are no blood vessels in it.

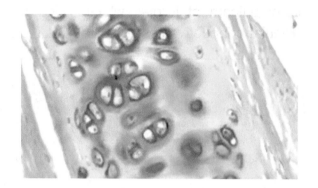

Figure J13   Hyaline cartilage of the trachea.

☑   Locate the lacunae and chondrocytes in Figure J13.

☑   Cartilage is avascular. What does this mean for the rate at which it heals? _____

_____

Bone makes up the skeleton, the framework of the body. Bone has a hard matrix containing collagen fibers and calcium and phosphorous salts. The matrix is secreted by cells that become trapped in the matrix. **Osteocytes** are present in liquid-filled pits in the matrix called lacunae. The lacunae are dark spots on the compact bone slide. The osteocytes are not present on the slide; they are lost during preservation. Lacunae are interconnected by **canaliculi** (singular: canaliculus). The canaliculi look like long eyelashes coming off the lacunae. Compact bone is laid down in concentric rings, called **lamellae**, around the **central canal** that contains blood vessels and nerves. A circular unit containing a central canal and multiple lamellae rings is called an **osteon**.

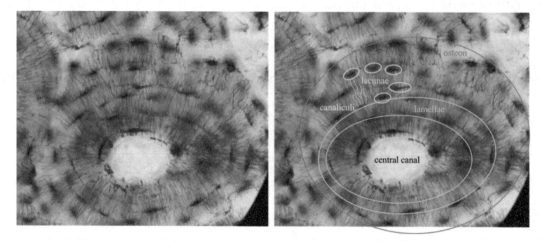

Figure J14   Compact bone with labeled features (right).

Adipose tissue is composed mainly of **adipocytes**, fat-storing cells, with little matrix. Each adipocyte is filled by a triglyceride droplet, which pushes the nucleus and cytoplasm to the edge of the cell. For most cells in the cross-section, the nucleus will not be visible. Adipose tissue stores energy and provides insulation and padding. Adipose tissue is found under the skin, around the kidneys and heart, and in other deposits throughout the body.

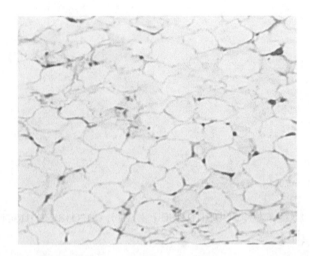

Figure J15   Rings of cell membrane of adipocytes.

☑   Why are most of the cells' nuclei not present in a cross-section of adipose tissue? Hint: Remember, cells are three-dimensional. _____

_____

Blood is a fluid connective tissue with a water-based ground substance (plasma) plus cells, proteins, and other compounds (see Cardiovascular System Lab K).

MUSCLE TISSUE

There are three types of muscle cells in the body: skeletal, cardiac, and smooth.

Skeletal muscles are connected to bone and are consciously controlled. The cells are shaped like long rods, contain multiple nuclei, and appear striped, or striated. The **striations** are caused by the alignment of the proteins that cause muscle contraction. Skeletal muscle cells are full of protein bundles, which push the nuclei to the cell periphery. Under the microscope, the nuclei look like lumps on the surface of the rods.

Cardiac muscle cells also have striations, though they are finer. Cardiac muscle cells are much shorter than skeletal muscles cells and branch; the cardiac muscle cells interconnect (via intercalated discs) to form a network in the heart. Cardiac muscle cells are only found in the heart and are autonomically controlled. Some cardiac muscle cells contain two nuclei. Nuclei are located in the middle of the cells.

Smooth muscle cells are also autonomic. They are found in the walls of hollow organs such as the stomach, intestines, and blood vessels, and provide peristaltic (wave-like) motion through these organs. Smooth muscle cells do not have striations. The cells are tapered at the ends (roughly diamond-shaped) and contain one centrally located nucleus per cell.

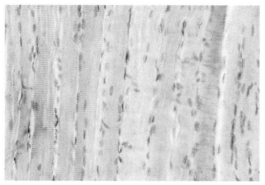 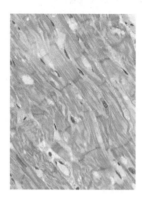 

© Choksawatdikorn/Shutterstock.com. Adapted by Kendall Hunt Publishing.

Figures J16, J17, J18   Skeletal muscle (left), cardiac muscle (middle), smooth muscle (right).

☑   Trace the striations in the skeletal and cardiac muscle tissue in Figures J16 and J17.

☑   Circle a few of the nuclei in the muscle tissues in Figures J16, J17, and J18.

☑   Trace a few cells in the muscle tissues in Figures J16, J17, and J18.

NERVOUS TISSUE

Nervous tissue is found in the brain and spinal cord of the central nervous system and in the nerves of the peripheral nervous system. There are two main categories of cells in nervous tissue: neurons and neuroglia. **Neurons** are the cells that send and receive signals. **Neuroglia** (glial cells) are the support cells. There are six types of neuroglia: Two types found in the peripheral nervous system and four in the central nervous system. Neurons look different from other cells of the body. They have a central **cell body** (stoma) that houses the nucleus, and two types of projections: the dendrites and the axon. **Dendrites** receive signals and communicate them to the cell body. The **axon** carries signals away from the cell body.

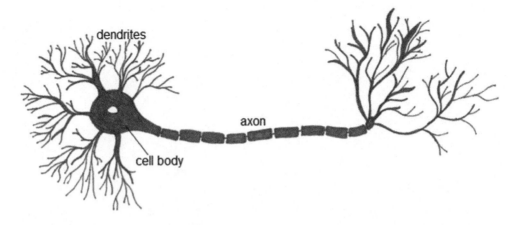

Figure J19 Neuron with labeled dendrites, axon, and cell body.

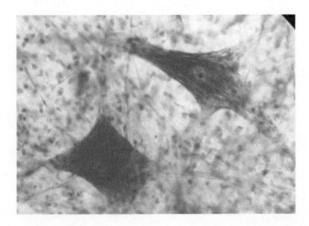

Figure J20 Two neurons under the microscope.

☑ Trace the two neurons in Figure J20 and circle each cell's nucleus.

Name _____ Section _____ Date _____

HISTOLOGY COMPLETION

Look at each of the slides indicated and draw the tissue.

1. **Epithelial tissues**

Simple Squamous (Oral)	Simple Squamous (Lung)
*The tissue inside the mouth is stratified, but the cells are broken apart when collected. We are viewing squamous cells from the top in this slide.	
Nonkeratinized Stratified Squamous	Keratinized Stratified Squamous
Pseudostratified Ciliated Columnar	Simple Columnar
Simple Cuboidal	Transitional

2. **Muscle tissues**

Skeletal	Cardiac	Smooth

3. **Connective tissues**

Loose Areolar	Tendon (Dense Regular)
Adipose Tissue	Blood
Compact Bone	Hyaline Cartilage

4. **Nervous tissue.** Look for a neuron. Once you find one, draw it:

5. Now that you've looked at the different types of tissues, look at the following organ cross-sections. For each, locate the epithelium and identify what type of epithelial tissue is present. Try to identify other layers of tissue, such as connective tissue or smooth muscle, as applicable.

   a. Small intestine: b. Kidney:

   c. Esophagus: d. Trachea:

   e. Stomach: f. Skin:

   g. Lung: h. Ureter:

Name _____ Section _____ Date _____

HISTOLOGY COMPREHENSION

1. For each box in the table, fill in the name of the epithelial tissue that is described by the column and row headings.

	One Layer of Cells	**Multiple Layers of Cells**
Short, wide cells		
Equal height and width cells		
Tall, narrow cells		

2. Complete the table below for the traits of the three types of muscle tissue.

Trait	**Skeletal Muscle**	**Cardiac Muscle**	**Smooth Muscle**
Location in body			
Shape			
Striations?			
# Nuclei			
Voluntary?			

3. Complete the table below for the traits of the fibrous connective tissues.

Trait	Areolar	Dense Regular	Dense Irregular
Composition of matrix			
Cell type(s) present			
Location in body			
Role			

4. Complete the table below for the traits of the specialized connective tissues.

Trait	Cartilage	Bone	Adipose	Blood
Composition of matrix				
Cell type(s) present				
Location in body				
Role				

5. Complete the table below for the traits of the epithelial projections.

	Simple Columnar Epithelium	Pseudostratified Columnar Epithelium
Location in body		
Type of projection		
Purpose of projection		
Protein providing structure		

Name _____ Section _____ Date _____

HISTOLOGY REVIEW QUESTIONS

1. Describe the following levels of organization: cell, tissue, organ.

2. Name the four types of tissues. Describe the role of each.

3. Describe the cell shapes and organizations possible in epithelial tissue.

4. Describe the relationship (packing) of cells in epithelial tissue.

5. Why is pseudostratified epithelium named that (what does it look like)?

6. Generally, what functions do simple epithelium, stratified epithelium, and transitional epithelium have?

7. Where is epithelial tissue found?

8. What is below epithelial tissue?

9. Describe the composition of connective tissue. What kinds of cells are present? What is the spatial relationship between cells?

10. Name and describe as many types of connective tissues as you can.

11. Describe the differences between the different kinds of fibrous connective tissues: loose and dense, regular and irregular.

12. Describe each of the specialized connective tissues, including the matrix composition, cells present, and where in the body each type of tissue can be found.

13. What does connective tissue supply to epithelial tissue?

14. In what special structure are cartilage and bone cells found?

15. Why do tendons heal slowly? Why does cartilage heal slowly?

16. Sketch a region of compact bone and label the components (hint: six terms).

17. Describe the cell appearance for each type of muscle.

18. Where is each muscle type found?

19. Which type(s) of muscle can you actively control and which are autonomic?

20. What kinds of cells are present in the nervous system and what is the role of each?

21. Describe the structure of a nerve cell.

22. Draw a sketch of the appropriate epithelial tissue in each box:

	Squamous	Cuboidal	Columnar
Simple			
Stratified			

23. Draw a sketch of the protein fibers in each box:

Loose Connective Tissue	Dense Regular Connective Tissue	Dense Irregular Connective Tissue

24. Draw a sketch of the appropriate muscle tissue in each box:

Skeletal Muscle	Cardiac Muscle	Smooth Muscle

25. Draw a sketch of a neuron. Label the parts.

<hr>

OBJECTIVES

- Learn about the anatomy and physiology of the heart.
- Learn about the formed elements of the blood.
- Learn about blood vessels and the vascular circuits.
- Learn about blood typing and compatibility.

<hr>

VOCABULARY

pericardium	epicardium	myocardium	endocardium
thoracic cavity	atrium	ventricle	valve
tricuspid valve	bicuspid valve	atrioventricular valve	semilunar valve
aortic valve	pulmonary valve	chordae tendineae	papillary muscles
artery	vein	arteriole	venule
capillary	oxygenated	deoxygenated	systemic circuit
pulmonary circuit	cardiac cycle	systole	diastole
lumen	vena cava	pulmonary artery	pulmonary vein
aorta	formed elements	leukocyte	erythrocyte
thrombocyte	sphygmomanometer	hypertension	arteriosclerosis
auscultate	bpm	HRR	antigen
agglutination	antiserum	"lub-dub"	

SKILLS

Identify the structures of a heart.
Use a stethoscope to measure your heart rate.
Use an automatic sphygmomanometer to measure your blood pressure.
Analyze agglutination with antisera to determine blood type.
Calculate your heart rate recovery.

ACTIVITY 1: HEART ANATOMY

INTRODUCTION

The cardiovascular system consists of the heart, blood vessels, and blood. Its main function is to pump blood through the body to supply cells with oxygen and nutrients.

Blood leaving the heart to the body is **oxygenated** (oxygen-rich). The cells of the body take up and use the oxygen from the circulating blood, thus the blood returning to the heart is **deoxygenated** (oxygen-poor).

The **heart** is a muscular organ located slightly left-of center in the **thoracic** (chest) **cavity**, behind the sternum (breastbone), between the lungs, and above the diaphragm. The human heart is roughly the size of your fist. The heart beats continuously, pumping blood through the body. The average resting heart rate is 60–100 beats per minute (bpm) and each contraction pumps 60–90 mL of blood out of the heart.

☑   Calculate approximately how many liters of blood are pumped through the heart each day. _____

The heart is suspended in a sac called the **pericardium**. The heart itself contains three layers of tissues. The outer layer of the heart is called the **epicardium**. The pericardium and epicardium produce fluid that lubricates and protects the heart.

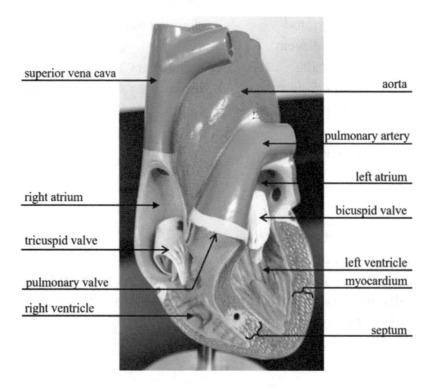

Figure K1   Features of heart model, interior frontal view.

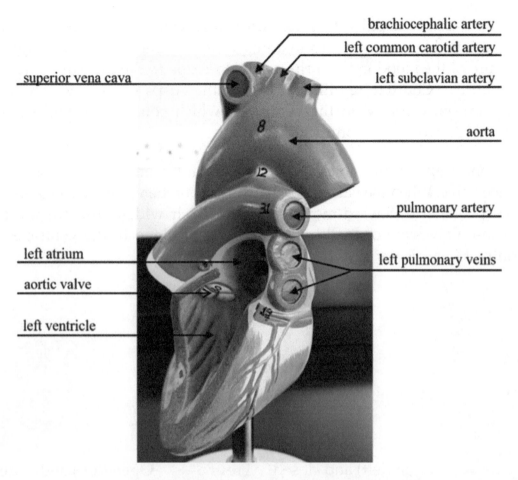

Figure K2 Features of heart model, left lateral view.

The middle layer of the heart is called the **myocardium** and contains the cardiac muscle (see Histology Lab J). The **endocardium** is the innermost layer of the heart and lines the heart chambers.

The heart is divided into four chambers: the **right atrium**, the **right ventricle**, the **left atrium**, and the **left ventricle**. The **atria** are the top chambers and the **ventricles** are the bottom chambers. The left and right designations are from the point of view of the subject. The chambers differ in size depending on their function; bigger chambers can hold more blood and pump harder. Left ventricle is the largest and strongest chamber because it pumps blood to the whole body. The wall of the human left ventricle is about half an inch thick.

The heart **valves** permit blood to flow in one direction and prohibit backflow. There are four valves in the heart: tricuspid, bicuspid (mitral), pulmonary, and aortic. The **tricuspid valve** is between the right atrium and right ventricle. The **bicuspid valve** is between the left atrium and left ventricle. The **pulmonary valve** is between the right ventricle and the pulmonary artery and the **aortic valve** is between the left ventricle and the aorta.

The tricuspid and bicuspid valves are **atrioventricular (AV) valves**, because each one is positioned between an atrium and a ventricle. These valves are opened by the pressure of the blood in the atrium and close due to the pressure of the blood in the ventricle. **Chordae tendineae** connect the cusps of the AV valves to the **papillary muscles** located in the ventricles, which contract to hold the valves closed when the ventricles contract.

The pulmonary and aortic valves are **semilunar valves**, named for the shape of the flaps in the valve. When the valve is open, the cusps of the valve are crescent-shaped. These cusps catch backward-moving blood, which widens them, shutting the valve. These valves are opened by the pressure of blood in the ventricles when they contract (ventricular systole).

Figure K3   Open (left) and closed (right) atrioventricular valve, with chordae tendineae and papillary muscles.

Figure K4   Open (left) and closed (right) semilunar valve.

Deoxygenated blood from the body returns to the heart by way of the **vena cava** and enters the right atrium. The blood passes through the tricuspid valve into the right ventricle. Blood from the right ventricle is forced through the pulmonary valve into the **pulmonary artery**, which carries the blood to the lungs, where it is oxygenated. The blood returns from the lungs to the heart by way of the **pulmonary veins** and enters the left atrium. The blood passes through the bicuspid valve into the left ventricle. Blood from the left ventricle is forced through the aortic valve into the **aorta**, which carries the oxygenated blood to the body.

Deoxygenated blood enters the vena cava→right atrium→tricuspid valve→right ventricle→pulmonary valve→pulmonary artery→lungs→oxygenated blood enters the pulmonary veins→left atrium→bicuspid (mitral) valve→left ventricle→aortic valve→aorta→body.

The movement of blood is a closed circulatory system and can be divided into two pathways: the systemic circuit and the pulmonary circuit. The **systemic circuit** transports oxygenated blood from the heart to the tissues and deoxygenated blood from the tissues back to the heart. The **pulmonary circuit** transports deoxygenated blood from the heart to the lungs and oxygenated blood from the lungs back to the heart.

ACTIVITY 2: MICROSCOPY OF THE CIRCULATORY SYSTEM

INTRODUCTION

Blood Vessels

Systemic circulation carries blood from the heart to the body and back in blood vessels. **Arteries** are large blood vessels that leave the heart; these branch and become narrower vessels called **arterioles**. Molecular exchange with the tissues of the body occurs at the **capillaries**. Blood returns to the heart from the capillary beds in **venules,** which merge to form larger diameter **veins**, which return blood to the heart.

Arteries and veins contain several layers of tissue. The blood in the lumen is in contact with a simple squamous epithelium layer. Beyond this are layers containing connective tissue with strong collagenous fibers and stretchy elastic fibers and smooth muscle (see the Histology Lab J). The elastic fibers allow the blood vessel to extend and recoil and the smooth muscle allows dilation and constriction. The smooth muscle layer is much thicker in arteries than in veins. This is because the

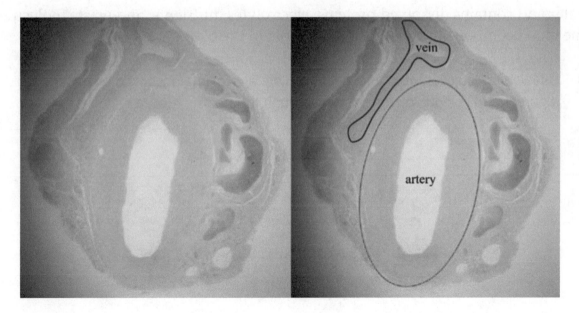

Figure K5 Microscope image of artery and vein (location indicated on right).

blood pressure is much higher, and fluctuating, in the arteries. Veins feel a low, constant blood pressure, so their walls are thinner. The majority of the body's blood is in the veins when the body is at rest. Thus, veins have a large **lumen** (inner space). Veins have one-way valves that prevent backflow. Blood is worked back to the heart by the movement of neighboring skeletal muscles. The contraction and thickening of muscles squeezes the veins, pushing the blood through the valves.

Capillaries are narrow and consist of a single layer of leaky simple squamous epithelial cells. The thinness of this tissue promotes exchange of molecules between the blood and the tissue. Capillary beds pervade the tissues of the body, so every cell is within a short distance (<50 μm) of a capillary.

☑ Arteries carry blood leaving the heart. What is the usual oxygenation state of blood in arteries? _____
What is the exception? _____

☑ Veins carry blood returning to the heart. What is the usual oxygenation state of blood in arteries? _____
What is the exception? _____

Blood

A person has 4–6 L of blood, depending on body weight. Blood is about 55% fluid plasma and 45% erythrocytes, with leukocytes and thrombocytes making up less than 1% of the blood volume. Erythrocytes leukocytes (white blood cells), and thrombocytes are the **formed elements** (cells) of the blood. The blood plasma is 92% water and contains dissolved proteins, electrolytes, nutrients, and waste molecules. The blood components help maintain the pH of the blood at 7.4.

☑ Use your calculation from above to calculate approximately how many times per day a person's full blood volume passes through the heart.

_____

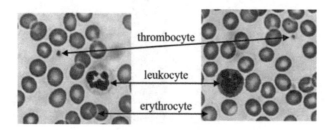

Figure K6   Microscope image of blood smears showing formed elements.

Erythrocytes (red blood cells, RBC) are red, biconcave "cells" that transport oxygen and carbon dioxide. Oxygen transportation is made possible by the protein hemoglobin, which contains four copies of a heme group, an organic molecule that contains a central iron atom that binds molecular oxygen. It is this complex that gives red blood cells their color. The disc shape of red blood cells gives them a high surface area, promoting oxygen diffusion, and is possible because RBCs lack a nucleus. This also makes the cells very flexible. Erythrocytes are not true cells since they lack a nucleus and most organelles. Instead, the space inside an erythrocyte is filled with hundreds of thousands of hemoglobin proteins. Since they lack a nucleus, erythrocytes don't live very long: They have a lifespan of about 120 days.

☑   Why does the lack of a nucleus cause erythrocytes to have a short lifespan?

_____

_____

☑   If one erythrocyte contains 270 million hemoglobin proteins, how many oxygen molecules can it carry? _____

Thrombocytes (platelets) are cell fragments that are important for blood clotting (coagulation). They are produced by the breakup of a precursor cell called a megakaryocyte. Platelets last about one week.

☑   Why do platelets have an even shorter lifespan?

_____

_____

Leukocytes, or white blood cells, (WBC), protect the body from disease. Leukocytes are true cells. There are five types of leukocytes. The shape of the nucleus is characteristic of each type of WBC. Leukocytes are divided into two categories: granular and agranular (not containing granules). The granules contain digestive enzymes. Neutrophils, eosinophils, and basophils are granular and lymphocytes and monocytes are agranular.

Neutrophils are the most common, making up 40–70% of the white blood cells present in the blood. Neutrophils are phagocytes: They engulf bacteria and other material. They can be identified by their multilobed (2–5) nucleus. Neutrophils are so named because they stain with pH-neutral dyes.

Lymphocytes make up 20–40% of leukocytes. Antibody-producing B cells, T cells, and natural killer (NK) cells are all lymphocytes. Lymphocytes are small WBCs with a large, round nucleus surrounded by a small ring of cytoplasm. Lymphocytes are present in the lymphatic system.

Monocytes are phagocytic cells that can become macrophages in tissue. Approximately 2–8% of leukocytes are monocytes. They contain a large kidney or U-shaped nucleus.

Eosinophils make up 1–4% of the WBC population. They play a role in allergies and fighting parasites. They are stained by eosin, an acidic dye, hence their name. Under the microscope, they display a bilobed nucleus and grainy cytosol, often dyed red/orange.

Basophils make up 1% or less of white blood cells. They are involved in inflammation and allergic reactions. They are identifiable by their dense, dark purple granules, which are stained with a basic dye.

☑   If neutrophils make up 65% of white blood cells, what percentage of whole blood do they constitute? _____

Blood Types

Proteins are expressed on the surface of red blood cells, and which proteins are present varies from person to person. These proteins will elicit an immune response (if they are foreign), so they are known as **antigens**. A person with type A blood expresses type A antigen (protein) on their red blood cells. Type B blood have type B antigen. Type AB blood has both A antigen and B antigen on each red blood cell. Type O blood has neither A nor B antigen. Each person has two alleles for blood antigens. Thus, a person with type A blood could be homozygous AA or heterozygous AO. A person with type O blood must be homozygous OO. A person with type AB blood must have the A allele on one chromosome and the B allele on the other chromosome. Another antigen that is important for blood typing is from the rhesus blood group system. Simply put, a person is either Rh+, and has the antigen on their red blood cells, or Rh−, and lacks the antigen. Again, a person who is Rh+ can be heterozygous or homozygous for this trait. A person's blood type is reported with their ABO type first and their Rh status (+ or −) afterward: AB+, O−, etc.

☑   The author's blood type is O−. What must her genotype be? (Hint: What must her two alleles for the ABO blood type be? What must her two alleles for Rh be?)

_____

☑   She has two children, one with B+ and one with B− blood types. What blood type must her husband have? _____

☑   What must their children's genotypes be? _____

☑ Given this information, what are her husband's possible genotype(s)?

_____

☑ If they had more children, what blood type would allow us to know the father's genotype for sure? _____

Blood donation is critical for saving lives, however, blood must be matched or a blood transfusion can be fatal. A person can only receive antigens their body already recognizes as self, otherwise they will mount an immune response that will attack the donated blood.

To ensure compatibility, blood is typed and cross-matched before administration. In addition to the ABO type and Rh status, there are other proteins present in the blood that may trigger an immune response in the patient. To test for this, a small amount of the patient blood and the donor blood are mixed together and viewed under the microscope to look for agglutination (clumping) caused by antibodies in the patient's blood.

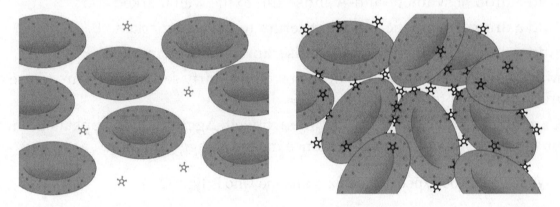

Figure K7 Left: Blood donation to a compatible recipient. Note that the anti-bodies (gray) do not bind to the antigens on the erythrocytes' surface. Right: Donation to an incompatible recipient. The antibodies (black) in the recipient's blood bind to the antigens (blue squares) on the donor's erythrocytes and agglu-tinate the cells, which can cause blocked blood vessels or hemolysis.

☑ A person has type A+ blood. Which antigens are recognized as self? _____
Which antigen(s) would be recognized as foreign? _____

☑ In an emergency situation, when a patient's blood type is unknown, type O− blood
is administered. Explain why this is. _____

_____

☑ A patient and potential donor's blood are mixed during a cross-match and agglutination is seen under the microscope. Is the donor's blood a match or not?

_____

ACTIVITY 3: DETERMINATION OF BLOOD TYPE

INTRODUCTION

Blood type can be determined by mixing blood with antisera that contain antibodies against the possible blood antigens and look for **agglutination**—the clumping of the blood caused by the antibodies binding to the antigens on the surface of the red blood cells. "**Antiserum**" is blood that contains antibodies. For example, "anti-A antiserum" is blood that contains antibodies against the A antigen. When anti-A antiserum is mixed with blood containing the A antigen, agglutination occurs.

PROTOCOL

*Replace each cap after using each dropper vial, before moving on.

1. Label the wells of a blood typing slide "A," "B," and "Rh."
2. Place a drop of synthetic blood into each well on the blood typing slide.
3. Add a drop of synthetic anti-A antiserum to the well marked "A."
4. Add a drop of synthetic anti-B antiserum to the well marked "B."
5. Add a drop of synthetic anti-Rh antiserum to the well marked "Rh."
6. Mix the blood and antiserum in each well for thirty seconds. Be sure to use a fresh toothpick for each well!
7. Carefully examine the blood film in each well. Agglutination appears grainy or spotty. A smooth, even appearance means no agglutination.

☑ What would you expect to see for someone who is type O−?

_____

☑ What would you expect to see for someone who is type AB+?

_____

ACTIVITY 4: HEART RATE AND BLOOD PRESSURE

INTRODUCTION

The **cardiac cycle** is the cycle of events that happens during a heartbeat, namely the contraction and relaxation of the heart muscle. **Systole** (pronounced with a long *ee* at the end) is the period when the heart is contracting; it occurs in two phases: atrial systole and ventricular systole. **Atrial systole** forces blood from the atria into the ventricles and **ventricular systole** pushes blood from the ventricles into the arteries. **Diastole** (with long *ee*) is when the heart muscle relaxes, during which time the heart chambers refill with blood.

The "**lub-dub**" sound of the heartbeat is caused by the closing of valves during the heart's contractions. The "lub" sound occurs when the AV valves close and the "dub" sound occurs when the semilunar valves close. The AV valves close first, as ventricular pressure rises. The rising pressure opens the semilunar valves. When the pressure drops, blood tries to return to the ventricles, which closes the semilunar valves. You can listen to your heartbeat using a stethoscope or feel your changing blood pressure by taking your pulse to determine your heart rate, in beats per minute (bpm). Your heart rate, or pulse, is the number of cardiac cycles that occur in one minute. A normal resting heart rate is 60–100 bpm. Some people with very high levels of cardiovascular fitness may have a resting heart rate of 40–60 bpm. During physical activity, the heart rate rises.

Blood pressure is the force of the blood against the blood vessel walls. It is measured as a diagnostic tool to assess the strength of the heart's contractions and the health of the arteries. Blood pressure is recorded as systolic pressure over diastolic pressure. The force of the blood in the artery as it is squeezed out of the heart during ventricular systole and the pressure of the blood against the walls of the artery when the heart is in diastole are measured using a **sphygmomanometer**. The blood pressure cuff is pressurized to the point where the artery in the upper arm is squeezed closed. The pressure is slowly released until the pressure of the blood during ventricular systole can force open the artery, allowing blood to pulse into the arm; this is the **systolic pressure**. The pressure in the cuff is further released until the artery stays open and blood is present in the artery continuously, including during diastole; this is the **diastolic pressure**.

Normal blood pressure ranges are 100–119 mmHg for systolic pressure and 60–79 mmHg for diastolic pressure. Chronically high blood pressure is called **hypertension**. Hypertension is a risk factor for arteriosclerosis. **Arteriosclerosis** is the thickening and hardening of the arteries. Arteriosclerosis is characterized by elevated systolic pressure and lowered diastolic pressure. Because the arteries have lost their ability to stretch and recoil, they can't expand to accept blood being forced out of the heart during ventricular systole, causing high systolic blood pressure, and the arteries can't contract to maintain blood pressure during diastole, causing low diastolic blood pressure.

$$healthy\ blood\ pressure = \frac{systolic\ blood\ pressure}{diastolic\ blood\ pressure} < \frac{120}{80}\ mm\ Hg$$

PROTOCOLS

To use a stethoscope:

We will use a stethoscope to **auscultate** (listen to) the heartbeat.

1. Place the earpieces of the stethoscope into your ears over your ear canals. The earpieces may curve; if they do, wear them so the earpieces point forward, toward your nose. This will help them cover your ear canals and block out background noise.

2. Place the diaphragm of the chestpiece against your chest, slightly above your left nipple. Gently move around the chestpiece until you can hear your heart's "lub-dub" sound.

3. Once you can clearly hear your heartbeat, count the number of heartbeats for 30 seconds. Remember, each "lub-dub" sound is one heartbeat.

4. Multiply the number of heartbeats you got by 2 to get your heart rate in bpm.

To use an automatic sphygmomanometer (blood pressure monitor):

1. Place the cuff of the sphygmomanometer snuggly around your upper arm, with the tube down and centered over the inside of your elbow.

2. Sit upright, with your feet flat on the floor and your arm resting on the table, breathe normally and don't talk during the measurement.

3. Press the start button on the blood pressure monitor. (If it doesn't start, turn it off and on again.)

4. Record the values reported by the monitor.

5. Do 30 seconds of jumping jacks and then measure your blood pressure and heart rate again.

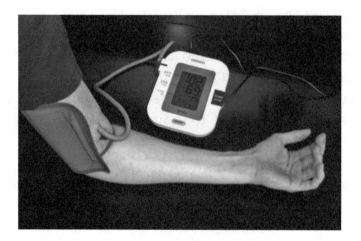

Figure K8   Placement of blood pressure cuff on upper arm.

ACTIVITY 5: HEART RATE RECOVERY

INTRODUCTION

Heart rate recovery (HRR) is how quickly your heart rate returns to normal after exercise. This can be an indicator of cardiac condition and health. People who are more physically fit have a faster HRR. To calculate HRR, you exercise until you are in your target heart rate range, then stop exercising and measure your pulse. Then you measure your pulse again two minutes later and calculate the difference in heart rate.

HYPOTHESES

Make a hypothesis about the average change in pulse between exercise and two minutes later for students in lab. Explain your reasoning. _____

_____

_____

Make a hypothesis about the range of the change in heart rate during recovery. What range in change do you think 68% of students in lab will fall in? (Make a hypothesis about what the standard deviation will be.) Explain your reasoning.

_____

_____

_____

Calculate your exercise target heart rate zone:

220 − your age = _____ = #

× 0.6 = _____ (low end of range)

× 0.8 = _____ (high end of range)

range: _____ bpm

Example: Jane is 100 years old. 220 − 100=120. 120 × 0.6=72, 120 × 0.8=96. Jane's target heart rate during exercise is 72–96 bpm.

PULSE MEASUREMENT

- To measure your pulse at your wrist, turn one hand over, palm up. Place one or two fingertips from your other hand on your wrist below your thumb. Move your fingers around until you can feel your pulse.

- To measure your pulse at your neck, place one or two fingertips to the side of your trachea, under your jawbone. Move your fingers around until you can feel your pulse.
- Count how many heartbeats you feel in 15 seconds. Multiply that number by four to get 4 heart rate in bpm.
- Practice measuring your pulse so you can quickly find the right spot.

EXPERIMENTAL PROTOCOL

1. While sitting, measure your resting pulse.
2. Go climb the stairs of the building quickly. Take a device that you can use for timing your pulse with you! As you climb, check your pulse. Keep climbing up and down the stairs until you reach your target heart rate.

    - Hint: Divide your target range by 4 to know how many beats per 15 seconds you are monitoring for. _____

3. Once you reach your target heart rate, when you get to the next stair landing, stop. Measure your pulse immediately after stopping (active pulse).
4. Measure your heart rate 2 minutes after stopping (recovery pulse).
5. Calculate the difference between your active pulse and your recovery pulse. This is your HRR.
6. Record your values on the completion sheet.

INTERPRETATION

- Less than 22: Your biological age is slightly older than your calendar age.
- 22–52: Your biological age is about the same as your calendar age.
- 53–58: Your biological age is slightly younger than your calendar age.
- 59–65: Your biological age is moderately younger than your calendar age.
- 66 or more: Your biological age is a lot younger than your calendar age.

Adapted from Improve Heart Health by Knowing Your Recovery Heart Rate, https://www.enhancedmedicalcare.com/2013/01/20/improve-heart-health-by-knowing-your-recovery-heart-rate/, accessed May 22, 2019.

Name _____ Section _____ Date _____

CARDIOVASCULAR SYSTEM COMPLETION

Activity 1

Look at the preserved cow and sheep hearts and the heart model. Make sure you can identify all the parts on each heart.

1. Identify the left ventricle. How can you tell which one it is?

_____

2. Identify the atrioventricular valves. What do they look like?

_____

3. Identify the aorta. What does it look like?

_____

4. Identify the myocardium. What does it look like?

_____

5. Identify the endocardium. What does it look like?

_____

6. Identify the epicardium. What does it look like?

_____

7. Why is the pericardium missing?

_____

Name _____ Section _____ Date _____

Activity 2

Look at the slide of the arteries and veins. Notice the thickness of the walls and the size of the inner space (lumen). Identify and sketch each.

Artery	Vein
total magnification: _____x	total magnification: _____x

Look at the slide of blood. Draw and label the cells you see. Can you identify the kind(s) of leukocytes you see?

total magnification: _____x

Activity 3

	A	B	Rh
Observations			

Name _____ Section _____ Date _____

Interpretation

What antigens are present in the blood you tested? What blood type is this? Explain your interpretation, linking your statements to your observations. _____

_____

_____

Activity 4

Use a stethoscope to determine your heart rate. Listen and count for 30 seconds. Remember, the "lub-dub" sound is one heartbeat. Multiply by 2 to get your heartbeats/minute.

1. Stethoscope heart rate _____

Use the blood pressure monitor to determine your blood pressure and heart rate:

2. Resting: systolic _____ diastolic _____ heart rate _____

Now, do thirty seconds of jumping jacks and measure again:

3. Active: systolic _____ diastolic _____ heart rate _____

Activity 5

Resting Pulse (bpm)	Active Pulse (Immediately After Exercise) (bpm)	Recovery Pulse (2 Minutes After Exercise) (bpm)

1. Calculate your heart rate recovery by subtracting your recovery pulse from your active pulse:

$HRR = active\ pulse - recovery\ pulse$

_____

2. Record your three heart rates on the class list.

Name _____ Section _____ Date _____

ACTIVITY 6: MICROSCOPY OF TISSUES

Identify each of the tissues and terms related to the cardiovascular system clued below and draw a picture of each tissue. Refer to the Histology Lab J as necessary.

1. This muscle tissue type is found only in the heart. What is it? _____

    Draw a picture of it:

total magnification: _____x

2. This muscle tissue type is in the thick middle layer of arteries and the thin middle layer of veins. What is it? _____

    Draw a picture of it:

total magnification: _____x

3. Blood brings oxygen and removes carbon dioxide from this muscle tissue type, which is under voluntary control. What is it? _____

   Draw a picture of it:

   ┌─────────────────────────────────────┐
   │   │
   │   │
   │   │
   │   │
   │   │
   │   total magnification: _____x │
   └─────────────────────────────────────┘

4. The nervous system controls muscle contraction. What kind of cell is this? _____

   Draw a picture of it:

   ┌─────────────────────────────────────┐
   │   │
   │   │
   │   │
   │   │
   │   │
   │   total magnification: _____x │
   └─────────────────────────────────────┘

Name _____ Section _____ Date _____

CARDIOVASCULAR SYSTEM EXTENDED ANALYSIS

1. Open the class data for heart rate recovery in Excel.

2. Use the histogram function to generate frequency data for resting heart rate and for active heart rate. Choose bins of an appropriate size.

3. Graph the two sets of frequency data **on the same axes**. Give the histogram a title, label the axes, and include a legend.

4. Calculate the change in heart rate between active and recovery pulse (HRR) for each person.

5. Create a histogram of the class' HRR. Include a title and axis titles.

6. Calculate the mean HRR for the class: _____

7. Calculate the standard deviation for HRR for the class: _____

8. Calculate the range for the first standard deviation for HRR for the class: _____

9. How does the calculated HRR compare to your hypothesis about the average change in pulse between exercise and two minutes later?

10. Interpret the class' average HRR. What does this number say about the cardiovascular health of students in the lab? Explain your interpretation.

11. How does the calculated standard deviation range of HRR compare to your hypothesis about range of change?

12. Interpret the class' standard deviation for HRR. Are students pretty similar in their cardiovascular health or is there a wide range of health indicated by this data? Explain your interpretation.

Submit your graphs and typed responses to Blackboard.

Name _____ Section _____ Date _____

CARDIOVASCULAR COMPREHENSION

1. Label the parts of the heart.

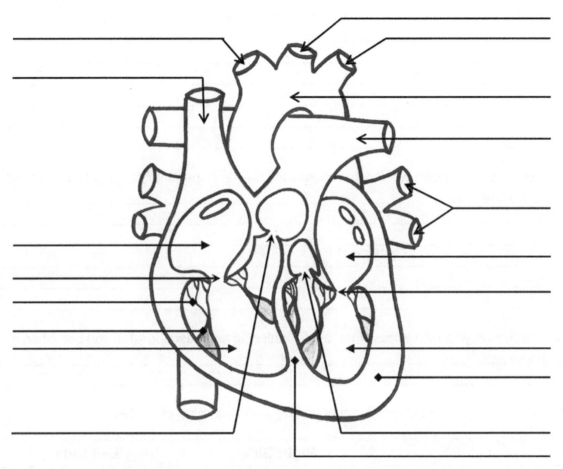

2. What is different about the pulmonary artery and vein compared to other arteries and veins in the body? _____

_____

_____

3. Describe the state of the heart muscles and the movement of blood during each step of the cardiac cycle.

   a. Diastole _____

   _____

   b. Atrial systole _____

   _____

   c. Ventricular systole _____

   _____

4. Describe the papillary muscles, chordae tendineae, and atrioventricular valves:

   a. When the heart is in diastole _____

   _____

   b. When the heart is in ventricular systole _____

   _____

5. In your own words, explain how a blood pressure cuff measures blood pressure.

   _____
   _____
   _____
   _____
   _____
   _____

6. Describe in your own words what causes the "lub" and the "dub" of the "lub-dub" sound
   of the heartbeat. _____

   _____
   _____
   _____
   _____
   _____

7. Describe in your own words what "agglutination" is and describe what you see when it
   happens. _____

   _____

8. Fill in the movement of blood though the right and left sides of the heart:

	Right Side	Left Side
From		
Blood Vessel		
Chamber		
Valve		
Chamber		
Valve		
Blood Vessel		
To		

9. Fill in the names of the blood vessels of the systemic circuit:

Heart → _____ → _____ → _____

→ _____ → _____ → heart

Name _____ Section _____ Date _____

CARDIOVASCULAR SYSTEM REVIEW QUESTIONS

1. What is the liquid part of blood called?

2. What is the scientific name for a red blood cell?

3. What is the scientific name for a white blood cell?

4. What is the scientific name for a platelet?

5. What makes your blood look red?

6. Describe what erythrocytes look like.

7. What is the main role of erythrocytes?

8. How long do erythrocytes live?

9. What is the main role of leukocytes?

10. What is the most common type of leukocyte?

11. What is the main role of thrombocytes?

12. How long do thrombocytes live?

13. Which of the formed elements is a true cell? Why aren't the others?

14. What type of blood vessel carries blood toward the heart?

15. What type of blood vessel carries blood away from the heart?

16. Why is there a pulse in an artery?

17. Why is there no pulse in a vein?

18. From what type of blood vessel does a capillary receive blood?

19. To what type of blood vessel does a capillary transport blood?

20. a. Where are veins heading (relative to the heart)?

    b. Do veins carry oxygenated or deoxygenated blood?

    c. Are there any exceptions?

21. a. Where are arteries heading (relative to the heart)?

    b. Do arteries carry oxygenated or deoxygenated blood?

    c. Are there any exceptions?

22. Describe how the structure of an artery and a vein differ.

23. Describe the structure of a capillary.

24. Blood from the body enters which chamber of the heart?

25. Blood leaves the heart for the body from which chamber of the heart?

26. Blood leaves the heart for the lungs from which chamber of the heart?

27. Blood returning from the lungs enters which chamber of the heart?

28. What prevents backflow of blood from the ventricles into the atria? Describe how these structures work.

29. What prevents backflow of blood from the arteries into the ventricles? Describe how these structures work.

30. Where are the chordae tendineae located? What is their role?

31. What type of muscle is found in the heart?

32. List the layers of tissue in the heart in order.

33. The period that the heart is in contraction is known as . . .

34. The period that the heart is at rest is known as . . .

35. What type of circulation reoxygenates the blood?

36. What type of circulation takes blood to and from the body?

37. Approximately what percentage of the blood volume is made up by erythrocytes?

38. Fill in the movement of blood though the right and left sides of the heart:

	Right Side	**Left Side**
From		
Blood Vessel		
Chamber		
Valve		
Chamber		
Valve		
Blood Vessel		
To		

39. Fill in the names of the blood vessels of the systemic circuit:

Capillary → _____ → _____ → _____

→ _____ → _____ → capillary

40. Label the chambers of the heart, the blood vessels, and the valves in this diagram.
    (Note that the blood vessels are not in anatomically correct positions.)

41. A blood typing experiment was carried out and the results for four students are given below. State each student's blood type.

	Anti-A Antiserum	Anti-B Antiserum	Anti-Rh Antiserum	Blood Type
Student 1	Agglutination	No	No	
Student 2	No	No	Agglutination	
Student 3	Agglutination	Agglutination	No	
Student 4	No	Agglutination	Agglutination	

42. Fill in the table for compatible and incompatible blood types for each of the patients, listed below, who need to receive blood:

Compatible	Patient	Incompatible
	AB+	
	AB−	
	A+	
	A−	
	B+	
	B−	
	O+	
	O−	

43. Determine the blood type for each of the patients below.

	Anti-A Antiserum	Anti-B Antiserum	Anti-Rh Antiserum	Blood Type
Patient 1				
Patient 2				
Patient 3				
Patient 4				

44. Determine the blood type for each of the patients below.

	Anti-A Antiserum	Anti-B Antiserum	Anti-Rh Antiserum	Blood Type
Patient 1				
Patient 2				
Patient 3				
Patient 4				

45. For each of the patents below, sketch what you'd expect to see in their blood typing test.

Patient 1: A−

Patient 2: B+

Patient 3: AB+

Patient 4: O−

46. Each person below could potentially receive or donate blood. Fill in each row indicating which blood type(s) the person can receive and which blood type(s) their blood can be donated to.

Can Receive Blood From	Person	Can Donate Blood To
	AB+	
	AB−	
	A+	
	A−	
	B+	
	B−	
	O+	
	O−	

47. Rh-status is important for pregnant women. If a woman is Rh− and she carries an Rh+ fetus, she may develop antibodies against Rh-factor. These antibodies can then attack an Rh+ fetus during a later pregnancy, leading to major complications. If a woman is Rh− and her husband is heterozygous for Rh, what percentages of pregnancies would you expect would result in an Rh+ fetus? _____

    What if the man were homozygous for Rh? (See Genetics Lab I for review.) _____

48. Two parents both have type A− blood.

    a. What are their possible genotypes?

    b. Given their possible genotypes, what blood types are possible for their children? (Refer to Genetics Lab I if necessary.)

49. A man has type B− blood and his wife has type B+ blood.

    a. What are each person's possible genotypes?

    b. Given their possible genotypes, what blood types are possible for their children?

50. A woman has type AB+ blood and her husband has type O− blood.

    a. What are each person's possible genotypes?

    b. Given their possible genotypes, what blood types are possible for their children?

51. A man has type A+ blood and his wife has type B+ blood.

    a. What are each person's possible genotypes?

    b. Given their possible genotypes, what blood types are possible for their children?

52. Two parents are both type AB+.

    a. What are their possible genotypes?

    b. Given their possible genotypes, what blood types are possible for their children?

53. A fertility clinic was not as careful with record keeping as it should have been and all egg and sperm identification is in doubt. Based on blood typing of the mother, father, and child, say whether it is possible for the child to be their parents' biological child or not. Justify your answers.

	Mother	**Father**	**Child**	**Response**
Family 1	Type O	Type B	Type A	
Family 2	Type A	Type A	Type O	
Family 3	Type A	Type A	Type AB	
Family 4	Type A	Type B	Type A	
Family 5	Type A	Type B	Type O	

54. Name the three types of muscle tissue. Describe the appearance of each one. For each type, give an example of where it is found.

55. James is 22. What is his target exercise heart rate zone? James measured an active pulse of 125 bpm and measured a recovery pulse two minutes later of 60 bpm. How would you describe James' cardiovascular health?

56. Lynda is 66. What is her target exercise heart rate zone? Lynda measured an active pulse of 100 bpm and measured a recovery pulse two minutes later of 80 bpm. How would you describe Lynda's cardiovascular health?

57. Andrei has a blood pressure of 114/67 mmHg. Which number is his systolic blood pressure and which one is diastolic? How would you describe his blood pressure?

58. Alexis has a blood pressure of 123/86 mmHg. Which number is her diastolic blood pressure and which one is systolic? How would you describe her blood pressure?

OBJECTIVES
- Learn about the anatomy and physiology of the respiratory system.
- Learn about lung volumes.

VOCABULARY

nose	pharynx	larynx	trachea
bronchi	bronchioles	lungs	lobes
alveoli	inhalation	exhalation	inspiration
expiration	respiration	tidal volume	IRV
ERV	vital capacity	residual volume	total lung capacity
diaphragm	intercostals	external respiration	internal respiration
cellular respiration	spirometer		

SKILLS

Measure exhaled lung volumes using a spirometer.
Calculate lung volumes.

INTRODUCTION

The respiratory system is composed of the nose, pharynx, larynx, trachea, bronchi, and lungs. Air is inhaled and exhaled through the **nose**. The **pharynx** is the region of the throat that is shared with the digestive system. The **larynx** is the voice box, where sound is produced. The **trachea** is the windpipe, which connects the upper and lower respiratory tract organs. The **bronchi** (singular: bronchus) branch from the trachea and carry air into the lungs. The **lungs** are housed inside the thoracic cavity, on the right and left sides of the heart and above the diaphragm. The right lung is bigger than the left lung and has three **lobes** (sections). The left lung has two lobes. Each lung is served by a primary bronchus and each lobe is served by a secondary bronchus. The bronchi branch into smaller **bronchioles**, creating a network of airways within the lung. The smallest bronchioles terminate in the alveoli (singular: alveolus). It is at the **alveoli** where gas exchange with the blood occurs. The alveoli are rounded membranes of simple squamous epithelium that are in close association with capillaries. The average lung has 300 million alveoli.

☑   The perfusing membrane of the lung, the alveolus, is curved, not flat. Explain why its shape is important for its function. _____

_____

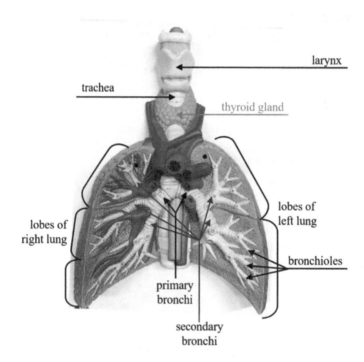

Figure L1   Structures of the respiratory system.

Lung Volumes

Air is moved into the body by **inhalation** or **inspiration** and out of the body by **exhalation** or **expiration**, which together comprise **respiration**.

Tidal volume (TV) is the amount of air inhaled and exhaled during normal breathing. **Inspiratory reserve volume (IRV)** is the lung volume over and above tidal volume, that can be filled with air (through forced inhalation). **Expiratory reserve volume (ERV)** is the lung volume that can be emptied (by forcefully exhaling) after exhaling the tidal volume. **Vital capacity (VC)** is the largest volume of air you can breathe. It is all of the air you can breathe in after a forced exhale, or, all the air you can breathe out after a complete inhale. Vital capacity is the sum of tidal volume, inspiratory reserve volume, and expiratory reserve volume. Vital capacity decreases with age due to loss of lung elasticity, increased chest wall rigidity, and loss of respiratory muscle strength. After exhaling the vital capacity volume, the lungs are not empty, and there is still air in the other structures of the respiratory tract. This air volume that cannot be exhaled is the **residual volume**. **Total lung capacity (TLC)** is the total volume of air that can be held by the respiratory tract. Total lung capacity is the sum of vital capacity and residual volume. Only the air that reaches the alveoli can participate in gas exchange with the blood (external respiration); the rest of the air in the respiratory tract (the dead space) does not. About 2/3 of tidal volume perfuses the alveoli.

☑ What would happen to your lungs and respiratory tract if you could exhale all of the air from them? _____

☑ About what volume of fresh air makes it to the alveoli with each normal breath?

_____

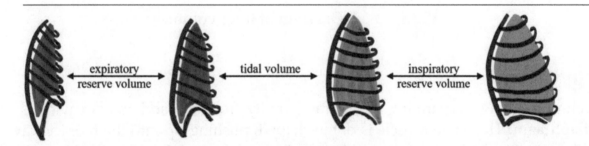

Figure L2 Cartoon of changes in lung size, rib position, and diaphragm position with changes in lung volume. Notice that the lungs get bigger, the ribs lift up and out, and the diaphragm gets lower and flatter with increased lung volume. Expiratory reserve volume is the exchange of air (inhale or exhale) below the exhaled position of tidal volume. Inspiratory reserve volume is the exchange of air (inhale or exhale) beyond the inhaled position of tidal volume.

Table L1 Mean lung volumes for males and females.

Volume	Males	Females
Tidal volume	500 mL	500 mL
Inspiratory reserve volume	3,100 mL	1,900 mL
Expiratory reserve volume	1,200 mL	700 mL
Vital capacity	4,800 mL	3,100 mL
Residual volume	1,200 mL	1,100 mL
Total Lung Capacity	6,000 mL	4,200 mL

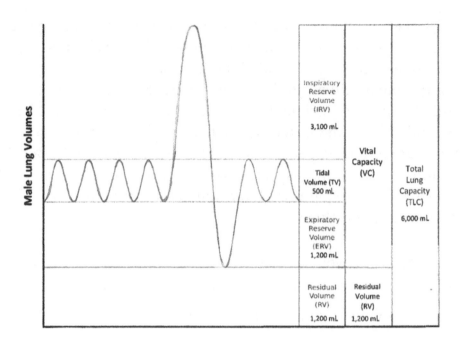

Figure L3   Diagram of lung volumes.

Muscles of Respiration

Below the lungs, separating the thoracic cavity from the abdominal cavity, is the **diaphragm**. This large muscle is dome shaped, pushing up into the thoracic cavity. When the diaphragm contracts, it gets smaller and flatter. When the diaphragm pulls down, the volume of the thoracic cavity increases. The lungs expand—by sucking air in from the external environment—to fill up the additional space. Thus, contraction of the diaphragm causes inhalation. When the diaphragm relaxes, it rises, decreasing the volume of the thoracic cavity. In response, air is pushed out of the lungs—exhalation.

The diaphragm does the majority of the work of inhalation. Additional muscles involved in breathing include the **intercostals**, which are located in between the ribs. During inhalation, the **external intercostals** lift the rib cage up and out, increasing the volume of the thoracic cavity and causing the lungs to expand. During forced exhalation, the **internal intercostals** contract, pulling the ribs down and in, decreasing the volume of the thoracic cavity.

☑   Contraction of a muscle is an active process-it requires energy-and relaxation of a muscle is a passive process-it does not require energy. Which part of respiration is active? _____. Which is passive? _____

Respiration

The air in the alveoli participates in **external respiration**, the exchange of gasses between the lungs and the blood in the capillaries that surround the alveoli.

Carbon dioxide diffuses out of the erythrocytes, through the blood plasma, through the epithelium of the capillary wall, through the epithelium of the alveoli, and into the lung and oxygen from the air makes the trip the other way, to the iron of the hemoglobin in erythrocytes (see Lab K for review).

The blood then cycles through the body through the cardiovascular system to the capillary beds where exchange occurs with the tissues. Here is the site of **internal respiration**. Oxygen diffuses out of the erythrocytes into the tissue fluid and carbon dioxide diffuses from the tissue fluid into the blood.

Oxygen is taken up by the cells and used by mitochondria during aerobic **cellular respiration**. Cellular respiration produces adenosine triphosphate (**ATP**), the energy currency of the cell. Without oxygen, we could not efficiently metabolize food into energy.

ACTIVITY 1: SPIROMETRY

PROTOCOL

Spirometry is the measurement of air volume and/or speed. It is used to assess pulmonary (lung) function. We will use a **spirometer** to measure exhaled air and use our measurements to calculate our inspiratory reserve volume. The spirometer's air pressure gauge measures exhaled air in milliliters (mL) or cubic centimeters (cc), which are equal.

1. Attach a paper mouthpiece to the end of the spirometer.
2. When using the spirometer, hold it level and grasp it with your fingertips along the bottom, so your hand doesn't cover any holes on the side of the spirometer.
3. Before each measurement, set the needle to zero by twisting the ring of the air pressure gauge. Conversely, because there is no gradation between 0 and 1,000, set the needle to 1,000 and then subtract 1,000 from your measured volume to get your lung volume.
4. You will measure three lung volumes: vital capacity, tidal volume, and expiratory reserve volume.
   a. **Vital capacity** is all the air you can breathe in and out. Take as large a breath in as you can, then exhale all the air out that you can into the spirometer. Read and record this volume.
   b. **Expiratory reserve volume** is the air left in your lungs after a normal exhale (after releasing the tidal volume). Hold the spirometer near your mouth and breathe normally several times. After a normal exhale, place the spirometer's mouthpiece in your mouth and forcefully exhale all the air you can into the spirometer. Read and record this volume.

c. **Tidal volume** is the amount of air you breathe in and out normally. Hold the spirometer near your mouth and breathe normally several times. After taking a normal breath in, place the spirometer's mouth piece in your mouth and exhale your normal volume through your mouth into the spirometer. Read and record this volume.

Figure L4   Spirometer with paper mouthpiece.

HYPOTHESIS

Hypothesize about the average vital capacity of men and of women in the lab compared to the "average" vital capacity for men and women given in Table L1. Explain your reasoning.

_____

_____

_____

Name _____ Section _____ Date _____

RESPIRATORY SYSTEM COMPLETION

1. Measure your exhaled lung volumes.

    Vital Capacity _____ mL

    Expiratory reserve volume _____ mL

    Tidal volume _____ mL

2. Calculate your inspiratory reserve volume. Show your work.

3. If you have the average residual volume for your sex, what would your total lung capacity be? Show your calculation.

4. How do your measured respiratory volumes compare to the average volumes for your sex? _____ _____

5. Calculate your vital capacity as a percent of the average vital capacity for your sex given in the lab manual. To do this, divide your vital capacity by the vital capacity for your sex given in the manual and multiply by hundred.

6. Now find your vital capacity as a percentage more or less than the average for your sex as given by the lab manual. If your vital capacity is less than the average for your sex, subtract the percentage you calculated in 5 from 100 (100 − %). If your vital capacity is greater than the average for your sex, subtract 100 from the percentage you calculated in 5 (% − 100).

    Percent above/below average _____

7. Record your vital capacity, height (in cm), and sex on the class list.

Name _____ Section _____ Date _____

RESPIRATORY SYSTEM EXTENDED ANALYSIS

1. Open the class data for vital capacity in Excel.

2. Sort the data by sex (refer to Lab B for directions).

3. Create bins of 500 mL and use the histogram function to generate frequency data for men and for women.

4. Graph the two sets of frequency data **on the same axes**. Include a title, axes titles, legend, and set the axes to appropriate scales to visualize the data.

5. Create a scatter plot of vital capacity (*y*-axis) versus height (*x*-axis). Include a title, axis titles, a linear trendline, and an R-squared value.

6. Is there a direct correlation between vital capacity and height? Explain your answer by referencing the appearance of the graph and the R-squared value.

   _____

   _____

7. Submit your graphs to Blackboard.

8. Calculate the mean vital capacity for each sex.

   Men _____ Women _____

9. How does the mean vital capacity you calculated from the class data for each sex compare to the values given in Table L1? Express your answers as percentages.

   _____

   _____

   _____

10. How does the difference in vital capacity between the class data and Table L1 compare to your hypothesis? _____

    _____

11. Calculate the difference between the average vital capacity of men and women in from the class data.

    _____

12. Calculate the difference between the average vital capacity of men and women using the values from Table L1. _____

13. How does the difference in average vital capacity between men and women you calculated for students in lab compare to the difference between the values in Table L1? Express your answer as a percentage.

    _____
    _____
    _____

14. What could be the reason for the differences between the vital capacity averages from the student data and the data presented in the lab manual? Give your answer in complete sentences.

    _____
    _____
    _____
    _____
    _____
    _____

Name _____ Section _____ Date _____

ACTIVITY 2: MICROSCOPY OF TISSUES

Identify each of the tissues and terms related to the respiratory system clued below and draw a picture of each tissue. Refer to the Histology Lab J as necessary.

1. The alveoli of the lung are composed of a single layer of thin cells.

    a. What is this epithelial tissue type called? _____

    b. Draw a picture of this tissue:

total magnification: _____x

2. The trachea is lined with tall cells with special structures that can move mucus.

    a. What is this epithelial tissue type called? _____

    b. What are the cellular projections called? _____

    c. What are the cells that produce mucus called? _____

    d. Draw a picture of this tissue:

total magnification: _____x

3. The trachea has tough, semicircular supports composed of a specialized connective tissue.

   a. What is this tissue called? _____

   b. What is the name of the specialized cells that make up the matrix of this tissue?

   _____

   c. What is the name for the liquid space in which these cells live?

   _____

   d. Draw a picture of this tissue:

total magnification: _____x

Name _____ Section _____ Date _____

RESPIRATORY SYSTEM COMPREHENSION

1. Label the parts of the respiratory system.

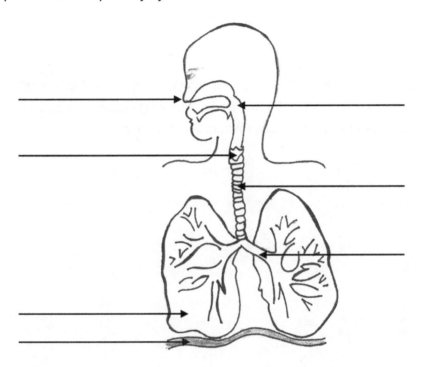

2. For each picture below, say which part of breathing it represents.

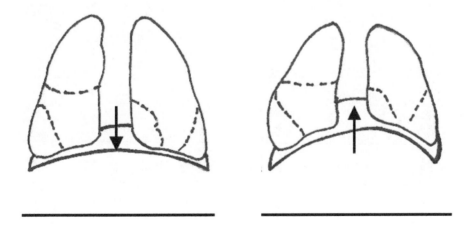

_____   _____

3. Sofia has a tidal volume of 500 mL, a vital capacity of 3000 mL, and an expiratory reserve volume of 700 mL. What is Sofia's inspiratory reserve volume? Show your work.

4. George has a tidal volume of 750 mL, an inspiratory reserve volume of 3000 mL, an expiratory reserve volume of 1250 mL, and a total lung capacity of 6000 mL. Calculate George's vital capacity and residual volume. Show your work.

Name _____ Section _____ Date _____

RESPIRATORY SYSTEM REVIEW QUESTIONS

1. How many lobes does the left lung have?

2. How many lobes does the right lung have?

3. How many primary bronchi go to the left lung?

4. How many primary bronchi go to the right lung?

5. How many secondary bronchi are in the left lung?

6. How many secondary bronchi are in the right lung?

7. In what structure of the lungs does gas exchange occur between the air in the lungs and the gas in the blood?

8. What muscle does most of the work of breathing?

9. Name each of the other two muscles discussed in this lab and match them to the type of forced air movement they participate in.

10. Describe the shape of the diaphragm when your lungs are full.

11. Describe the shape of the diaphragm when your lungs are empty.

12. What is the volume of air your normally breathe in and out called?

13. You are startled and gasp. What volume of air have you taken in?

14. You have a lot of candles on your birthday cake. You inhale as deeply as you can and then exhale as hard as you can to get the last candle blown out. What volume of air have you just cycled through your body?

15. You are being dramatic and after a normal sigh you choose to keep sighing. What additional volume of air are you breathing out?

16. What is the volume of air left in your respiratory tract called after you breathe out all the air you can?

17. Jordan has a tidal volume of 500 mL, a vital capacity of 4000 mL, an expiratory volume of 800 mL, and a residual volume of 1000 mL. Calculate Jordan's inspiratory reserve volume and total lung capacity.

18. Mali has a tidal volume of 450 mL, an inspiratory reserve volume of 2000 mL, an expiratory reserve volume of 1000 mL, and a residual volume of 1500 mL. Calculate Mali's vital capacity and total lung capacity.

19. AJ has a tidal volume of 0.5 L, an inspiratory reserve volume of 3.0 L, an expiratory reserve volume of 1.0 L, and a residual volume of 1.0 L.

    a. What is AJ's vital capacity?

    b. What is AJ's total lung capacity?

    c. What sex is AJ?

20. DC has a tidal volume of 0.5 L, an inspiratory reserve volume of 2.0 L, an expiratory reserve volume of 0.75 L, and a residual volume of 1.0 L.

    a. What is DC's vital capacity?

    b. What is DC's total lung capacity?

    c. What sex is DC?

21. Tonya has a total lung capacity of 4200 mL and a residual volume of 1100 mL. She has a tidal volume of 500 mL and an expiratory reserve volume of 750 mL.

    a. What is Tonya's vital capacity?

    b. What is Tonya's inspiratory reserve volume?

22. Felipe has a tidal volume of 550 mL, an expiratory reserve volume of 1250 mL, a vital capacity of 5000 mL, and a total lung capacity of 6100 mL.

    a. What is Felipe's inspiratory reserve volume?

    b. What is Felipe's residual volume?

23. Aja has a tidal volume of 600 mL, an inspiratory reserve volume of 2000 mL, an expiratory reserve volume of 800 mL, and a residual volume of 1200 mL.

    a. What is Aja's vital capacity?

    b. What is Aja's total lung capacity?

24. David has a vital capacity of 5.0 L, a tidal volume of 0.5 L, an inspiratory reserve volume of 3.0 L, and a residual volume of 1.5 L.

    a. What is David's expiratory reserve volume?

    b. What is David's total lung capacity?

25. Adriane has a vital capacity of 3.0 L, a tidal volume of 500 mL, an inspiratory reserve volume of 2.0 L, and a residual volume of 1100 mL.

    a. What is Adriane's expiratory reserve volume?

    b. What is Adriane's total lung capacity?

26. Brad has a tidal volume of 500 mL, an inspiratory reserve volume of 3200 mL, a vital capacity of 4.8 L, and a total lung capacity of 6.2 L.

    a. What is Brad's expiratory reserve volume?

    b. What is Brad's residual volume? Express your answer in milliliters.

OBJECTIVES

- Learn about the organs of the urinary system.
- Learn about the structures and functions of the nephron.

VOCABULARY

kidney	ureter	bladder	urethra
renal capsule	renal cortex	renal medulla	renal pyramid
renal pelvis	hilum	renal artery	renal vein
sphincter	glomerulus	glomerular capsule	renal corpuscle
proximal convoluted tubule	distal convoluted tubule	nephron loop	collecting duct
afferent arteriole	efferent arteriole	peritubular capillaries	glomerular filtration
tubular reabsorption	tubular secretion		

SKILLS

Interpret urinalysis test results.

INTRODUCTION

The urinary system is responsible for removing metabolic waste from the body and maintaining homeostasis of the aqueous environment of the body. Metabolic wastes include H^+ and CO_3^- from metabolism of carbohydrates and lipids, urea from metabolism of proteins, and uric acid from metabolism of nucleic acids.

The urinary system is composed of the **kidneys**, **ureters**, **bladder**, and **urethra**. The two kidneys are each connected by a ureter to the bladder, which empties to the outside of the body via the urethra. The kidneys serve many roles in homeostasis, most notably filtering the blood to maintain the composition, pH, and volume of the blood.

The kidneys are covered by a protective connective tissue membrane called the **renal capsule**. Under this, the outer layer of the kidney (about 1 cm) is called the **renal cortex** and the inner region of the kidney is the **renal medulla**. The renal medulla is divided into triangular regions called **renal pyramids**. You can think of the kidney like a watermelon: the renal medulla is the inner red part, the renal cortex is the whitish part near the rind, and the renal capsule is the outer green skin. The **renal pelvis** is the region near the ureter where the urine produced in the renal medulla is collected. The **hilum** (hilus) is the indented region at the center, inner curve of the outside of the kidney where the **renal artery** enters the kidney and the **renal vein** and **ureter** exit the kidney.

The **ureters** connect the kidneys to the bladder. These tubes are about 25 cm long and are composed of several layers of tissue. The inner layer, which is in contact with the urine, is composed of transitional epithelium. Recall that transitional epithelium is stretchy. This allows boluses of urine to pass through. The middle layer of the ureter contains smooth muscle, which generates peristaltic waves that move urine in the right direction, from the kidney to the bladder, even when the body is

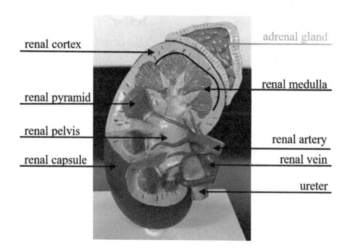

Figure M1   Structures of the kidney.

horizontal or upside down. The outer layer of the ureters is composed of connective tissue that embeds the ureters in the surrounding abdomen.

The **bladder** stores urine until it is convenient to eliminate it from the body. The empty bladder is about the size of a walnut and a full bladder can hold about 800 mL. The inner layer of the bladder, which is in contact with the urine, is composed of stretchy transitional epithelium.

The **urethra** is short in women, 3–4 cm, and long in men, about 20 cm, and connects the bladder to the outside of the body. The short length of the female urethra makes women more susceptible than men to urinary tract infections (UTIs), which are generally caused by bacteria that travel from outside the body up the urethra to the bladder.

Urine is maintained inside the body by two sphincters: the internal and external urethral sphincters. A **sphincter** is a ring of muscle that is normally contracted to block passage through an opening or tube. When relaxed, the sphincter opens and allows passage forward. The **internal urethral sphincter** is at the junction of the bladder and urethra and is under involuntary control. The **external urethral sphincter** is located at the pelvic floor and is under voluntary control.

☑ What kind of muscle do you think is present in each of the urethral sphincters? Why? (Refer to Lab J if necessary.)

_____

Nephron

The renal medulla is composed of over a million nephrons, the filtering unit of the kidney. The nephron is composed of the renal corpuscle, proximal convoluted tubule, nephron loop, distal convoluted tubule.

Each nephron is served by an **afferent arteriole**, which provides blood to the **glomerulus**, a ball of capillaries surrounded by the **glomerular capsule** (Bowman's capsule). The glomerulus and the glomerular capsule together make up the **renal corpuscle**. Small components of the blood, such as water, glucose, amino acids, and ions, are forced through the simple squamous epithelium of the glomerulus and through the epithelial cells of the glomerular capsule to enter the nephron during **glomerular filtration**. About 20% of the plasma passing through the glomerulus leaves the blood and enters the nephron, forming the glomerular filtrate. The rest of the blood exits the glomerulus and enters the **efferent arteriole**. The filtered fluid moves from the glomerular capsule into the proximal convoluted tubule.

Proximal means near and **convoluted** means twisty, so the **proximal convoluted tubule** is the coiled, folded part of the nephron near the beginning. Here **tubular reabsorption** of nutrients, ions, and water from the tubular fluid occurs. The reabsorbed molecules travel through the walls of the nephron, into the interstitial

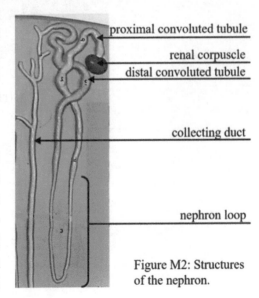

proximal convoluted tubule

renal corpuscle

distal convoluted tubule

collecting duct

nephron loop

Figure M2: Structures of the nephron.

fluid, and through the walls of the **peritubular capillaries**, which wrap around the nephron, to rejoin the blood.

Next the nephron descends deeper into the medulla and then ascends, forming the **nephron loop**. The medulla contains a salt gradient that increases with greater depth. This gradient aids the reabsorption of water and salts in the nephron loop.

The remaining tubular fluid then enters the **distal** (far) **convoluted tubule**. Here **tubular secretion** occurs: Molecules too large to enter the nephron at the renal corpuscle are actively transported into the nephron at the distal convoluted tubule. Excess ions are also transferred into the distal convoluted tubule from the blood in the peritubular capillaries.

From the distal convoluted tubule the fluid passes into the **collecting duct**, which carries the urine to the renal pelvis.

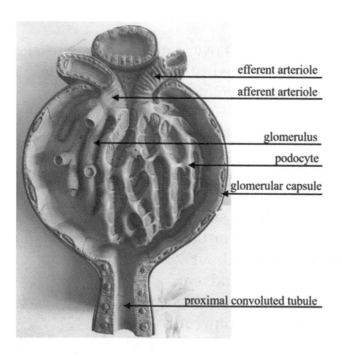

Figure M3   Structures of the renal corpuscle.

ACTIVITY 1: URINALYSIS

INTRODUCTION

Normal urine is yellow or amber in color, clear (when fresh), and mildly smelly. The more vibrant the color or stronger the smell, the more concentrated the urine. The color and odor of urine can also be affected by some foods. Urine has a **pH** of 4.6–8; a diet high in meat results in urine that is more acidic and a vegetarian diet results in urine that is more basic. Urine has a **specific density (SG)** of 1.005–1.030 g/mL (pure water is 1.000 g/mL).

The nephrons reabsorb almost all of the useful molecules they filter; very little is lost in the urine. The percentage excreted in the urine is 0% for glucose, 0.5% for sodium, 1% for water, and 50% for urea (urea is used to maintain a concentration gradient in the kidneys, so this waste molecule is not efficiently eliminated).

The presence of some substances in the urine is indicative of health problems. The following things should not be present in the urine. (Abbreviations from the urinalysis interpretation chart provided.)

(LEU) **Leukocytes** are white blood cells. They are too big to enter the nephron at the glomerular capsule. As immune cells, the presence of leukocytes in the urine suggest infection, such as a urinary tract infection (UTI) in the bladder or kidney.

(NIT) **Nitrites** are produced by bacteria from nitrates. nitrates are normally found in urine; nitrites are not. During a UTI, the bacteria causing the infection may have an enzyme that converts nitrates to nitrites, which leads to the presence of nitrites in the urine.

(URO) **Urobilinogen** is a metabolized version of bilirubin. Presence of urobilinogen in the urine at levels higher than 1 mg/dL is indicative of hemolytic anemia, hepatitis, jaundice, or other blood or liver problem.

(PRO) **Albumin** is a protein present in the blood that is too big to transfer through the renal corpuscle. Presence of albumin in the urine indicates unusually high permeability of the glomerulus. This can be caused by injury, disease, or high blood pressure.

(BLO) **Erythrocytes,** or red blood cells, are too big to enter the nephron, so they must be entering from another point in the urinary system. Inflammation, kidney stones, tumors, trauma, or kidney disease can result in the presence of erythrocytes in the urine.

(KET) **Ketone bodies** are found in the urine when fatty acids are metabolized for energy. Presence of ketone bodies in the urine is a sign of a low-carb diet, anorexia, starvation, or diabetes mellitus type I.

(BIL) **Bilirubin** is a product of heme degradation in the normal turnover of red blood cells. bilirubin is normally added to bile, which is produced by the liver, to be eliminated in the feces. Presence of bilirubin in the urine indicates a liver problem, such as cirrhosis, hepatitis, or liver disease.

(GLU) **Glucose** should be completely reabsorbed from the nephron. Presence of glucose in the urine indicates diabetes mellitus. However, glucose can appear in the urine during stress.

Casts are hard lumps that can form in the nephrons from proteins and cells or minerals. The presence of casts in the urine indicates serious kidney trouble.

Urine is sterile until it comes into contact with the external environment. Therefore the **microbe** concentration should be very low. Presence of microbes in the urine indicates infection.

PROTOCOL

1. With a partner, pour some synthetic urine into the provided cup. Make sure you use the appropriate color-coded lab equipment to avoid contamination between urine samples.
2. Remove a urinalysis test strip from the container. Recap the container (the strips absorb water from the air). Do not touch the pads with your fingers.
3. Wet all of the pads on the urinalysis test strip in the urine. You may need to bend the strip to get them all wet. The strip only needs to be in the urine long enough to get wet.
4. Lay the strip on a paper towel or, better yet, hold it on its side against a paper towel.
5. Wait the specified amount of time (30, 40, 45, 60, or 120 seconds) and then compare the color of the pads to the interpretation chart on the label of the urinalysis bottle. Start from the bottom of the strip and work up. These observations are qualitative, so make your best judgment about the colors.
6. Write down the value from the interpretation chart that best matches the color for each pad on the strip.
7. Use Table M1 to determine what, if any, health problem(s) the urinalysis indicates.

Table M1 Abnormal urine components and their associated disorders.

Abbreviation	Indicator	Normal Value	Presence
LEU	Leukocytes	-	UTI
NIT	Nitrite	-	UTI
URO	Urobilinogen	-	Liver disease
PRO	Protein	-	Kidney disease
pH	pH	4.6–8.0	Low pH: type I diabetes high pH: dehydration
BLO	Blood	-	Infection or inflammation
SG	Specific gravity	1.005–1.030 *Numbers vary with testing method	1.001–1.003: excessive fluid consumption, diabetes insipidus, or tubular damage High end of range or above: dehydration
KET	Ketone	-	Diabetes mellitus type I
BIL	Bilirubin	-	Liver or gallbladder problems
GLU	Glucose	-	Diabetes mellitus

Name _____ Section _____ Date _____

ACTIVITY 1: URINALYSIS COMPLETION

1. Make observations about the appearance and smell of the urine sample:

_____

_____

2. Test the patient's urine and record your results:

   Patient _____

Leukocytes (LEU)	120 seconds (2 minutes)	_____ leu/µL
Nitrite (NIT)	60 seconds (1 minute)	_____
Urobilinogen (URO)	60 seconds (1 minute)	_____ mg/dL
Protein (PRO)	60 seconds (1 minute)	_____ mg/dL
pH	60 seconds (1 minute)	_____
Blood (BLO)	60 seconds (1 minute)	_____ ery/µL
Specific Gravity (SG)	45 seconds	_____
Ketone (KET)	40 seconds	_____ mg/dL
Bilirubin (BIL)	30 seconds	_____ mg/dL
Glucose (GLU)	30 seconds	_____ mg/dL

3. Which urine components are present at an abnormal level in the patient's urine?

_____

4. What are the health implications of your findings? _____

_____

_____

Name _____ Section _____ Date _____

ACTIVITY 2: MICROSCOPY OF TISSUES

Identify each of the tissues and terms related to the urinary system clued below and draw a picture of each tissue. Refer to the Histology Lab J as necessary.

1. Most of the length of the nephron tubule is composed of a single layer of cells that are about as wide as they are tall.

    a. What is this epithelial tissue type called? _____

    b. Draw a picture of this tissue:

    total magnification: _____x

2. The inner layer of the ureters and bladder are composed of a stretchy epithelial tissue.

    a. What is this tissue called? _____

    b. Draw a picture of this tissue:

    total magnification: _____x

3. The role of the kidney nephrons is to filter this specialized connective tissue, which is critical for maintaining homeostasis of the body's fluids.

a. What is this tissue called? _____

b. What is the scientific name of the most common cells seen in this tissue?

_____

c. What is the scientific name of the large, rare cells, which are stained purple, in this tissue? _____

d. What is the scientific name for the small cell fragments found in this tissue?

_____

e. Draw a picture of this tissue:

total magnification: _____x

Name _____ Section _____ Date _____

URINARY SYSTEM COMPREHENSION

1. Label the organs of the urinary system.

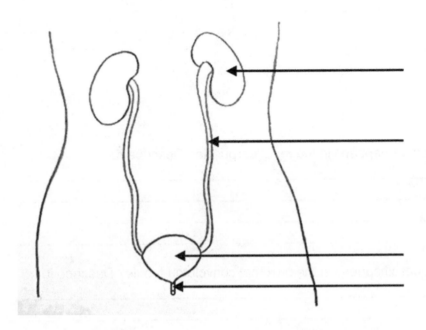

2. Label the structures of the kidney.

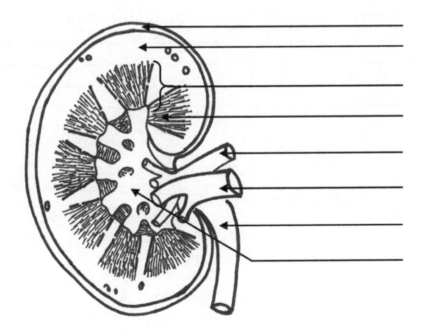

3. Label the structures of the nephron. (Blood vessels are indicated by open arrowheads.)

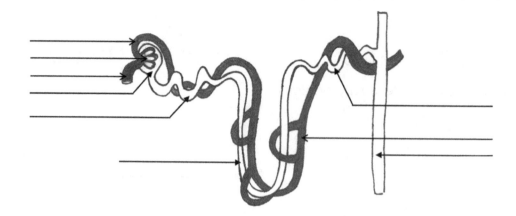

4. What process happens in the renal corpuscle? Describe it.

_____

_____

_____

_____

5. What process happens in the proximal convoluted tubule? Describe it.

_____

_____

_____

_____

6. What process happens in the distal convoluted tubule? Describe it.

_____

_____

_____

_____

Name _____ Section _____ Date _____

URINARY SYSTEM REVIEW QUESTIONS

1. Name the organs of the urinary system in order. Indicate how many of each we have.

2. a. What leaves the blood and enters the renal corpuscle?

   b. What is this process called?

3. a. What leaves the nephron tubule and returns to the blood?

   b. What is this process called?

   c. Where in the nephron does this mainly occur?

4. a. What leaves the blood and enters the distal convoluted tubule?

   b. What is this process called?

5. Name some normal components of the urine.

6. Name some things that should not be found in the urine.

7. Label the structures of the kidney:

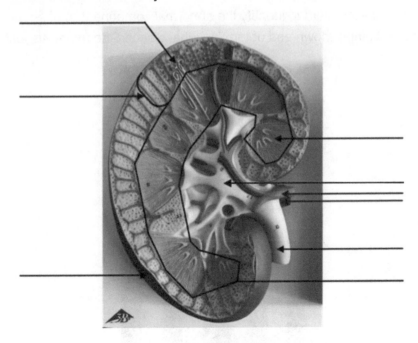

8. Label the parts of the nephron. Note that there are three nephrons in this image.

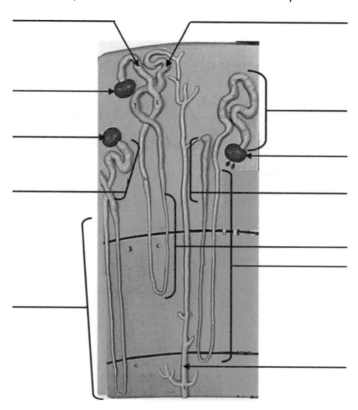

9. Use the interpretation chart to identify the abnormal component(s) (if any) in the urine for each of the test strips shown and determine what disease the urinalysis test indicates.

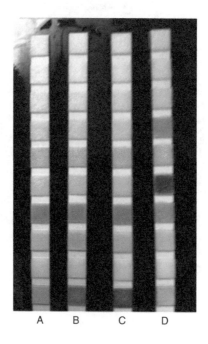

A   B   C   D

10. a. If a person has a urinary tract infection (UTI), what abnormal components would you expect to see in their urine?

b. If a person has liver disease, what abnormal components would you expect to see in their urine?

Digestive System

OBJECTIVES
- Learn about the organs and enzymes of the digestive system.
- Learn about the factors that affect digestion efficiency.

VOCABULARY

mouth	pharynx	esophagus	stomach
small intestine	large intestine	salivary gland	pancreas
liver	gallbladder	enzyme	catalyze
substrate	product	digestion	amylase
protease	lipase	pepsin	pancreatic juice
pancreatin	amylase	bile	emulsify
chyme	colorimetric reagent	Biuret solution	phenol red
Lugol's solution (KI)	negative	control	

SKILLS

Identify the organs of the digestive system.
Run an experiment testing the effect of a variable and interpret the results.

ACTIVITY 1: ANATOMY

INTRODUCTION

The digestive system is composed of the gastrointestinal tract, or alimentary canal, and the associated accessory structures. Food is ingested through the **mouth** and travels through the **pharynx** and **esophagus** to the **stomach**. From there it passes through the three regions of the **small intestine**, the duodenum, jejunum, and ileum. The final remnants of the ingested food then travel through the cecum; the ascending, transverse, descending, and sigmoid colon; and the rectum of the **large intestine** to be eliminated from the body. Along the way, enzymes produced by the salivary glands, stomach, pancreas, and small intestine aid digestion.

In the mouth, the teeth crush ingested food, the tongue pushes around the food, and the **salivary glands** produce saliva to wet the food, creating a bolus that can be swallowed. The bolus passes through the pharynx and down the esophagus to the stomach. The stomach stores and mashes the food, mixes it with pepsin and lipase, and shifts the pH to 2, which kills almost all microorganisms. The slurry of food and stomach acid leaving the stomach is called **chyme**. Chyme slowly exits the stomach into the small intestine, where absorption takes place. At the beginning of the small intestine, chyme is mixed with pancreatic juice, released from the **pancreas**. **Pancreatic juice** contains enzymes that digest fats, proteins, and carbohydrates, and also has a basic pH, which neutralizes the stomach acid and raises the pH of the chyme to around neutral. The enzymes of the pancreatic juice, along with enzymes expressed in the epithelium of the small intestine, complete molecular digestion of the chyme; so nutrients can be absorbed across the small intestine wall. The small intestine has a huge amount of surface area. The large surface area provides the necessary contact with the chyme for complete absorption of nutrients. Amino acids and sugars cross the epithelial cells of the small intestine to join the blood stream. Larger lipids are too big to enter the blood capillaries and so enter lymphatic capillaries instead. The material remaining at the end of the small intestine passes into the large intestine where water is removed to concentrate the material into feces.

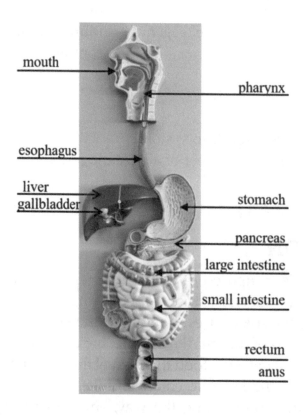

Figure N1   Organs of the digestive system.

Name _____ Section _____ Date _____

ACTIVITY 2: MICROSCOPY OF THE DIGESTIVE SYSTEM

INTRODUCTION

The digestive tract is composed of several layers of tissue. In contact with the food passing through it is a layer of epithelium. Most of the GI tract contains simple columnar epithelium, but the ends—the mouth, upper esophagus, and rectum (where the material passing through may be rough)—contain stratified squamous epithelium. Below the epithelium are layers of connective tissue and smooth muscle. The outside of the GI tract is covered with connective tissue and simple squamous epithelium (see the Histology Lab for review).

Look at the tissue slides of the **stomach** (may be from the cardia, fundus, or pyloric region of stomach), **small intestine** (may be from duodenum or jejunum, or from the salamander necturus), and, if available, the esophagus–stomach junction, and draw what you see.

_____ total magnification: _____x	_____ total magnification: _____x
_____ total magnification: _____x	_____ total magnification: _____x

Name ——————————————— Section ——————— Date ——————

ACTIVITY 3: MICROSCOPY OF TISSUES

Identify each of the tissues and terms related to the digestive system clued below and draw a picture of each tissue. Refer to the Histology Lab as necessary.

1. Food is ingested through the mouth. Teeth do mechanical processing of food, crushing and grinding it into smaller pieces. The teeth rest on compact bone of the jaw.

   a. What are the cells of the compact bone called? ————————————————

   b. What is the name for the liquid space in which these cells live? ————————————

   c. These spaces form the boundaries of the concentric rings that make up the compact bone. What are these rings called? ————————————————————

   d. Several concentric rings make up a round unit of bone. What is the whole round unit called? ————————————————————————

   e. At the center of the round unit is a hole through which blood vessels and nerves pass. What is this hole called? ————————————————————

   f. Draw a picture of this specialized connective tissue:

   total magnification: ——— x

2. When you chew, your temporomandibular joint (TMJ) acts as a sliding hinge, allowing you to open and close your mouth, moving your jaw against your skull. The TMJ is a complex joint composed of a disc between a ball and socket and is made up of muscles, bones, fibrocartilage, and ligaments. Ligaments are composed of fibrous connective tissue.

   a. What is this tissue called? _____

   b. Draw a picture of this tissue:

total magnification: _____x

3. After chewing, food passes from the mouth to the esophagus. Both organs are lined with many layers of small cells.

   a. What is this epithelial tissue type called? _____

   b. Draw a picture of this tissue:

total magnification: _____x

4. The stomach, small intestine, and large intestine are lined with a single layer of tall cells.

   a. What is this epithelial tissue type called? _____

   b. The epithelium of the small intestines contains cellular projections to increase surface area. What are these projections called? _____

   c. What are the cells that produce mucus called? _____

   d. Draw a picture of this tissue:

   ┌─────────────────────────────────┐
   │   │
   │   │
   │   │
   │   │
   │   │
   │   │
   │   total magnification: _____x │
   └─────────────────────────────────┘

5. The epithelium of the gastrointestinal tract is supported by a layer of connective tissue, the lamina propria of the mucosa, which also supplies nutrients from the blood to the epithelial cells above.

   a. What is this tissue called? _____

   b. Draw a picture of this tissue:

   ┌─────────────────────────────────┐
   │   │
   │   │
   │   │
   │   │
   │   │
   │   │
   │   total magnification: _____x │
   └─────────────────────────────────┘

6. Excess calories are stored as triglycerides in a specialized connective tissue.

    a. What is this tissue called? _____

    b. What are the cells that store fat called? _____

    c. Draw a picture of this tissue:

total magnification: _____x

ACTIVITY 4: DIGESTION

INTRODUCTION

Digestion of the macronutrients- carbohydrates, proteins, and lipids- by enzymes provides fuel and building blocks for the body. Carbohydrates are digested into simple sugars; starch is digested to oligosaccharides, maltose, and glucose by **amylases** from saliva and the pancreas. Proteins from animal meat and plant matter are composed of amino acids linked by peptide bonds. Proteins are digested into short peptides and free amino acids by **proteases** or peptidases. Pancreatic juice contains several proteases and the stomach lining produces the protease **pepsin**. Triglycerides are the most common type of dietary fat. A triglyceride has three fatty acids connected to a glycerol molecule. **Lipases** digest triglycerides by removing the fatty acids from the glycerol. Lipases are produced by the mouth, stomach, and pancreas. Digestion of fats is aided by bile. **Bile** contains bile acids, steroid acids that **emulsify** fat: The bile acids work like soap to break up large drops of fat into lots of small droplets of fat. (Note that bile does not have enzymatic activity.) Bile is produced by the **liver** and stored in the **gallbladder**.

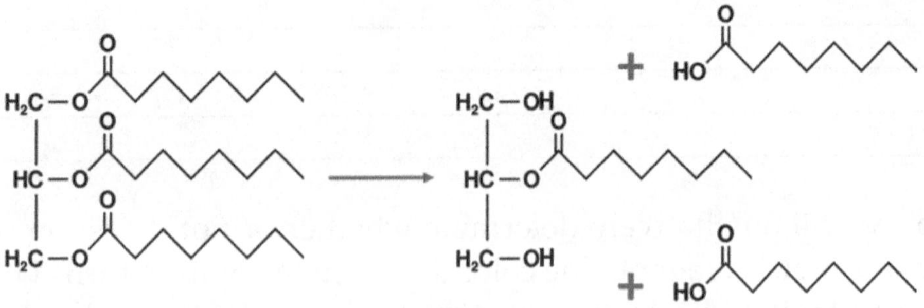

Figure N2 A triglyceride, composed of a glycerol and three fatty acids (left) is digested by pancreatic lipase to free the fatty acids in the first and third positions.

Enzymes

Enzymes are molecules that **catalyze** (speed up) reactions. Almost all enzymes are proteins. An enzyme binds to a specific substance (**substrate**) and forces a chemical reaction to produce the **product**. An enzyme can only work on the right molecule; it can't bind to other molecules. To get a chemical reaction, the right substrate-enzyme pair must be present. The enzyme and the substrate float around in solution and the enzyme can only work on the substrate if they meet. Increasing the concentration of the enzyme and/or the substrate will increase how often the chemical reaction occurs and how quickly product appears. Increasing the digestion time increases how completely the reaction occurs. The more time the enzyme is given to run into and react with the substrate, the more product will be produced.

The rate at which an enzyme is able to convert a substrate into its product is influenced by temperature. All enzymes have an optimal temperature at which they work most efficiently; as the temperature moves away from this, either warmer or colder, the rate of the reaction decreases. Human enzymes work best at human body temperature, 37°C. Enzymes also have an optimal pH. They work efficiently at their optimal pH and will stop working if the pH is too far from optimal. Stomach enzymes work in very acidic solutions—the stomach has a pH of about 2. Enzymes from the small intestine work around neutral pH 7.

In the laboratory, enzymatic reactions are stopped by stopping the activity of the enzyme. This can be done by changing the pH, freezing, or boiling the reaction sample. Boiling causes the enzyme to unfold; proteins are only active if they are properly folded.

☑   List five factors that affect how much product is produced.

_____

_____

_____

_____

_____

In this lab we will qualitatively determine whether or not digestion occurred by adding a **colorimetric reagent**. The color the reaction solution turns with the colorimetric reagent will indicate the presence or absence of the molecule of interest. The negative control included in each experiment will show the color produced when no digestion occurs, which we will use as a comparison for the other reaction tubes.

Name _____ Section _____ Date _____

ACTIVITY 4 DIRECTIONS

Read the protocols for each of the experiments in Activity 4 and complete the questions for each. You and your partner will conduct one of the four experiments. You will need to collect the experimental results from the other pairs at your table to finish the Digestion Completion.

PURPOSE

1. What do we aim to discover with this activity? (What are we testing?)

_____
_____
_____

2. What data will you collect from these experiments?

_____
_____

For the experiment you are going to conduct, fill in each of the tubes below with the volumes of each of the reagents you will use.

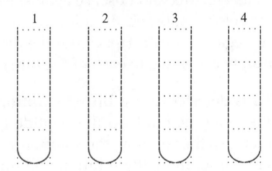

EXPERIMENT 1: EFFECT OF pH ON PROTEIN DIGESTION

In this experiment we will test the effect of pH on protein digestion. We will digest proteins from powdered milk (casein) and powdered egg white (albumin) using the enzyme pepsin. **Pepsin** is produced by the stomach, which has a pH of about 2, which is very acidic. To achieve this low pH, we will use hydrochloric acid (HCl). Do not get this on you!

Protocol

1. In each tube, add 2 mL (40 drops) of protein solution.
2. In tubes **1** and **2**, add 1 mL (20 drops) of 1 N HCl. (Be very careful!)

   In tube **3**, add 8 drops of 1 N HCl + 12 drops of water.

   In tube **4**, add 1 mL of water.
3. In tube **1**, add 1 mL of water.

   In tubes **2–4**, add 1 mL (20 drops) of 1.5% pepsin solution.
4. Cover each tube with a piece of Parafilm, place your thumb over the Parafilm, and gently invert the tube several times to mix.
5. Use pH strips to determine the pH of each tube. Record the results.
6. Incubate the tubes at 37°C for 45 minutes (or more).
7. Add Biuret solution with gentle mixing. You will need 5–25 drops of Biuret solution to see color change. Mix and observe against something white every 1–2 drops because the color is pale and the addition of too much Biuret solution can cause a false-negative result. Tip: Count the drops you add to tube 2, then add the same number of drops to each of the other tubes.

Digestion of the proteins is detected using **Biuret solution**. Biuret solution contains copper sulfate. This molecule binds to the peptide bonds in peptides and proteins. If there are proteins in the solution, the solution will turn purple. If there are only small peptides in the solution, the solution will turn pink. If there are no peptide bonds in the solution, the solution will look blue due to the copper sulfate.

Clean-up: Thoroughly rinse out tubes and place upside down in test tube rack by sink.

Questions

1. What are we testing with tubes 2–4? _____
2. Why do we have tube 1? _____
3. After digestion, what color do you expect each tube to turn?

   Tube 1 _____   Tube 2 _____

   Tube 3 _____   Tube 4 _____

EXPERIMENT 2: EFFECT OF CONCENTRATION ON LIPID DIGESTION

In this experiment we will test the effect of concentration on the amount of digestion that occurs. We will digest lipids from heavy cream (36% fat minimum), whole milk (3.25% milkfat), and skim milk (0% fat) with pancreatic lipase. We will use a resuspension of a dried, powdered extract from pancreatic juice, **pancreatin**, which contains a range of enzymes including lipase. Pancreatic juice is secreted from the pancreas into the small intestine, where it digests molecules that have left the stomach. Pancreatic juice also contains bicarbonate to increase the pH of the chyme coming from the stomach to neutral pH (~7). Pancreatin and the lipase in it work optimally at body temperature, 37°C.

Protocol

1. In each tube, add 2 mL (40 drops) of phenol red.
2. In tube **1**, add 1 mL (20 drops) of water.

   In tubes **2–4**, add 1 mL (20 drops) of 1% pancreatin solution.
3. In tubes **1** and **2**, add 5 drops of heavy cream.

   In tube **3**, add 5 drops of whole milk.

   In tube **4**, add 5 drops of skim milk.
4. Cover each tube with a piece of Parafilm, place your thumb over the Parafilm, and gently invert the tube several times to mix.
5. Record the initial appearance of each tube.
6. Incubate tubes at 37°C for 30 minutes.

Digestion of the triglycerides is detected using phenol red. **Phenol red** is a pH-indicator, which means it changes color when the pH changes. At pH 7, phenol red is red. At higher pH values, phenol red turns pink. At lower pH values, phenol red turns orange or yellow. Digestion of triglycerides results in the creation of free fatty acids. Fatty acids are so named because they are acidic. Thus, during digestion, the pH of the solution goes down (the acidity goes up), so the color of phenol red changes.

Clean-up: Thoroughly rinse out tubes and place upside down in test tube rack by sink.

Questions

1. What are we testing with tubes 2–4? _____
2. Why do we have tube 1? _____
3. After digestion, what color do you expect each tube to turn?

   Tube 1 _____   Tube 2 _____

   Tube 3 _____   Tube 4 _____

EXPERIMENT 3: EFFECT OF TIME ON CARBOHYDRATE DIGESTION

In this experiment we will test the effect of time on the amount of digestion that occurs. To do so, we will digest starch with amylase for different amounts of time and then detect the starch remaining in the tube. Starch is a polysaccharide—a large molecule composed of hundreds or thousands of glucose molecules. In our bodies, starch is digested by various enzymes to break it down into smaller pieces. One of the enzymes is amylase. Amylase is produced both by the salivary glands and the pancreas. **Amylase** breaks starch into fragments of two glucose molecules linked together, called maltose. Maltose is a sweet-tasting simple sugar. In this experiment we will digest starch from potatoes with salivary amylase. Salivary amylase works optimally at body temperature, 37°C. Salivary amylase is present in saliva, which has a pH near neutral, about pH 7.

Protocol

1. In each tube, add 1 mL (20 drops) of 0.5% amylase solution.
2. In each tube, add 5 drops of 1% starch solution (swirl starch solution before dispensing, for each tube).
3. Cover each tube with a piece of Parafilm, place your thumb over the Parafilm, and gently invert the tube several times to mix.
4. Incubate each tube at 37°C for the indicated amount of time:
   - Tube 1: 0 minute
   - Tube 2: 10 minutes
   - Tube 3: 30 minutes
   - Tube 4: 60 minutes
5. After incubation, add 3 drops of KI and gently shake.

The presence of starch in solution can be detected by **Lugol's solution**, which is **potassium iodide (KI)**. If starch is present, it reacts with the KI and forms a dark black-purple solution or solid precipitate. If there is no starch in the solution, then the solution looks yellow or orange due to the iodide.

Clean-up: Thoroughly rinse out tubes and place upside down in test tube rack by sink.

Questions

1. What are we testing with tubes 2–4? _____
2. Why do we have tube 1? _____
3. After digestion, what color do you expect each tube to turn?
   Tube 1 _____   Tube 2 _____
   Tube 3 _____   Tube 4 _____

EXPERIMENT 4: EFFECT OF TEMPERATURE ON CARBOHYDRATE DIGESTION

In this experiment we will test the effect of temperature on the amount of digestion that occurs. To do so, we will digest starch with amylase at different temperatures and then detect the starch remaining in the tube. Starch is a polysaccharide—a large molecule composed of hundreds or thousands of glucose molecules. In our bodies, starch is digested by various enzymes to break it down into smaller pieces. One of the enzymes is amylase. Amylase is produced both by the salivary glands and the pancreas. **Amylase** breaks starch into fragments of two glucose molecules linked together, called maltose. Maltose is a sweet-tasting simple sugar. In this experiment we will digest starch from potatoes with salivary amylase. Salivary amylase works optimally at body temperature, 37°C. Salivary amylase is present in saliva, which has a pH near neutral, about pH 7.

Protocol

1. In tube **1**, add 1 mL (20 drops) of water.
2. In tubes **2–4**, add 1 mL (20 drops) of 0.5% amylase solution.
3. In each tube, add 5 drops of 1% starch solution (swirl starch solution before dispensing).
4. Cover each tube with a piece of Parafilm, place your thumb over the Parafilm, and gently invert the tube several times to mix.
5. Incubate each tube for 30 minutes at the indicated location
   - Tube 1: water bath
   - Tube 2: water bath
   - Tube 3: benchtop
   - Tube 4: refrigerator
6. Measure and record the temperature of each location.
7. After incubation, add 3 drops of KI to each tube and gently shake.

The presence of starch in solution can be detected by **Lugol's solution**, which is **potassium iodide (KI)**. If starch is present, it reacts with the KI and forms a dark black-purple solution or solid precipitate. If there is no starch in the solution, then the solution looks yellow or orange due to the iodide.

Clean-up: Thoroughly rinse out tubes and place upside down in test tube rack by sink.

Questions

1. What are we testing with tubes 2–4? _____

2. Why do we have tube 1? _____

3. After digestion, what color do you expect each tube to turn?

   Tube 1 _____ Tube 2 _____

   Tube 3 _____ Tube 4 _____

Name _____ Section _____ Date _____

DIGESTION COMPLETION

Experiment 1: Protein Digestion

Macromolecule used: _____

Enzyme used: _____

Variable tested: _____

Colorimetric indicator used: _____

Molecule detected with indicator: _____

Molecule presence color: _____

Molecule absence color: _____

Tube	1	2	3	4
pH				
Color after incubation				
Extent of digestion?				

What effect did the variable tested have on digestion? _____

_____

Name _____ Section _____ Date _____

Experiment 2: Lipid Digestion

Macromolecule used: _____

Enzyme used: _____

Variable tested: _____

Colorimetric indicator used: _____

Molecule detected with indicator: _____

Molecule presence color: _____

Molecule absence color: _____

Tube	1	2	3	4
Color before incubation				
Color after incubation				
Extent of digestion?				

What effect did the variable tested have on digestion? _____

_____

Name _____ Section _____ Date _____

Experiment 3: Carbohydrate Digestion

Macromolecule used: _____

Enzyme used: _____

Variable tested: _____

Colorimetric indicator used: _____

Molecule detected with indicator: _____

Molecule presence color: _____

Molecule absence color: _____

Tube	1	2	3	4
Incubation time				
Color after incubation				
Extent of digestion?				

What effect did the variable tested have on digestion? _____

_____

Name _____ Section _____ Date _____

Experiment 4: Carbohydrate Digestion

Macromolecule used: _____

Enzyme used: _____

Variable tested: _____

Colorimetric indicator used: _____

Molecule detected with indicator: _____

Molecule presence color: _____

Molecule absence color: _____

Tube	1	2	3	4
Temperature				
Color after incubation				
Extent of digestion?				

What effect did the variable tested have on digestion? _____

_____

Name _____ Section _____ Date _____

DIGESTIVE SYSTEM COMPREHENSION

Label the organs of the digestive system.

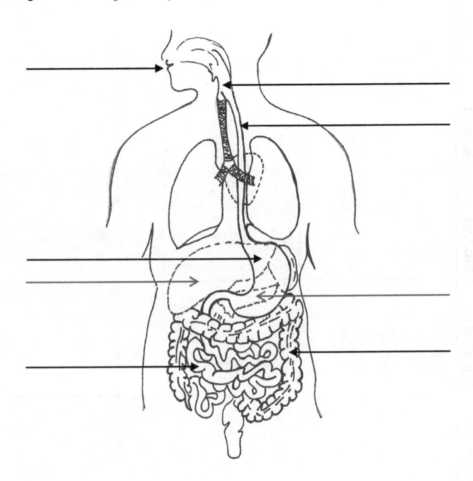

Enzyme	Conditions for Optimal Activity	Produced by (Organ)	Molecule Digested	Reaction Product	Detected by Colorimetric Reagent	Digestion Color	No Digestion Color
Pepsin	Temp: pH:						
Lipase (pancreatin)	Temp: pH:						
Salivary amylase	Temp: pH:						

Name _____ Section _____ Date _____

DIGESTIVE SYSTEM REVIEW QUESTIONS

1. Name the organs of the digestive system (gastrointestinal tract) in order.

2. Name three locations that produce digestive enzymes.

3. Where are most nutrients taken up?

4. What is the main role of the large intestine?

5. What are the main roles of the stomach?

6. What molecule does Biuret's solution detect? What color(s) does it turn if the molecule is present? What color is it if the molecule is absent?

7. What molecule does Lugol's solution detect? What color(s) does it turn if the molecule is present? What color is it if the molecule is absent?

8. What does phenol red detect? What color(s) does it turn?

9. Explain why the color of phenol red is indicative of lipid digestion.

10. What molecule is Lugol's solution? What is that molecule's chemical formula?

11. If you were to mix lipase, melted butter, and phenol red, what color would you expect to see after digestion at 37°C? Why?

12. If you were to mix starch, amylase, and Biuret's solution, what color would you expect to see after digestion at 37°C? Why?

13. A negative control is missing a key component to ensure a negative result. For each digestion experiment, state what key component is missing from the negative control.

14. What can you do to promote complete digestion of a molecule by an enzyme?

15. Why was HCl added to tubes 1–3 of Experiment 1 of Activity 4?

16. For Experiments 3 and 4, what does a positive result with Lugol's solution tell us about the extent of digestion?

17. Benedict's solution is used to detect maltose. If no maltose is present, the solution is blue. If maltose is present, the solution may be green, yellow, orange, or red, depending on concentration (red is highest). For each tube in experiments 3 and 4 of Activity 4,

state what color you would expect each tube to turn if tested with Benedict's solution. Explain your logic.

18. Which organs have a neutral pH? Which organ has an acidic pH?

19. Why is there no mention of digestive enzymes produced in the large intestine?

20. You set up an experiment with two tubes. Both tubes contain starch and one tube contains amylase. After incubation, when you add Lugol's solution, both tubes turn black. Explain these results.

21. You set up an experiment with two tubes. Both tubes contain starch and one tube contains amylase. After incubation, when you add Lugol's solution, both tubes turn yellow. Explain these results.

22. You set up an experiment with two tubes. Both tubes contain pepsin and one tube contains milk protein. After incubation, when you add Biuret solution, both tubes turn purple. You are sure you set up everything correctly. Explain these results.

23. You repeat Experiment 2 from Activity 4, using gastric (stomach) lipase instead of pancreatin. To optimize digestion, you add HCl to change the pH to 2, the pH of the stomach. All of your tubes, including the negative control, turn yellow. Explain these results.

24. You repeat Experiment 3 from Activity 4, but instead of putting the tubes in the water bath you leave them on the benchtop. What effect will this have on the results?

25. You conduct an experiment testing the effect of pH on starch digestion. You set up tubes containing starch and amylase and add 1 mL of 1 N HCl to tube 1, 0.5 mL of 1 N HCl plus 0.5 mL water to tube 2, and 1 mL of water to tube 3. After digestion at 37°C, you add Lugol's solution to each tube and observe that tube 1 is black, tube 2 forms a small amount of black precipitate, and tube 3 is yellow. Explain your results.

26. You conduct an experiment testing the effect of temperature on lipid digestion. You set up tubes with phenol red, cream, and pancreatin lipase. You incubate tube 1 at 3°C, tube 2 at 20°C, and tube 3 at 37°C. After incubating for thirty minutes, you observe that tube 1 is red, tube 2 is orange, and tube 3 is yellow. Explain your results.

27. You want to test the effect of time on lipid digestion. Design this experiment. State what results you expect to observe and why.

28. You want to test the effect of enzyme concentration on digestion. Using the reagents and equipment available in the Experiments from Activity 4, design an experiment to test this variable. State what results you expect to observe from your experiment and why.

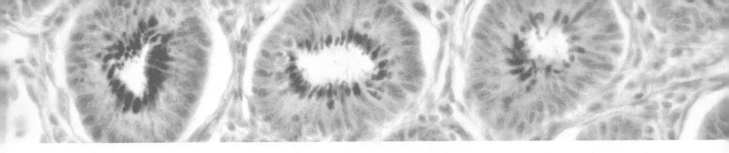

Review Question Answers

LAB A MICROSCOPY REVIEW QUESTION ANSWERS

1. See text (13 terms).
2. See text (8 terms).
3. See text.
4. See text (last paragraph of "Microscope Parts" section).
5. The image will appear out of focus to the lab partner. Each person will need to adjust the fine focus knob to bring the image into crisp focus after the other person uses the microscope.
6. Both refer to the appearance of the image when magnification (objective) changes.
7. Depth of Field: As magnification increases, the depth of the image that is in focus decreases.
8. Field of View: As magnification increases, the diameter of the image that is visible decreases.
9. See text (Introduction to Activity 2).
10. See text (Introduction to Activity 2).
11.

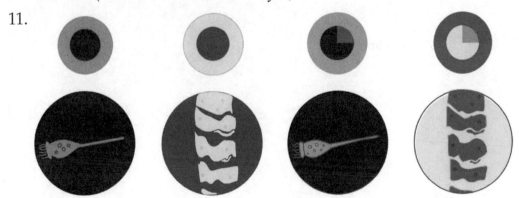

12. Dark-field microscopy (different densities).
13. Dark-field microscopy (fine structure).

14. Bright-field microscopy (India ink gives contrast to vacuoles, so can use bright field with its high light levels to view specimen).

15. TEM and compound microscopy are both the higher magnification method of their pairs and uses thin samples and send particles (electrons or photons) through it. SEM and dissecting microscopes are relatively low magnification methods and bounce particles off of the surface of a sample.

LAB B DATA ANALYSIS REVIEW QUESTION ANSWERS

1. a. Independent variable: month
   b. Dependent variable: average daytime temperature
   b. x-axis would have months
   c. y-axis would have temperatures

2. a. x-axis: age (years)
   b. y-axis: height (centimeters)

3.

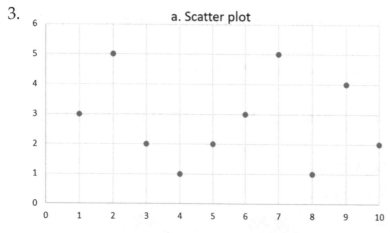

a. Scatter plot

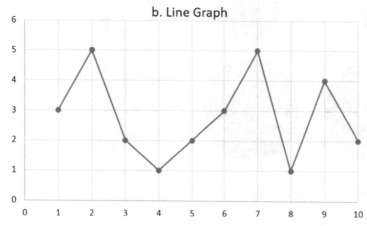

b. Line Graph

c. Histogram

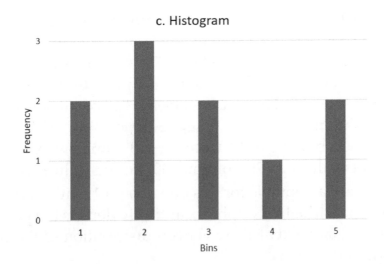

The x-values of the histogram are the y-values of the data set (1–5). I'm using a bin size of 1.

4. a. Mean = 3, median = 2, mode = 1, range = 5 or 1–6
   b. Mean = 20, median = 10, mode = 5, range = 45 or 5–50
   c. Mean = 20, median = 15, mode = 40, range = 39 or 1–40
   d. Mean = 50, median = 30, mode = 100, range = 95 or 5–100

5. =stdeva() (or other *stdev* options)

6. Spring = 2 (nesting birds, daffodils)   Summer = 3 (snorkel, beach ball, ice cream)

   Fall = 1 (orange leaves)   Winter = 3 (wreath, ice skating, snowman)

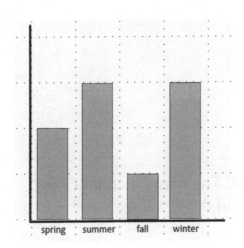

7. a. Graph 1 has a bin size of 1. The first bin counts the number of times the value "1" appears in the data set, bin 2 contains "2," bin 3 contains "3." Graph 2 has a bin size of 2. The column labeled "2" counts the frequency of the values 1 and 2. The column labeled "4" counts 3 and 4. "6" counts 5 and 6. Graph 3 has a bin size of 5. The column labeled "5" counts the frequency of values 1–5, column "10" counts values 6–10, column "15" counts values 11–15. Graph 4 has a bin size of 10. Column "10" counts values 1–10, column "20" counts values 11–20, column "30" counts values 21–30.

   b. A number of arguments are acceptable for this one. Graph 1, with a bin size of 1, shows all the data individually. Graph 2 beautifully depicts the periodicity of the data. Graph 4 shows that there is even distribution of the data across the range, if grouped by tens.

8. a. i. is graph C, ii. is graph B, iii. is graph A (note irregular x-axis values), iv. is graph D

   b. i. 68% range: 85–115, 95% range: 70–130; ii. 68% range: 70–130, 95% range: 40–160; iii. 68% range: 158.5–161.5, 95% range: 157–163; iv. 68% range: 55–85, 95% range: 40–100

9. a. When knowing the y-value at any x-value would be useful: You can extrapolate from a finite set of collected data to all values by connecting the data points with a smooth curve.

   b. When the data is not continuous (connecting the data points would have no meaning because intervening x-axis points have no meaning).

10. a. Mean = 2.98, median = 2.85, standard deviation = 1.114

    b.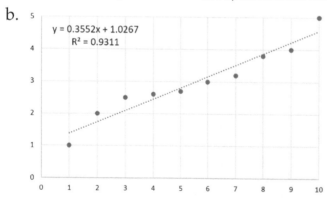

    c. Yes, there is good fit. The trendline follows the overall upward progression of the data points and the R^2 value of 0.9311 is very close to 1.0, which indicates good fit.

11. a. Mean = 3.78, median = 2.75, standard deviation = 2.814

b.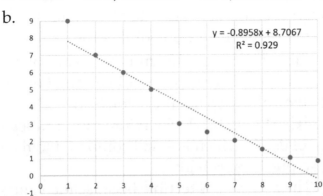

$y = -0.8958x + 8.7067$
$R^2 = 0.929$

c. Yes, there is good fit. The trendline follows the overall downward progression of the data points and the R^2 value of 0.929 is very close to 1.0, which indicates good fit.

12. a. Mean = 5.37, median = 5.5, standard deviation = 3.416

b.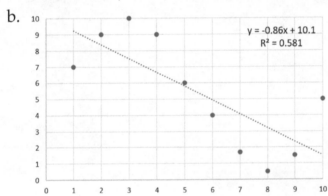

$y = -0.86x + 10.1$
$R^2 = 0.581$

c. No, the trendline does not follow the sinusoidal path of the data—a straight line is not a good fit for this data. The R^2 value of 0.581, deviating significantly from 1, reflects that this is not a good fit.

LAB D METRIC SYSTEM REVIEW QUESTION ANSWERS

1. d

2. d

3. a. Accuracy is high because values are all close to the true value of an "inch" worm, 2.54 cm. Precision is high because the values fall in a range of 0.04 cm which is small compared to the magnitude of the true value.

   b. A standard door is 80 inches tall, or 203 cm. 110 cm is 43 inches, which is 3.5 feet. Therefore the accuracy is low. The values fall in a range of 25 cm, which is a large percentage of the values, so the precision is low.

   c. Room temperature is about 20°C. 64°C is 147°F. Therefore the accuracy is low. The values fall in a range of 0.5°C, which is small compared to the magnitude of the true value, so precision is high.

   d. A sugar packet weighs 2–4 g. The accuracy is terrible because the values are in kilograms. The values range from 0.82 to 8.02, so the precision is terrible.

   e. 0.5 L is 500 mL. All values are too high, so accuracy is low. Values fall in a range of 33 mL. 33 is 6.6% of 500, so would characterize the precision as low.

4. a. 0.99 g/mL

   b. 8 kg

   c. 25 mL

   d. 0.032 µg

5. Qualitative

6. Quantitative

7. Graduated cylinder

8. Micropipette

9. 5 mL: It is big enough and the smallest option that would work.

10. Because the weigh boat is lighter. The weight of the water causes a larger change in the gross mass with the weigh boat than with the beaker when weighing tiny volumes.

11. 167 µL

12. 34 µL

13. 0.25 mL, 250 µL

14. 9.8 µL

15. P200, because 50 µL is in range

16. P200, because 100 µL is in the center of the range, so it would be more accurate

17. 0.1 µL = 0.0001 mL or $1*10^{-4}$ mL = 0.0000001 L or $1*10^{-7}$ L

18. 0.2 nm = 0.0002 µm ($2*10^{-4}$ µm) = 200 pm

19. This systematic instrument error could be corrected by subtracting 2°C from each measurement.

20. Systematic observational error

21. Systematic environmental error

22. Random error

23. Random error

24. Human error

25. Human error

26. You would expect the height data to show a Gaussian distribution; people are different heights, with most people being near average and the number of people of any given height dropping off as you move away from the average. Normal body temperature is 37°C, so we would expect only one bar in the histogram. In reality, normal body temperature varies between people, from 36.5°C to 37.5°C, so we would expect nonzero values for more than one bin in the histogram. However, we would not expect the measured temperature to taper off from 37°C, so we do not expect a Gaussian distribution.

27. a. $1.234*10^3$

    b. $3.7*10^{-3}$

    c. $1.068*10^1$

    d. $1.2*10^{-1}$

    e. $1.50*10^2$

    f. $1.73*10^1$

28. a. 100

    b. 0.125

    c. 1,500,000

    d. 0.00011

    e. 3,141.59

    f. 4.12

29. a. Greater than one

    b. Less than one

    c. Greater than one

    d. Less than one

    e. Greater than one

    f. Less than one

    g. Greater than one

    h. Less than one

    i. Less than one

30. a. 900 cm
    b. 8,000 mm
    c. 7,000,000 μm (7*10^6 μm)
    d. 6*10^9 nm
    e. 5*10^{12} nm

31. a. 4*10^{-12} m
    b. 3*10^{-9} m
    c. 2*10^{-6} m
    d. 1*10^{-3} m (0.001 m)
    e. 0.5*10^{-2} m (5*10^{-3} m or 0.005 m)

32. a. 0.95 cL
    b. 15 mL
    c. 8.5*10^{-3} mL (0.0085 mL)
    d. 2.5*10^3 μL (2,500 μL)
    e. 7.5*10^{-3} nL (0.0075 nL)
    f. 3.5*10^3 pL (3,500 pL)
    g. 6.5*10^{-6} μL
    h. 4.5*10^6 pL

33. a. 2,000 g (2*10^3 g)
    b. 300,000 cg (3*10^5 cg)
    c. 4,000,000 mg (4*10^6 mg)
    d. 5*10^9 μg
    e. 6*10^{12} ng
    f. 7*10^{15} pg
    g. 8*10^{-15} kg
    h. 9*10^{-12} kg
    i. 10*10^{-9} kg (1*10^{-8} kg)
    j. 11*10^{-6} kg (1.1*10^{-5} kg)
    k. 12*10^{-5} kg (1.2*10^{-4} kg)

34. a. 50.8 cm
    b. 508 mm
    c. 23.622 inches
    d. 2.7559 in

35. a. 86°F
    b. 68°F
    c. 50°F
    d. −17.78°C
    e. 4.44°C
    f. 37.78°C

36. a. 100 g
    b. 90 mL
    c. 80 cm^3
    d. 70 mL
    e. 60 g
    f. 50 cm^3

37. a. $0.5*10^{15}$ pg ($5*10^{14}$ pg)
    b. $0.6*10^{10}$ pg ($6*10^9$ pg)
    c. $0.7*10^9$ pg ($7*10^8$ pg)
    d. $0.8*10^6$ pg ($8*10^5$ pg)
    e. $0.9*10^3$ pg ($9*10^2$ pg or 900 pg)
    f. $0.5*10^{12}$ nL ($5*10^{11}$ nL)
    g. $0.6*10^7$ nL ($6*10^6$ nL)
    h. $0.7*10^6$ nL ($7*10^5$ nL)
    i. $0.8*10^3$ nL ($8*10^2$ nL or 800 nL)
    j. $0.9*10^{-3}$ nL ($9*10^{-4}$ nL)
    k. $0.5*10^9$ μm ($5*10^8$ μm)
    l. $0.6*10^4$ μm ($6*10^3$ μm)
    m. $0.7*10^3$ μm ($7*10^2$ μm or 700 μm)
    n. $0.8*10^{-3}$ μm ($8*10^{-4}$ μm)
    o. $0.9*10^{-6}$ μm ($9*10^{-7}$ μm)
    p. $0.5*10^6$ mg ($5*10^5$ mg)
    q. $0.6*10^1$ mg (6 mg)
    r. $0.7*10^{-3}$ mg ($7*10^{-4}$ mg)
    s. $0.8*10^{-6}$ mg ($8*10^{-7}$ mg)
    t. $0.9*10^{-9}$ mg ($9*10^{-10}$ mg)
    u. $0.5*10^5$ cm ($5*10^4$ cm)
    v. $0.6*10^{-1}$ cm ($6*10^{-2}$ cm or 0.06 cm)
    w. $0.7*10^{-4}$ cm ($7*10^{-5}$ cm)
    x. $0.8*10^{-7}$ cm ($8*10^{-8}$ cm)
    y. $0.9*10^{-10}$ cm ($9*10^{-11}$ cm)
    z. $0.5*10^{-5}$ kg ($5*10^{-6}$ kg)
    aa. $0.6*10^{-6}$ kg ($6*10^{-7}$ kg)
    ab. $0.7*10^{-9}$ kg ($7*10^{-10}$ kg)
    ac. $0.8*10^{-12}$ kg ($8*10^{-13}$ kg)
    ad. $0.9*10^{-15}$ kg ($9*10^{-16}$ kg)

38. a. 0.018288 km
    b. 304.8 μm
    c. 330,200 nm ($3.302*10^5$ nm)
    d. $3.556*10^8$ pm
    e. $1.9685*10^{-8}$ inches
    f. $1.5748*10^{-5}$ inches
    g. $1.181*10^{-2}$ inches (0.01181 inch)
    h. 984.25 inches

39. a. 39.2°F
    b. 37°C
    c. 140°F
    d. −40°C
    e. 212°F
    f. 0°C
    g. 14°F
    h. 176.67°C
    i. 122°F

40. a. 300 cm³
    b. 50 mL

41. 5.217%

42. −4.25%

43. −2.8%

44. 3.2%

LAB E DIFFUSION REVIEW QUESTION ANSWERS

1. a. Hypotonic—lower solute (black dot) concentration
   b. Isotonic—same concentration on both sides
2. a. C (two solute "molecules" versus four in reference)
   b. A (8 versus 4)
   c. B (4 in both)
3. a. Hypotonic (concentration of cell = 4 solutes/1 space; concentration of solution = 4 solutes/5 spaces, so solution has lower concentration)
   b. Water
   c. Water will osmose into the cell, causing it to swell, perhaps pop

4. a. Hypertonic (concentration of cell = 2 solutes/4 spaces; concentration of solution = 2 solutes/2 spaces, so solution has higher concentration)

   b. Water

   c. Water will osmose out of the cell, causing it to shrivel

LAB E CELL BIOLOGY REVIEW QUESTION ANSWERS

1. A positive control should show you what a positive result looks like. A positive control is set up using reagents that should give a positive result. If you don't see the expected positive result, then you know something is wrong with the experiment and that you can't trust your experimental results.

2. A negative control should show you what a negative result looks like. A negative control is set up using reagents that should give a negative result. If you don't see the expected negative result, then you know something is wrong with the experiment and that you can't trust your experimental results.

3. a. The extracellular fluid is hypotonic—it has a lower sugar concentration than the cells.

   b. The membrane is impermeable to extracellular glucose because the solute can't go up its concentration gradient.

4. Impermeable, Na^+ and Cl^- are ions (carry a charge), so they can't cross the cell membrane by passive diffusion.

5. Impermeable, too large to cross by passive diffusion.

6. Yes, carbon dioxide can cross the cell membrane by passive diffusion.

7.

Colorimetric Reagent	Benedict's Solution	Lugol's Solution / Potassium iodide	Silver nitrate
Detects	Glucose	Starch	Sodium chloride salt
Present color(s)	Green, yellow, orange, red solution	Purple or black solution or dark precipitate	Cloudy solution or white precipitate
Absent color	Blue solution	Yellow solution	Clear solution

8. To allow diffusion to occur. If the incubation were shorter, less diffusion would take place. Thirty minutes may not be enough to reach equilibrium. If this is so, a longer incubation would allow diffusion to get closer to or reach equilibrium.

9. See Figure E1 and accompanying text.

10. See Figure E2 and accompanying text.

11. The dialysis membrane is permeable to molecules that are small enough to move through its pores, in the direction that is down their concentration gradient. The dialysis membrane is impermeable to molecules that are too big to fit through the holes in the membrane.

12. A living cell is permeable to small, uncharged molecules, in the direction that is down the molecule's concentration gradient. The membrane is impermeable to large or charged molecules and to molecules that would be moving up their concentration gradient.

13. Hot days, summer

14. a. Experiment 1 has sugar in the cell and water in the bath, so the surrounding solution is hypotonic. Experiment 2 has water in the cell and sugar in the bath, so the bath solution is hypertonic. I would conclude from this that a hypotonic solution causes mass loss and a hypertonic solution would cause mass gain.

    b. The larger the solute molecule, the less diffuses out of the membrane.

LAB F MICROBIOLOGY REVIEW QUESTION ANSWERS

1. a. $2*10 = 20$
   b. 200
   c. 2,000
   d. 20,000
   e. 200,000

2. a. $281/10 = 28$
   b. ~3

3. a. $397*10 = 3,970$
   b. ~40

4. a. $8*2 = 16$
   b. 4

5. a. 26 CFU/0.1 mL $= 260$ CFU/mL
   b. 37 CFU/0.1 mL $= 370$ CFU/mL
   c. 194 CFU/0.5 mL $= 388$ CFU/mL
   d. 41 CFU/0.075 ≈ 547 CFU/mL

6. a. 130 CFU/mL
   b. 1,300 CFU/mL
   c. 13,000 CFU/mL
   d. 130 colonies
   e. 1,300 colonies

7. a. 17/0.25 mL = 68 CFU/mL
   b. 68*15 = 1,020 CFU/mL
   c. 1,020 CFU/mL * 0.25 mL = 255 colonies (or 17*15)
   d. 15,3000 CFU/mL
   e. 3,825 colonies

8. a. ~254 colonies
   b. ~10 colonies
   c. ~84,827 CFU/mL
   d. ~3,393 CFU/mL
   e. ~136 CFU/mL

9. a. 1:10
   b. 21
   c. 0.1 mL
   d. 210 CFU/mL
   e. 21 CFU/mL
   f. 210,000 CFU/mL
   g. 210 colonies
   h. ~2 colonies

10. a. 1:5
    b. 55
    c. 0.25 mL
    d. 220 CFU/mL
    e. 1,100 CFU/mL
    f. 137,500 CFU/mL
    g. 11
    h. 275

11. a. 1:10
    b. 1:25 (1,875/75 = 25; 75/3 = 25)
    c. 1:12 (1,008/84 = 12; 84/7 = 12)
    d. 1:8 (256/32 = 8, 32/4 = 8)

12. a. $\dfrac{3\ CFU}{60\ CFU} * \dfrac{1\ mL}{1\ mL} * \dfrac{1000\ \mu L}{1\ mL} = 50\ \mu L$

   b. $\dfrac{40\ CFU}{80\ CFU} * \dfrac{1\ mL}{1\ mL} * \dfrac{1000\ \mu L}{1\ mL} = 500\ \mu L$

   c. $\dfrac{24\ CFU}{160\ CFU} * \dfrac{1\ mL}{1\ mL} * \dfrac{1000\ \mu L}{1\ mL} = 150\ \mu L$

13. Fastidious bacteria, which need something special to live.

14. You have grown bacteria that are gram negative and can ferment lactose.

15. The bacteria are gram negative and cannot ferment lactose.

16. *E. coli*

17. The bacteria are gram positive.

18. The bacteria must be fastidious for blood, that is, they can only grow in the presence of blood. Green color indicates alpha-hemolysis.

19. The bacteria must be gram positive.

20. a. Both. The ten colonies that grew on the EMB plate must be gram negative, which means the thirty additional colonies on the NA plate must be gram positive.

   b. 10/40 = 25% gram negative; 30/40 = 75% gram positive

   c. Yes. The four purple colonies on the EMB plate are lactose fermenting. The white colonies are not.

   d. 4/40 = 10%

   e. Yes. The six green colonies on the blood agar plate are alpha-hemolytic. The four colonies with clear halos are beta-hemolytic. The thirty white colonies on this plate are gamma-hemolytic (nonhemolytic).

   f. 10/40 = 25%

   g. I expect the hemolytic bacteria are gram negative because there are the same number of hemolytic colonies on the BA plate as there are colonies on the EMB plate. I would assume the thirty nonhemolytic colonies are gram positive, analogous to the additional thirty colonies on the NA plate.

   h. 120 bacteria (40 bacteria were transferred to each plate).

21. a. Some fastidious bacteria that require red blood cells must have grown on that plate, and were unable to grow on any of the others.

   b. Green

   c. No. Because the cells require blood to grow and there isn't any blood in the EMB plate, we cannot learn anything about their Gram state.

   d. They are gram negative because there are the same number of colonies on the nutrient agar plate and the EMB plate and the ones on the EMB plate must be gram negative.

e. Yes. Since the bacteria on the nutrient agar plates are the same as the bacteria on the EMB plate and the bacteria on the EMB plate are pink, which indicates lactose-fermenting, the bacteria on the nutrient agar plate would have this ability, too, if lactose were available.

f. No. The eighty colonies on the blood agar plate that correspond to the colonies on the nutrient agar and EMB plates are white, so gamma- (non-) hemolytic.

22. An autoclave sterilizes

23. It got contaminated and became turbid.

24. A clone is an identical cell created by bacterial cell division.

25. A colony is a pile of clones, from the cell division of the bacterium that was placed on that spot.

26. Lawn

27. a. 1 hour → 8 bacteria; 4 hours → 4,096; 12 hours → $6.87*10^{10}$
    b. 1 hour → 16 bacteria; 4 hours → 8,192; 12 hours → $1.37*10^{11}$
    c. 1 hour → 80 bacteria; 4 hours → 40,960; 12 hours → $6.87*10^{11}$

28. Bacteria continue to grow in the refrigerator and pathogenic bacteria produce wastes and toxins that make people sick. These molecules increase as the bacterial population increases. By throwing away food in a timely manner it will keep a person from eating food that is heavily contaminated.

29. a. 8
    b. 32

30. Anabaena looks like a chain of round cells, some of which look different than the rest. These cells (heterocysts) fix nitrogen (instead of doing photosynthesis).

31.

	Round	Rod-shaped
Pairs	Diplococcus	Diplobacillus
Chains	Streptococcus	Streptobacillus
Clusters	Staphylococcus	Staphylobacillus

32.

	Prokaryotes	Eukaryotes
Nucleus?	No	Yes
Organelles?	No	Yes
Cell size?	Smaller	1–10x bigger
Multicellular?	No	Can be
Organism types?	Bacteria, archaea	Plants, animals, protists, fungi

33.

	NA	EMB	MAC	BA
Full name	Nutrient agar	Eosin methylene blue agar	MacConkey agar	Blood agar
Composition	Carbohydrates, amino acids, vitamins, nitrogen source, salt, seaweed	Nutritional components + eosin and methylene blue dyes	Nutritional components + bile salts and crystal violet	Nutritional components + blood
Differential?	No	Yes, for lactose fermentation	Yes, for lactose fermentation	Yes, for hemolysis
Selective?	No	Yes, for gram-negative bacteria	Yes, for gram-negative bacteria	No
Grows	Most microorganisms	Gram-negative bacteria	Gram-negative bacteria	Most microorganisms, including bacteria fastidious for blood
Color of colonies and meaning	Natural color	Metallic green, purple, pink, brown: lactose fermentation; white: no fermentation	Red, pink: lactose fermentation; white: no fermentation	Green: alpha-hemolysis; clear halos in agar around colony: beta-hemolysis; white: gamma-(no) hemolysis

LAB G MOLECULAR BIOLOGY REVIEW QUESTION ANSWERS

1. DNA fragments of known size in a buffer that will sink into the gel.

2. We can compare the horizontal position of the unknown bands and the DNA ladder bands on the gel to make an estimate of the size (length, molecular weight) of the unknown DNA fragments.

3. If the gel is not run long enough, the top bands in the ladder will be clumped together; if the gel is run too long, the bottom band(s) may run off the bottom of the gel. Having an extra-bright band in the middle allows you to work up and down from the middle of the ladder to identify the other bands.

4. Because there are twice as many fragments that are 3,000 bp long as there are fragments of the other lengths.

5. DNA gel electrophoresis uses charge to separate DNA fragments by size in a gel.

6. Because it separates DNA by size. This can be used to identify a desired DNA fragment or to compare DNA samples.

7. DNA extraction: Mix cells with detergent to disrupt lipid membranes. Add alcohol to precipitate the DNA (separate it from the water layer). (See Activity 3.)
   Restriction digestion: Mix DNA with restriction enzyme and appropriate buffer. Incubate at 37°C.
   Running a gel: Prepare gel, buffer, and rig. Mix DNA samples with loading dye and load into wells. Attach lid and start current. Stop current and image gel once the bands have separated.

8. DNA is separated using charge (DNA is negatively charged and migrates toward the positive electrode). Speed of migration is affected by length of DNA fragment (longer fragments travel more slowly than smaller ones); amount of agarose in the gel (higher agarose concentration slows down migration); type of agarose used (different seaweeds have different crosslinking abilities); buffer used (ions are required to complete the circuit–no migration would occur if pure, deionized water were used); voltage used (lower voltage results in slower migration; higher voltage speeds up migration, but also runs the risk of melting the gel!); the shape of the DNA (particularly important when working with plasmids from bacteria).

9. Loading dye contains two important things: glycerol and dye. Glycerol adds weight to the sample, weighing it down so it stays in the gel well instead of floating away when pipetted into the gel. The dye has two roles: it adds color to the DNA sample to aid in loading the sample into the gel well and the dye migrates through the gel, giving a visual for migration progress (note that the dye runs independently from the DNA).

10. DNA bands can be visualized due to ethidium bromide incorporated into the gel when it is made. EtBr intercalates into the DNA—it physically gets into the DNA between the nucleotide pairs. The fluorescence of EtBr is increased by being in the DNA. EtBr absorbs UV light and emits orange light. This orange light can be seen and photographed.

11. Two hazards are used: ethidium bromide and UV light. Wear gloves and goggles to prevent contact of ethidium bromide with the skin or eyes. Wear goggles and use appropriate shielding to protect the skin and eyes from UV radiation.

12. Guanine to cytosine because it has three hydrogen bonds, whereas adenine to thymine has two.

13. Adenine (A) is colored purple and thymine (T) is blue and the two bases are linked by two dotted lines representing the hydrogen bonds. Guanine (G) is colored red and cytosine (C) is green and the two bases are linked by three dotted lines representing the hydrogen bonds.

14. The deoxyribose sugars (pentagons with oxygen at one position) have the O up on the left side and the O down on the right side.

15. The phosphodiester bonds link the deoxyribose sugars vertically on the left and right sides of the image. The bonds are (sugar)C-O-P(O_2)-O-C(sugar). The hydrogen bonds are in the middle, between the bases, and are represented by dotted lines.

16. BsrBI: 213, 241, 586 bp; HicII: 521, 294, 225 bp; HpaI: 815, 225 bp; Hpy166II: 521, 277, 17, 225 bp; MlyI: 252, 264, 524 bp; MspA1I: 322, 718 bp; PvuII: 322, 718; RsaI bp: 754, 286 bp

17. RFLP analysis uses digestion of DNA by a restriction enzyme and the natural presence of SNPs in people's genomes to create or destroy recognition sequences to generate DNA fragments that can be run on a gel to separate by size so that different people can be told apart/identified.

18. A restriction endonuclease is a protein enzyme that breaks the phosphodiester bond of both DNA polynucleotide strands at a predicable location.

19. DNA fragments are seen separated by size (length, molecular weight). The distance from the top of the gel tells you about the fragment's size: shorter pieces migrate farther and longer pieces stay closer to the top of the gel.

20. See Figure G4 to identify ladder bands. A: 1,300 and 3,500 bp; B: 900 and 6,400 bp; C: 2,200 and 9,000 bp, D: 400, 1,100, and 4,100 bp (Estimates may vary by as much as 500 to 1,000 bp.)

21. See Figure G4 to identify ladder bands. A: 600 and 7,000 bp; B: 1,100 and 4,500 bp; C: 1,900 and 3,800 bp; 700, 1,600, 2,950 bp. (Estimates may vary by as much as 500 to 1,000 bp.)

22. A & G; B & H

23. C & F; G & J

24. A child gets half their DNA from each parent and each parent gives half of their DNA to their child. Thus, each of the child's DNA bands should correspond to a band in one of their parents, but some of the parents' bands will not be present in the child. Counting down the gel from the well, the first band in the child's

sample is from the mom; the second band must be from the dad, since the mother has no band at the same horizontal position on the gel; the third band is also from dad; the fourth band is from mom. Man 3 is the only man with bands at the same positions as bands 2 and 3 in the child, so he is the father.

25. Counting down the gel from the well, band 1 is from mom, band 2 is from dad, band 3 is from dad, band 4 is from mom, 5 is from dad, 6 is from mom, 7 is from mom, 8 is from dad. The only man with bands in the same position as bands 2, 3, 5, and 8 in the child is Man 1, so he is the father.

LAB H CELL REPRODUCTION REVIEW QUESTION ANSWERS

	Mitosis	**Meiosis**
What is the purpose of this process? (What kind of cells are made from this process?)	To make more diploid body cells, identical to the original cell	To make haploid cells for sexual reproduction
Where does this process occur in humans?	Throughout the body	In the ovaries of females and the testes of males
When in a person's lifetime does this process occur?	Throughout life	During the fetal stage and between puberty and menopause in women and from puberty on in men
Describe the parent cell for this process.	Diploid	Diploid
What happens to the parent cell before this process can occur? (Phase name and what happens.)	Interphase: chromosomes duplicate to make sister chromatics	Interphase: chromosomes duplicate to make sister chromatics
How many cells are produced by this process?	2	4 sperm in males 1 function egg and 3 polar bodies in females
Are the cells produced diploid or haploid?	Diploid	Haploid
Describe the chromosomal makeup of the produced cells: are the identical to or distinct from the mother cell?	Identical	Distinct (due to crossing-over)

(continued)

	Mitosis	**Meiosis**
What are the steps of this process?	Prophase Metaphase Anaphase Telophase	Prophase I Metaphase I Anaphase I Telophase I Prophase II Metaphase II Anaphase II Telophase II
Generally, explain the overall procedure and outcome of this process.	The sister chromatids are aligned in the center of the cell, then the sister chromatids are pulled apart and one moves to each side of the cell.	Meiosis I: the homologous chromosomes are matched up and homologous recombination occurs. The tetrads are aligned at the center of the cell. Homologous chromosomes are separated to move to opposite sides of the cell (with their attached sister chromatid). Meiosis II: The sister chromatids are aligned in the center of the cell, then the sister chromatids are pulled apart and one moves to each side of the cell.
When are sister chromatids separated in this process?	During anaphase	During anaphase II
When are homologous chromosomes separated in this process?	They aren't	Anaphase I
Does anything special happen in this process that does not happen in the other process?		Synapsis and homologous recombination
Anything else important to remember about this process?		

	Spermatogenesis	**Oogenesis**
What kind of cell division is this?	Meiosis	Meiosis
What is the name of the gamete formed?	Spermatozoon	Ovum
In which sex does this process occur?	Males	Females

	Spermatogenesis	**Oogenesis**
Where in the body does the process take place?	Testes	Ovaries
When during a person's life does the process occur?	From puberty to death	Begins as fetus; resumes at puberty and ends at meno-pause
How many functional gametes are produced per cell division?	4	1
Describe the appearance of the pro-duced cells.	Small head contain-ing DNA and long flagellum tail	Big, round cell

LAB I GENETICS REVIEW QUESTION SET A ANSWERS

1. a. Dd   b. dd

2. a. ff   b. FF

3. a. $X^h Y$ b. $X^H X^H$

4. a. $X^H Y$ b. $X^H X^h$

5. a. Hh   b. Hh   c.

	H	h
H	HH	Hh
h	Hh	hh

     d. 75%   e. 25%

6. a. Hh   b. hh   c.

	H	h
h	Hh	hh
h	Hh	hh

     d. 50%   e. 50%

7. a. $X^E Y$ b. $X^E X^e$ c.

	X^E	X^e
X^E	$X^E X^E$	$X^E X^e$
Y	$X^E Y$	$X^e Y$

     d. 50%   e. 0%

8. a. $X^F Y$ b. $X^f X^f$ c.

	X^f	X^f
X^F	$X^F X^f$	$X^F X^f$
Y	$X^f Y$	$X^f Y$

d. 0%   e. 100%

LAB I GENETICS REVIEW QUESTION SET B ANSWERS

1.

	a	a
A	Aa	Aa
A	Aa	Aa

AA : Aa : aa ratio = 0:4:0
Dominant : recessive ratio = 4:0
aa would be affected by disorder

2.

	a	a
A	Aa	Aa
a	aa	aa

AA : Aa : aa ratio = 0:2:2
Dominant : recessive ratio = 2:2
AA and Aa would be affected by disorder

3.

	X^D	X^d
X^D	$X^D X^D$	$X^D X^d$
Y	$X^D Y$	$X^d Y$

$X^D X^D : X^D X^d : X^d X^d : X^D Y : X^d Y$ ratio = 1:1:0:1:1
Female dominant : female recessive : male dominant : male recessive
ratio = 2:0:1:1
$X^d X^d$ and $X^d Y$ would be affected by disorder

4.

	X^d	X^d
X^D	$X^D X^d$	$X^D X^d$
Y	$X^d Y$	$X^d Y$

$X^D X^D : X^D X^d : X^d X^d : X^D Y : X^d Y$ ratio = 0:2:0:0:2
Female dominant : female recessive : male dominant : male recessive ratio = 2:0:0:2
$X^D X^D$, $X^D X^d$, and $X^D Y$ would be affected by disorder

5.

	a	a
A	Aa	Aa
a	aa	aa

AA : Aa : aa ratio = 0:2:2
Dominant : recessive ratio = 2:2
aa would be affected by disorder

6.

	A	a
A	AA	Aa
a	Aa	aa

AA : Aa : aa ratio = 1:2:1
Dominant : recessive ratio = 3:1
AA and Aa would be affected by disorder

7.

	X^D	X^d
X^d	$X^D X^d$	$X^d X^d$
Y	$X^D Y$	$X^d Y$

$X^D X^D : X^D X^d : X^d X^d : X^D Y : X^d Y$ ratio = 0:1:1:1:1
Female dominant : female recessive : male dominant : male recessive
ratio = 1:1:1:1
$X^d X^d$ and $X^d Y$ would be affected by disorder

8.

	X^D	X^d
X^D	$X^D X^D$	$X^D X^d$
Y	$X^D Y$	$X^d Y$

$X^D X^D : X^D X^d : X^d X^d : X^D Y : X^d Y$ ratio = 1:1:0:1:1
Female dominant : female recessive : male dominant : male recessive ratio =
2:0:1:1
$X^D X^D$, $X^D X^d$, and $X^D Y$ would be affected by disorder

LAB I GENETICS REVIEW QUESTION SET C ANSWERS

1. a. Autosomal   b. Aa (WT) and aa (mutant)
2. a. Autosomal   b. Aa (WT) and Aa (WT)
3. a. Autosomal   b. AA (WT male) and aa (mutant female)

4. a. Sex-linked   b. X^dX^d (mutant female) and X^DY (WT male)

5. a. Sex-linked   b. X^DX^d (WT female) and X^DY (WT male)

6. a. Sex-linked   b. X^dX^d (WT female) and X^DY (mutant male) (dominant mutation)

7. a. Autosomal   b. Aa (mutant) and Aa (mutant) (dominant mutation)

8. a. Autosomal   b. AA (mutant male) and aa (WT female) (dominant mutation)

LAB J HISTOLOGY REVIEW QUESTION ANSWERS

1. Cell: the smallest unit of life, composed of cytoplasm and organelles enclosed in a phospholipid membrane. Tissue: a collection of similar cells (and perhaps extracellular matrix) that form a functional unit. Organ: a collection of tissues that forms a functional unit.

2. Epithelial: lines surfaces of the body; forms a barrier. Connective: binds the body together; provides support, cushioning, and insulation. Muscle: provides movement. Nervous: sends and receives signals.

3. Epithelial tissues can have squamous, cuboidal, or columnar cells, either as a single layer (simple) or in multiple layers (stratified).

4. Epithelial tissue is composed of tightly connected cells.

5. Pseudostratified epithelium is really simple, because all of the cells attach to the bottom of the tissue, but because the cells vary in height, their nuclei are at different heights, so the tissue looks stratified.

6. Simple epithelium is more common in areas where diffusion takes place. Stratified epithelium allows cells to be lost and still maintain the epithelial barrier. Transitional epithelium is stretchy and found in expandable organs.

7. At boundaries: the innermost layer of hollow organs, the outermost layer of body structures; and glands are epithelia.

8. Connective tissue with blood vessels, which supply nutrients to the epithelium above.

9. Connective tissue is usually mostly noncellular matrix, which contains water and protein fibers. Connective tissue contains fibroblasts and other cells such as adipocytes and specialized cells. These cells are usually scattered throughout the matrix.

10. Seven tissues, see text

11. "Loose" has a lower protein fiber content and "dense" has a higher concentration of fibers. "Regular" tissue has all of the fibers running the same way; in "irregular" tissue the fibers take all orientations.

12. Cartilage: matrix is firm and rubbery from collagen; cells are chondrocytes; found in ears, nose, respiratory tract. Bone: matrix is ossified calcium phosphate and collagen; cells are osteocytes; found in skeleton. Adipose tissue: matrix is very limited; cells are adipocytes; found under skin and around organs. Blood: matrix is plasma, mostly water; cells are red blood cells, white blood cells, and platelets; found in cardiovascular system.

13. Nutrients from blood

14. Lacunae

15. These tissues have few (tendon) or no (cartilage) blood vessels; so molecules needed for repair must diffuse across a long distance to get to these tissues, which is a slow process.

16. See Figure J14

17. Skeletal: long, parallel cylinders with striations and multiple nuclei. Cardiac: branched cells with striations and single (or two) nuclei. Smooth: Tapered/diamond-shaped cells with a single nucleus, no striations.

18. Skeletal: attached to bone; cardiac: in the heart; smooth: lining hollow organs

19. Can control skeletal; cardiac and smooth are involuntary

20. Neurons receive and send signals; neuroglia are support cells that take care of the neurons

21. A neuron has an axon, branching dendrites, and a central cell body (soma)

22.

	squamous	cuboidal	columnar
simple			
stratified			

23.

loose connective tissue	dense regular connective tissue	dense irregular connective tissue

24.

skeletal muscle	cardiac muscle	smooth muscle

25. See also Figure J19.

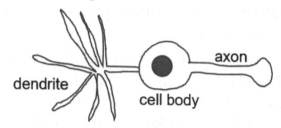

LAB K CARDIOVASCULAR SYSTEM REVIEW QUESTION ANSWERS

1. Plasma
2. Erythrocyte
3. Leukocyte
4. Thrombocyte
5. The iron in the heme of the hemoglobin in erythrocytes
6. Erythrocytes are biconcave—they look like disks with the middle pushed in on both sides (they look hourglass from the side)
7. To carry oxygen
8. 120 days (4 months)
9. Immune response
10. Neutrophils
11. Blood clotting
12. One week
13. Leukocytes are the only true cells. Erythrocytes are missing the nucleus and thrombocytes are cell fragments.
14. Vein
15. Artery
16. The force of the periodic expulsion of blood from the heart
17. Veins are far away from the heart and do not feel the heartbeat
18. Arteriole
19. Venule
20. a. Toward the heart   b. Deoxygenated   c. Pulmonary vein
21. a. Away from the heart   b. Oxygenated   c. Pulmonary artery

22. Arteries have thick walls full of smooth muscle and elastin (tunica media) to withstand the high, changing pressure of the heartbeat; this layer is much thinner in veins. Veins have a much larger lumen (inner space) than arteries do.

23. Capillaries are one simple squamous epithelial cell thick.

24. Right atrium

25. Left ventricle

26. Right ventricle

27. Left atrium

28. Atrioventricular valves. The pressure of blood in the ventricles pushes the AV valves closed and the chordae tendineae and the papillary muscles are tight, holding the valve flaps (cusps, leaflets) in position so they valve doesn't prolapse.

29. Semilunar valves. When the pressure in the ventricles drops the blood in the arteries tries to reverse and re-enter the ventricles; the blood catches in the cusps of the valve, which pushes open/widens the cusps, closing the valve.

30. The chordae tendineae attach between the cusps of the atrioventricular valves and the papillary muscles. They hold the AV valve flaps taut during ventricular systole.

31. Cardiac muscle

32. Pericardium, epicardium, myocardium, endocardium (innermost)

33. Systole

34. Diastole

35. Pulmonary circulation

36. Systemic circulation

37. 45%

38.

	Right side	**Left side**
From	Body	Lungs
Blood vessel	Vena cava	Pulmonary vein
Chamber	Right atrium	Left atrium
Valve	Tricuspid	Bicuspid
Chamber	Right ventricle	Left ventricle
Valve	Pulmonary valve	Aortic valve
Blood vessel	Pulmonary artery	Aorta
To	Lungs	Body

39. capillary → venule → vein → heart → artery → arteriole → capillary

40.

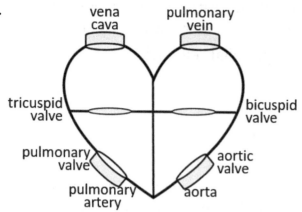

41. Student 1: A−   Student 2: O+   Student 3: AB−   Student 4: B+

42.

Compatible	Patient	Incompatible
AB+, AB−, A+, A−, B+, B−, O+, O−	AB+	
AB−, A−, B−, O−	AB−	AB+, A+, B+, O+
A+, A−, O+, O−	A+	AB+, AB−, B+, B−
A−, O−	A−	AB+, AB−, A+, B+, B−, O+
B+, B−, O+, O−	B+	AB+, AB−, A+, A−
B−, O−	B−	AB+, AB−, A+, A−, B+, O+
O+, O−	O+	AB+, AB−, A+, A−, B+, B−
O−	O−	AB+, AB−, A+, A−, B+, B−, O+

43. Patient 1: A+, Patient 2: B−, Patient 3: AB+, Patient 4: O−

44. Patient 1: AB−, Patient 2: B+, Patient 3: O+, Patient 4: A−

45. Patient 1: agglutination for A; Patient 2: agglutination for B and Rh; Patient 3: agglutination for A, B, and Rh; Patient 4: no agglutination

46.

Can Receive Blood from	Person	Can Donate Blood to
AB+, AB−, A+, A−, B+, B−, O+, O−	AB+	AB+
AB−, A−, B−, O−	AB−	AB+, AB−
A+, A−, O+, O−	A+	AB+, A+
A−, O−	A−	AB+, AB−, A+, A−
B+, B−, O+, O−	B+	AB+, B+
B−, O−	B−	AB+, AB−, B+, B−
O+, O−	O+	O+, O−
O−	O−	O−

47. Heterozygous: half of pregnancies. Homozygous: all pregnancies

48. a. AA Rh−/− or AO Rh−/−   b. A− or O−

49. Man: BB Rh−/− or BO Rh−/−
Woman: BB Rh+/+ or BO Rh+/+ or BB Rh+/− or BO Rh+/−
Children's phenotypes: B+, B−, O+, O−

50. Woman: AB Rh+/+ or AB Rh+/−
Man: OO Rh−/−
Children's phenotypes: A+, B+, A−, B−

51. Man: AA Rh+/+ or AA Rh+/− or AO Rh+/+ or AO Rh+/−
Woman: BB Rh+/+ or BB Rh+/− or BO Rh+/+ or BO Rh+/−
Children's phenotypes: AB+, AB−, A+, A−, B+, B−, O+, O−

52. a. AB Rh+/+ or AB Rh+/−   b. AB+, AB−, A+, A−, B+, B−

53.

Mother	Father	Child	Response
Type O	Type B	Type A	Not possible (no A antigen from either parent)
Type A	Type A	Type O	Possible (if both parents have the AO genotype)
Type A	Type A	Type AB	Not possible (no B antigen from either parent)
Type A	Type B	Type A	Possible (if dad has BO genotype)
Type A	Type B	Type O	Possible (if both parents are heterozygous)

54. Cardiac, skeletal, smooth. Cardiac muscle is branched, striated, and has a single nucleus (or two) per cell. Skeletal muscle has long, parallel, cylindrical, striated, multinucleated cells. Smooth muscle is tapered at the ends, has a single nucleus per cell, and no striations.

55. ~119–158 bpm. Change of 65 bpm = good cardiovascular health
56. ~92–123 bpm. Change of 20 bpm = poor cardiovascular health
57. 114 is systolic and 67 is diastolic; he has normal blood pressure
58. 123 is systolic and 86 is diastolic; she has high blood pressure

LAB L RESPIRATORY SYSTEM REVIEW QUESTION ANSWERS

1. 2
2. 3
3. 1
4. 1
5. 2
6. 3
7. Alveoli
8. Diaphragm
9. External intercostals: inhalation; internal intercostals: forced exhalation
10. Diaphragm is down, closer to flat, at the bottom of the thoracic cavity
11. The diaphragm is bowed up, into the thoracic cavity
12. Tidal volume
13. Inspiratory reserve volume
14. Vital capacity
15. Expiratory reserve volume
16. Residual volume
17. IRV: 2,700 mL   TLC: 5,000 mL
18. VC: 3,450 mL   TLC: 4,950 mL
19. a. 4.5 L   b. 5.5 L   c. Most likely male
20. a. 3.25 L   b. 4.25 L   c. Most likely female
21. a. 3,100 mL   b. 1,850 mL
22. a. 3,200 mL   b. 1,100 mL
23. a. 3,400 mL   b. 4,600 mL

24. a. 1.5 L   b. 6.5 L
25. a. 500 mL (0.5 L)   b. 4,100 ml (4.1 L)
26. a. 1,100 mL   b. 1,400 mL

LAB M URINARY SYSTEM REVIEW QUESTION ANSWERS

1. Kidneys (2), ureters (2), bladder (1), urethra (1)
2. a. Small molecules   b. Glomerular filtration
3. a. Useful molecules   b. Tubular reabsorption   c. Proximal convoluted tubule
4. a. Large wastes, pH-affecting ions   b. Tubular secretion
5. Water, salts (ions), urea, uric acid, metabolic wastes
6. Erythrocytes (red blood cells), leukocytes (white blood cells), urobilinogen, bilirubin, albumin, nitrites, ketone bodies, glucose, casts, microbes
7.

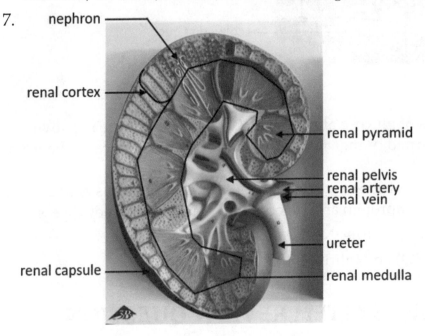

nephron

renal cortex

renal pyramid

renal pelvis
renal artery
renal vein

ureter

renal capsule

renal medulla

8.

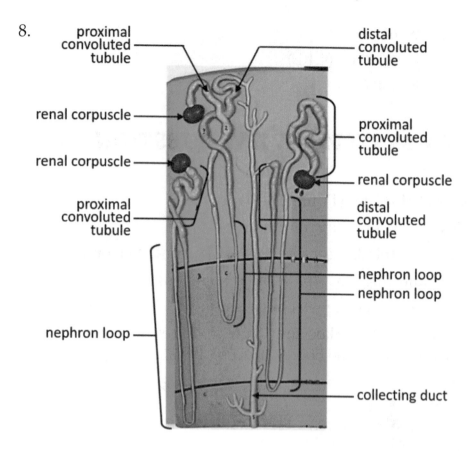

proximal convoluted tubule

distal convoluted tubule

renal corpuscle

proximal convoluted tubule

renal corpuscle

renal corpuscle

proximal convoluted tubule

distal convoluted tubule

nephron loop

nephron loop

nephron loop

collecting duct

9. A: Normal

   B: Abnormal levels of glucose and ketones (ketones are not the negative color (though turned orange instead of purple), which indicates diabetes mellitus type 1.

   C: Abnormal level of glucose, which indicates diabetes mellitus type 2.

   D: Abnormal levels of protein and blood, which indicates kidney disease.

10. a. Leukocytes (LEU) and nitrite (NIT)

    b. Urobilinogen (URO) and bilirubin (BIL)

LAB N DIGESTIVE SYSTEM REVIEW QUESTION ANSWERS

1. Mouth, pharynx, esophagus, stomach, small intestine, large intestine

2. Salivary glands of mouth, stomach, pancreas, small intestine

3. Small intestine

4. Absorb water (and vitamins) to transform waste into semi-solid feces. (Note that 80–90% of fluid in the digestive system is absorbed in the small intestine)

5. To hold food, and convert it into chyme, so it can pass slowly into the small intestine.

6. Biuret solution detects peptide bonds. It turns purple when proteins are present and pink when only small peptides are present. If no protein is present, Biuret solution is blue.

7. Lugol's solution (KI) detects starch and causes the formation of a solid precipitate or dark (black or purple) solution. If no starch is present, Lugol's solution is yellow or orange.

8. Phenol red is a pH indicator. It is red at neutral pH (7) and changes to orange and then yellow as pH decreases. (It turns pink in basic conditions.)

9. When triglycerides are digested, H^+ is produced, decreasing the pH, which is detected by the pH indicator.

10. potassium iodide, KI

11. Butter contains fat. Lipase will digest the fat at 37°C. Therefore the phenol red should turn orange or yellow, indicating the digestion.

12. Biuret's solution detects peptide bonds. Amylase is an enzyme that digests starch. The amylase will digest the starch at 37°C; however, Biuret's solution is the wrong colorimetric reagent for this experiment. The solution will turn faintly purple because the enzyme amylase is a protein, so protein is present in the solution.

13. Experiment 1: Tube 1 is missing pepsin, so the protein cannot be digested.
    Experiment 2: Tube 1 is missing pancreatin, so the fat cannot be digested.
    Experiment 3: Tube 1 is not incubated (0 minutes), so there is no time for the digestion of starch to take place.
    Experiment 4: Tube 1 is missing amylase, so the starch cannot be digested.

14. Incubate at the optimum temperature and pH for an extended amount of time, add more enzyme.

15. Pepsin requires low pH to work and HCl is an acid.

16. A positive result shows the presence of starch, which means it hasn't been digested: It shows that digestion is incomplete, weak, or failed.

17. Experiment 3, tube 1: blue (no digestion of starch, so no maltose present).
    Experiment 3, tube 2: green (some, though low digestion of starch to produce maltose).
    Experiment 3, tube 3: orange (significant digestion of starch to maltose).
    Experiment 3, tube 4: red (complete digestion of starch to maltose).
    Experiment 4, tube 1: blue (no digestion of starch, so no maltose present).
    Experiment 4, tube 2: orange (optimal conditions for digestion of starch to maltose).
    Experiment 4, tube 3: yellow (amylase will be partially active at room temperature, 22°C).
    Experiment 4, tube 4: green (amylase will have low activity in the fridge, 3°C).

18. Neutral pH: mouth, intestines. Acidic: stomach.

19. All nutrients have already been extracted from ingested food before it makes it to the large intestine, so there's no need for digestive enzymes there.

20. Black indicates the presence of starch. This is the color expected for the negative control. The experimental tube being black means that the starch didn't digest—perhaps because the incubation wasn't long enough or was at the wrong temperature.

21. Yellow means no starch present. You'd expect this for the tube containing amylase, but you'd expect a dark solution for the other tube (negative control). Something was wrong with this experiment (the negative control was contaminated with amylase or what was thought to be starch wasn't starch, etc.) and you can't use your experimental results.

22. The negative control tube should be purple because pepsin is a protein, so protein is present when tested with Biuret solution. Pepsin digests protein, which should yield a pink color upon addition of Biuret solution in the experimental tube. Purple means no digestion. Perhaps the experiment wasn't incubated long enough or was at the wrong temperature.

23. HCl is acidic so it caused the phenol red to change to yellow in all tubes. A different test would be necessary to detect digestion of lipids by gastric lipase.

24. By shifting the enzyme from its optimal temperature (37°C) to a lower temperature (20°C) you are lowering its activity, so the rate of the reaction would be slowed. Each time point will have more undigested starch to react with the KI than in the version of the experiment in the text. To compensate, this experiment should be extended: I would suggest adding a two-hour and perhaps a three-hour tube.

25. Salivary amylase works at approximately neutral pH. Tube 1 has a very acidic pH, so the amylase was unable to digest the starch, so the starch turns black in the presence of KI. Tube 2 is also acidic, but not as much as tube 1. Some digestion occurred, resulting in less black product upon addition of KI. Tube 3 had no HCl added, so the amylase was able to digest the starch, leaving only the yellow color of KI when added to the tube.

26. Pancreatic lipase works at 37°C. Tube 1 is red because no digestion took place at 3°C. Tube 2 is orange because a small amount of digestion took place at 20°C, and tube 3 is yellow because lots of digestion occurred at 37°C.

27. Set up tubes with phenol red and pancreatin solution as in Experiment 2. Add 5 drops of heavy cream to each tube. Observe the color of the tubes at different times, such as 0, 5, 10, 20, and 30 minutes. At 0 minutes, the solution should be red (no digestion). As the digestion time lengthens, the color should shift to orange and then yellow as more acid is produced.

28. One possible answer: Design an experiment based on Experiment 2. Place phenol red and 5 drops of cream to each tube. Add 0 drops of pancreatin solution (and 20 drops of water) to tube 1; 5 drops of pancreatin (and 15 drops of water) to tube 2; 10 drops of pancreatin (and 10 drops of water) to tube 3; and 20 drops to tube 4. Tube 1 should be red, for no digestion should take place. Tube 2 may be reddish-orange. Tube 3 may be orange. Tube 4 should be yellow. The degree of color shift from red toward yellow indicates the amount of digestion (yellow is most).